To Linda and Brian
with best wishes

Quentin Morton

IN THE
HEART OF THE DESERT

The Story of an Exploration Geologist
and the Search for Oil in the Middle East

Michael Quentin Morton

GREEN MOUNTAIN PRESS

Printed in the UK

In the Heart of the Desert

Copyright © Michael Quentin Morton 2006

ISBN: 09552212-0-X / 978-0-9552212-0-0

A catalogue record of this book is available from the British Library.

Published by:

Green Mountain Press
P. O. Box 348, Aylesford ME6 9AP
www.greenmountainpress.co.uk
Telephone and fax: 01732 220823

Typesetting and production by:

Able Publishing
13 Station Road, Knebworth, Herts SG3 6AP
www.ablepublishing.co.uk

Printed in the UK by:
Impress Print, Northampton

To Heather

'*So in the heart of the desert, on the naked rind of the planet, in an isolation like that of the beginnings of the world, we built a village of men.*'

Antoine de Saint-Exupéry[1]

'*Exploration required a special breed of men who could react effectively to difficulties and respond sensibly to strange customs.*'

E. W. Owen[2]

1   Excerpt from *Wind, Sand and Stars* by Antoine de Saint-Exupéry, by permission of Gallimard; © 1939 by Antoine de Saint-Exupéry and renewed 1967 by Lewis Glanantiere, reprinted by permission of Harcourt, Inc.
2   E. W. Owen, *AAPG Trek of the Oil Finders*, © AAPG 1975. Reprinted by permission of the AAPG whose permission is required for further use.

Contents

Maps and Tables

A note on the spelling of names

Throughout the text of this book, I have kept to my father's spellings of place names. However, many of these names are spelt differently on modern maps. For example, the place Mike knew as Ghaida is spelt Al Ghaydah on some modern maps (others spell it differently again); Sei'un is spelt Say'un; and so on. It should not take much guesswork to match up the old spellings with the new, but any errors are entirely my own.

I have described the Gulf as the 'Persian Gulf' because it was so described in Company documents of the time; however I am aware that today it is more diplomatically referred to as 'The Gulf'. For historical reasons only, I have kept to the Persian Gulf.

Prologue

'It was not quite a favourable atmosphere in which to geologize.'

On a faintly misty morning, a small fleet lay at anchor off the desert coast, brooding on the becalmed waters of the Indian Ocean. From the deck of a vehicle landing-craft, anxious eyes scanned the shoreline for signs of hostile activity, for this was the coast of Oman, a wild and barren country and the home of untamed tribesmen renowned for their ferocious ways. A shore landing – albeit on this occasion with peaceful intent – was always going to be a hazardous affair.

A small party of native troops, or 'wild goats' as their British commander liked to call them, was ready to clamber down from the main vessel into the infantry landing-craft, to be driven at top speed and tumble out on to the shore. This was when the landing party would be at its most vulnerable, easy pickings for the Bedouin snipers imagined to be lying in wait behind the dunes.

The expedition had come to open up an undiscovered land, negotiating with some tribes and avoiding the bullets of others, securing safe passage for the geologists, surveyors, and numerous other oil Company personnel who would follow in their wake. For riding on board the landing-craft were the plans and ambitions of an international oil company. The Iraq Petroleum Company (IPC), a conglomerate of international oil interests designed to dominate the exploration and extraction of oil in the Middle East, had planned and paid for this venture.

It was 15 February 1954. Company ships, ex-World War II landing-craft renamed *Jamila*, *Jesoura* and *Jawada*, had appeared off the Omani coast at Ras Duqm, with a Royal Navy frigate in attendance: *HMS Wild Goose* lay just over the horizon.

The ships moved almost imperceptibly on the swell; it was too early to land. From the decks the Company men could see some movement on the beach, but nothing of a warlike nature – with a small group of fishermen squatting on the shore, and a thin trace of smoke rising from behind the dunes, it was a scene of primitive tranquillity. These were men of the Janubah tribe, who spent time on the coast in autumn and winter, fishing and grazing their camels until the summer monsoons and dust storms arrived.

Surely the fishermen had never seen anything quite like this before: a mini-armada poised off the coast, nervous soldiers waiting to disembark, Company men anxious to proceed, vehicles, provisions – tins of bully-beef, salmon, sardines, tinned steak, stew, bags of rice, water and beer – and nothing ahead of them but sea and sand.

The geologists' thoughts would have roamed farther to the north, some 320 kilometres to be precise, where they could picture a mountain known as Jebel Fahud. In 1949–50 the English explorer Wilfred Thesiger had travelled through the area disguised as a Bedouin and had identified Fahud by name. Jebel Fahud meant 'Leopard Mountain'. From what the geologists had seen from the aerial photographs, it looked more like an Arctic whale; how strange to be looking for a whale so far from the Arctic sea.

Yet it wasn't fanciful notions that brought the expedition to this place. Fahud had been identified from the photographs as a highly promising site for the discovery of oil, described by the Company's chief geologist as an 'absolute natural',[1] and planned to be the ultimate prize of the Duqm task force.

Movement broke the tranquillity of the scene. A few hundred metres away, the tribesmen – who had until now been squatting peacefully on the shore – got up and walked over to their boats, pushing them out across the beach and launching them into the sea. With sails raised, the boats headed directly towards the Company fleet.

From the deck of the *Jawada*, Company representative Edward Henderson looked on with some dismay: this was not meant to happen. It was too late to take evasive action, too late to launch the landing-craft to intercept the little flotilla. The fishing boats were quickly upon the fleet and, for a brief moment, the Company men held their breath. But for some reason the fishermen appeared strangely disinterested in their presence, sailing right past and heading for the open sea. There was a collective sigh of relief. Henderson turned to a local guide, Salim, and asked him what the fishermen were doing. Salim replied calmly: 'Oh, they are going fishing. They do that every morning this time of year.'[2]

Soon, the soldiers climbed on board the infantry landing-craft and were carried to the shore. Although their progress was conspicuous enough to those Janubah left behind on the shore, the beaching of the landing-craft seemed to attract no attention.

As the craft hit the beach, the Company general manager on board lost his grip and fell into the sea. Rather than arriving with a bang, the twentieth century had arrived with an unremarkable and inconsequential splash.

TODAY, THE LANDING of a party of geologists, oil company officials and men of the Muscat and Oman Field Force on the coast of Oman is little more than a footnote in the history of that country. Yet at that time it was an enormously risky venture, and the event that triggered the emergence of Oman from its medieval past into the modern nation of today.

In ancient times, Omanis, much like the British, were known as merchants, sailors and pirates. They created a trading empire stretching from Zanzibar to India, and cultivated the frankincense that was carried to the markets of the Mediterranean. They also had a reputation for wildness. Tribal conflict was a constant feature of Omani life, and still posed a real danger to travellers in the mid-twentieth century.

Foreign interventions added spice to the history of the land. Invasions were driven by different motives: religious fanaticism from the north, such as that demonstrated by the followers of Wahabism who invaded late in the eighteenth century; acquisitive designs on the land and resources of the region, like those expressed by the Ottoman Empire and later by the Kingdom of Saudi Arabia; and the need to protect factories and trading routes to the East from pirates that prompted the Portuguese and then the British to intervene.

Admiral Afonso D'Albuquerque announced his presence in ferocious style, arriving with a fleet off the port of Muscat in 1508. After conducting an unsuccessful parley with a local deputation, the Portuguese proceeded to bombard the town into submission and sliced off the noses and ears of the unfortunate survivors.

The British, too, had their share of brutal encounters. In 1820, a messenger was sent ashore from a British ship, swimming through the surf to deliver a letter to the Abu Ali tribe warning them to desist from piracy. The messenger was hacked to death as he made to return to the ship. An ill-fated expedition ensued, resulting in the death of 256 men that was described as a defeat 'in which British arms sustained a disgrace which they had never before experienced in Asia'.[3] A larger expedition returned the following year to crush the tribe, demolish their fort, cut down their date palms, and destroy their cultivation channels.

The deserts, mountains and plains of southern Arabia held little attraction for the passing traveller. Among a trickle of intrepid explorers who ventured into the interior, one came in search of coal. Sir Percy Cox described an expedition in the early 1900s:

> We got near the place, which was about three miles [4.8 km] inland, but there we were held up for six weeks in the middle of the hot weather, endeavouring to get through to the coal-bearing hills. I was quite determined to get there, but finally I had to wait for the Sultan to come down and square the unruly sheikhs, and we were at last able to go on. We continued, however, to meet with extraordinary difficulty and obstruction, and finally the geologist and I were able to dig one bag of coal, and being sniped all the time! We agreed that it was not quite a favourable atmosphere in which to geologize, and got away with our bag.[4]

The Arabian Peninsula remained of little interest to geologists until the 1920s.

The first oil was struck on Bahrain Island at Awali on 31 May 1932, in porous limestone of Cretaceous age. This was followed in subsequent years by major finds in Saudi Arabia, Kuwait and Qatar. It was not until after World War II, when the Company commissioned a geological survey of southern Arabia, that my father, Mike Morton, first became involved in that part of the world.

Mike began his journey of exploration through the Middle East in 1945. His main focus was along the southern rim of Arabia, although he undertook many other assignments. Each stage of the journey was very much a team effort, working with a number of talented geologists, geophysicists, surveyors, and political liaison officers, and always backed up by the logistic resources of the Iraq Petroleum Company. A quarter of a century later, in 1971, Mike completed his journey when he visited the northernmost tip of the Arabian Peninsula as Deputy Leader of the Royal Geographical Society expedition to the Musandam Peninsula.

On 15 February 1954, travelling on the tank-landing-craft *Jawada* from Aden, Mike arrived off Ras Duqm as a member of the Duqm Expeditionary Force. 'On a faintly misty morning,' he wrote, 'who musters behind the dunes?'

THE MOUNTAINS OF north Oman in April 1970 presented a safer prospect, safe enough for my father to take the family to the coast for a holiday break. We left Abu Dhabi in a Land Rover and headed for Dubai, Sharjah and then to the fishing village of Khor Fakhan. In those days the area was relatively unexplored, with few Westerners visiting, so that excited locals would crowd around our vehicle and point to the curly-tailed Alsatian inside crying '*dhib! dhib!*', believing him to be a wolf.

We left Khor Fakhan and drove northwards along a deserted shore for miles, scattering crabs and seagulls as we motored along the strand. At one point we pulled up and walked along the glistening sands, marvelling at the mighty rollers of the Indian Ocean and imagining the distant shores of India lying over the horizon. We collected sand dollars[5], marvelling at their detail and perfect symmetry. Our dog Blocky chased the gulls without success.

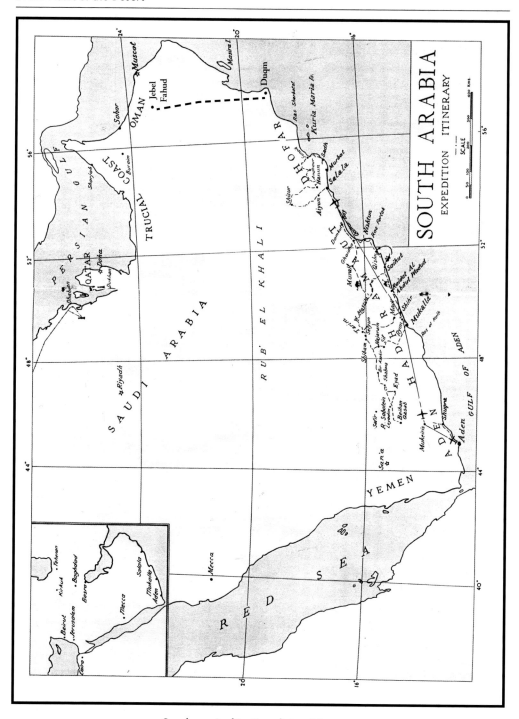

Southern Arabia Expedition Itinerary

We returned to the Land Rover and drove farther up the coast until we reached the entrance to a wadi, and turned inland. As dusk was falling, we made a simple camp and my father prepared the evening meal – an event usually accompanied by the crashing of tins and the swearing of many oaths. But on this occasion Mike proceeded with remarkable stealth, making sure that his usual tendency towards self-harm with a tin opener was kept in check. 'Open the tins,' he whispered to my mother, Heather, handing her the tin opener as he crouched over the fire, fanning its fledgling flames with an old copy of the *Daily Telegraph*. The radio, usually blasting out the BBC Foreign Service at full volume, was silent.

We were in bandit territory, my father had warned us. A notorious camel track, used by a tribe of cut-throat bandits, lay on the other side of the low mountain saddle that ran alongside the wadi where we were camped. After dinner, our stomachs still reeling from the gastronomic onslaught of bully-beef hash *brulée*, we climbed to the top of the saddle to witness those bandits passing by. We watched and waited.

There in the darkness it was easy to imagine a group of robed figures shuffling quickly along the dusty path, leading a few camels and trailed by several small children, no voices, no faces, no noise even from the children, only the padding flip-flop of their sandals as they passed beneath our secret hideaway. We watched intently, scarcely daring to breathe.

When no one came, we scrambled back down the scree slope, trying not to make any noise as we slithered back down to our camp. Then my father checked the perimeter of the camp, shone his torch into the darker recesses of the wadi, and gave the all clear. We settled down on camp beds in the open air. But the thought of Omani bandits, armed to the teeth with razor-sharp daggers, breech-loading rifles and creeping up the wadi to disembowel the Nasrani intruders, kept me awake and watchful as a full moon slowly climbed across a glittering night sky.

The stories he would tell. Could it really be true that Mike had crawled into an apparently dried-up well and drunk the last drops of water extracted from camel droppings squeezed through a blanket? And that he had – purely by chance – avoided being shot through the head by a tribesman's bullet? Had he really witnessed the exorcism of a camel or provided a sheet from his sleeping bag for a Bedouin burial?

Or were these stories, and many others, as imaginary as Bedouins gathering in the night?

IT WAS ONLY in 1990, when we began to index his collection of photographs and, with my father, began putting names to places, that the stories started coming to life. But the indexing work became increasingly difficult as Mike's mind wandered erratically – the tracks to his past were becoming harder to follow.

My father passed away on 22 November 2003 at the age of 79. 'Mike's history is the Company's history,' wrote his former boss, Dr Tom Harris. Mike's experience represented the full geographical range of the Company's operations, and told of events in a bygone, half-forgotten world. Resolute in exploring a harsh terrain, cheerfully accepting the hardships of the assignment in hand, Mike and his colleagues laid a path into territories where others had feared to tread. 'Mike's full story remains to be told,' concluded Dr Harris in his obituary.[6]

This book takes up that challenge, making use of Mike's letters and journals, and the writings of his contemporaries, to present a picture of what it was like to be an exploration geologist in his day. With my mother's help, it also tells of life in the Company, of living in places such as

Tripoli, Kirkuk and Dukhan. I hope that it fulfils my father's wish to set down his account of his travels and that, also, it does justice to the contribution of the many others who made up the Iraq Petroleum Company and its subsidiaries.

As it became necessary to make sense of the journals, books, maps, and geological reports that lay scattered around my father's study – the last testament of an explorer's life – something else emerged. I became aware of the strength of the desert to capture the traveller's soul, drawing him back there, time and again. As it developed, the book became a journey to discover how a young man from a bleak northern town became entranced by the spell of an unknown and desolate land.

1   D. M. Morton, The Geology of Oman. Proc. *5th World Petroleum Congress*, 1959, p. 293.
2   Edward Henderson, *This Strange Eventful History*, 1988, p.100 (expanded and republished in 1999 as *Arabian Destiny – The Complete Autobiography* – for publisher details, please refer to 'Acknowledgements' p. 258).
3   Sir Charles Belgrave, *The Pirate Coast*, 1966.
4   Sir Percy Cox, comments to a Royal Geographical Society meeting, from The *Geographical Journal* 1929, vol. LXXIII, no. 3, with permission from Blackwell Publishing.
5   A type of thin, circular echinoderm.
6   *IPC Society Newsletter*, January 2004.

Chapter 1: Baba Gurgur

The Middle East, 1900–1945

'Then these men were bound in their coats, their hosen, and their hats, and their other garments, and were cast into the midst of the burning fiery furnace.'
Daniel 3:21

In a letter to his wife, Mike wrote: 'One stage of our journey is now over, and I snatch a brief respite to write to you … it's wonderful to be back in the clean dry air of the desert,' describing his feelings at the start of a new expedition. The allure of the wilderness, whether at midnight in the Kurd-Dagh mountains of north-western Syria, in the middle of the burning day on the Dhahira Plain in Oman, or early morning on the fringes of the seemingly endless dunes of the Rub al Khali, was already irresistible to the young geologist:

> It's wonderful … to be chilled in the early morning, and awake in a fresh crisp atmosphere. The temperature ranges about 50 degrees Fahrenheit during twenty-four hours, but as there's no humidity it's a healthy climate … I get a terrific kick being in a new country. I feel electrified and nervous, and I want to see everything.

By this time, late 1949, Mike was 25 years old and a well-travelled man. The four years' experience gained from exploring the Hadhramaut, Mahra and Dhofar regions, and from Company expeditions to Syria, Trans-Jordan, Qatar and Oman, had not dimmed his enthusiasm for the job: quite the reverse. 'I wish I'd lived 100 years ago when there was much more of the world unexplored,' he concluded. The irony was that the opportunities Mike enjoyed were not available 100 years before.

Mike worked for the Iraq Petroleum Company (IPC), which had come into being in October 1928. IPC represented an attempt by several large oil companies to protect their interests in the Middle East.[1] At the heart of this arrangement was the 'Red Line Agreement', an arrangement whereby the participating companies agreed to act jointly in the Middle East through IPC (see map on p. i of colour section). Rumour had it that an American – or possibly the oil tycoon C. S. Gulbenkian himself – formulated the agreement by taking a thick red pencil to a map of the Middle East and drawing a line around the borders of the former Ottoman Empire. The red line marked IPC's sphere of operations.

Although opinions about this arrangement would soon diverge, there could be no doubt about its long-term impact; Stephen Longrigg noted that 'the Red Line Agreement, variously assessed as a sad case of wrongful cartelization or as an enlightened example of international co-operation and fair-sharing, was to hold the field for twenty years and in large measure determined the pattern and tempo of oil development over a large part of the Middle East.'[2]

IPC's *modus operandi* was simple: its parent companies would apply for concessions together, under the auspices of IPC, not individually or with other companies; IPC would then survey the territory and, if successful, hand over the extracted oil in apportioned shares to its parent companies.

Until its demise in November 1948, when the two American partners broke free to develop their interests in Saudi Arabia, the Red Line Agreement was remarkably successful in keeping others out. It was inevitable that negative charges would be levelled against the Company, the most common being that its main purpose was simply to pre-empt other companies in the exploration and discovery of oil. Amongst Iraqis there developed an enduring suspicion that IPC was not exploiting its concession to the full so that higher oil prices could be maintained elsewhere.

Since the heart of the Company lay in Iraq, such complaints did not bode well for the future. Still, it would take more than a few grumbles to divorce the Company from the country, for theirs was a relationship that had been created in the very earth of Iraq, forged out of a violent eruption at Baba Gurgur.

THE ROCKS AND fossils of the earth tell a story. The ageing of the earth, described through sediments laid down over many millions of years, is evidenced today in exposed rock faces across the globe which, like an open book, can tell a geologist about the history of the earth and the processes that shaped it – and a petroleum geologist about the possible location of crude oil, from which petroleum products such as gasoline, kerosene and fuel oil are refined.

Because oil and gas are captured by rocks below the surface of the Earth, great pressure can build up. Some of this pressure escapes naturally as oil seeps to the surface, and gas leaks or burns away.

The presence of gas at Baba Gurgur had been evident for thousands of years. Baba Gurgur means 'the father of underground rumblings', and it was well known for its burning gases escaping through faults in the structure of the earth. Visitors to Kirkuk were encouraged to visit the fires at night, when the effects of the flames were at their most spectacular. This was believed to be the site of the biblical 'burning fiery furnace' into which Nebuchadnezzar cast three Jews, only for them to emerge unscathed by the heat and flames. And it was here that, according to Plutarch, people had gathered oil from seepages and used it to illuminate the streets in order to impress Alexander the Great.

Strategic and trading interests – not oil – first drew the British to Iraq (or Mesopotamia as it was sometimes called), when the East India Company established a factory in the port of Basrah in 1763. By the early twentieth century, however, British interests in the region were being driven by the growing need to find oil. The discovery of oil at Masjid-i-Sulaiman in Persia in 1908 hinted at good oil prospects for the region as a whole while the British Government's decision to convert its naval fleet from coal to oil, and coal shortages during World War I, created pressure to find new reserves.

The Treaty of Versailles, 1918, confirmed Britain and France as the leading powers in the Middle East. Britain established the Hashemite monarchy in Iraq, and a series of protracted negotiations took place between the Turkish Petroleum Company (the forerunner of IPC) and the Iraqi Government for concession arrangements in that country. In the 1920s, the first Iraqi wells were spudded-in at Pulkhana, Injana and Khashm al Ahmar. These wells were expected to strike oil quickly and there was an air of relaxed confidence in the main camp of the Turkish Petroleum Company:

The long summer of 1927 was drawing to a close and the first signs of approaching autumn were in the air. The Headquarters of the Turkish Petroleum Company at Tuz-

Khurmatu, south east of Kirkuk, was still largely a tented camp and had assimilated itself to the surrounding low and bare hills through accumulation of dust over the past hot weather. This camp had been sited as conveniently central for the control of the exploratory drilling programme which had commenced in different areas in the spring of that year.[3]

Another well was constructed to the north of Kirkuk in the wadi known as Baba Gurgur, a single derrick situated in an unremarkable depression in the desert. Expectations of an early strike were not so strong here as in the south. Night after night the drillers went about their routine business, hearing only the familiar hissing sounds of locomotive boilers and a steam engine while the drill bit churned its way ever downward toward a silent black lake which – unbeknown to them – lay some 460 metres below their feet.

LIKE AN ERUPTION from Hell, first with a rumble and then with a deafening roar, oil burst out of the ground and rose above the derrick, raining down black crude and rocks on the surrounding wadi and filling nearby hollows with poisonous gas.

Oil was struck at 3 a.m. on 15 October 1927. Next day, from 20 kilometres away, the huge spraying column of oil looked like a clump of trees in the distance. To the people of Kirkuk only eight kilometres away, crowding the roof tops for a view, it looked like the vengeance of an angry God.

At first, when the drill bit cracked through the cement at the casing shoe and into the oil reservoir, the routine on the surface was undisturbed. When the driller pulled out the drill bit to clean the cuttings, he had no inkling that anything was amiss: the drill bit was raised as usual, bull ropes flying in the driller's face, the cable rising towards him.

Suddenly there was a piercing, hissing sound. The drilling tools were about six metres from the derrick floor when the driller suddenly realized that gas and oil were rushing up the hole. In that moment, realizing the risk of fire, his first thought was to extinguish the flame of the boiler, which he did just as a fountain of oil spurted over the crown of the derrick to a height of 42 metres.

When the call of an oil strike came to headquarters, it was a great surprise that it came from Baba Gurgur. An eye witness to the aftermath reported:

At 3:30 a.m. on 27th October 1927, the insistent ringing of the telephone in my tent awakened me from deep slumber to the feeling that something was wrong. Sleepily removing the receiver, I heard an excited Field Manager urging me to be ready to accompany him to Kirkuk. It was not clear what had happened but something serious had gone wrong with well No.1 at Baba Gurgur. Hastily donning clothes I dashed away to find the Field Manager who was already waiting in his car, and we were soon speeding along in the half light of the early dawn determined to be the first on the spot from the locations outside Kirkuk.[4]

A two-hour drive brought them to within sight of the town and, on rounding an olive grove, they saw away in the distance a huge column of what appeared to be smoke rising well above the top of the No.1 derrick.

'My God!' the Field Manager ejaculated. 'She's gone on fire!'

While I, not having seen an oil well in my life, felt comment was out of place and remained silent. I remember, however, instinctively feeling what a tragedy for us all, including Iraq generally, that our first success should be attended by such unfortunate circumstances.

It was clear that the Company had a major environmental crisis on its hands:

While it was attractive to stand just away from the worst of the roaring of the gusher and watch the spectacle of the oil being sprayed falling in billowy clouds to the ground, yet urgent and far-reaching measures were necessary if tremendous losses were not to be suffered by the Company on account of loss of oil and by the local inhabitants whose property stood in danger of being destroyed. There was also the additional fear of water supplies being polluted.[5]

The No.1 well had been sited in a depression that carried water off the low foothills to the open desert, and the oil was escaping down this wadi. The surrounding villages, and Kirkuk itself, were at risk of being drowned in a deluge of crude oil. Being unable to stop the flow immediately, the problem for the Company was how to contain the oil:

Eventually it was decided to commence building dams in the wadi (known as Wadi Naft) at distances of about 1.5 kilometres apart and a piece of low ground was selected about 24 kilometres away from the well location which it was calculated could be easily dammed to hold several weeks of production from the well.[6]

It was estimated that 2,000 men would be required to build the dams. Men from the Jubur tribe scattered down the Zab river settlements, and the Obaid tribe on the Hawija plain, were soon converging on Kirkuk. Vehicles collected a few of the men but the main body walked the whole way, in some cases of distances up to 60 kilometres.

A blue mist formed at night in the hollows of the low hills caused by gas pockets. On one still night the poisonous effects of gas collecting in a depression killed two drillers and three Iraqi workers. The risk of fire was ever-present since the men worked day and night to complete the dam, and the vision that confronted the visitor was one of hell without the flames:

For hundreds of metres around everything was smothered in oil. Men were working in gas masks almost naked in an endeavour to get near enough to rig up some control appliances. The oil fell evenly in clouds all around the derrick and draw-works due to the windless autumn days.[7]

At length the cloud of oil was blown away from the derrick to allow work to start on the well head. This was achieved by setting up an aero engine which, when started, created the necessary draught to clear one side of the derrick. It took ten days from the first eruption to close the control valve and shut off the supply of oil. The roar of the gusher was abated, the 'terrible enemy had been vanquished and now, tied down and controlled, could be looked upon as our greatest friend'.[8]

The relief was short-lived, however, as the approaching rainy season raised the spectre of another disaster. If the rains came and the wadi flooded, the oil would be carried down to the river and pollute water supplies across the whole country. Pumps were urgently installed to pump the oil back into the wells, but they made little impression. Desperate to remove the oil, large quantities were set alight. When the rains came the area was clear of oil.

By the time the well was capped, over 95,000 barrels of oil a day had spewed forth into the desert. Work on clearing up the area was completed by Christmas Day 1927 and, for those departing, a new idea of the Company had emerged:

> No longer would we be regarded with the pitying eyes of those who looked upon our quest as hopeless, no longer would we writhe under the cynical comments of those offered to wager they would drink all the oil found in Iraq. Our heads were up, we had done a good job, we knew it and were already thinking of the way out to the world for Iraq oil. Up until this time we had merely been an exploratory company. Overnight our status had changed and from now on we were really on the map.[9]

Consequently, when the Iraq Petroleum Company came into being in October 1928, replacing the Turkish Petroleum Company, it was clear where its immediate future lay. Following the discovery of oil at Baba Gurgur, drilling operations in less promising areas were suspended so that the Company could focus its full resources on the development of the Kirkuk field. Roads, water supply, power plant, together with offices and dwellings, stores and workshops quickly followed. Two 30 cm (12 inch) pipelines were planned to carry crude oil from the Kirkuk oilfield to the Mediterranean coast, the northern line passing through Syria and Lebanon to a terminal at Tripoli, and the southern line routed across Jordan to reach Haifa on the coast of Palestine.

The Company saw itself engaged in a mighty task. There was a whole infrastructure to support the lines: twelve pumping stations; 100 wells and 320 kilometres of water pipeline in the desert, serviced by twelve smaller pumping stations to provide drinkable water; terminals with eight underwater lines to mooring berths 1.5 kilometres from the shore; a network of telegraph, telephone and wireless communications to support operations; an air transport system; four main railheads; workshops, offices and a labour force numbering hundreds of men.

At one stage, the Iraqi Government tried to open up the country to competition – an ill-fated venture, for the company taking up the new concession was bought out by IPC and, under the name of the Mosul Petroleum Company, was duly gathered into the IPC 'family' of subsidiary companies. The Company's Iraq portfolio was now complete: the southern oil concession area had been snapped up by the Basrah Petroleum Company, which was identical in composition and share-holding to IPC.

The Company did not rest there, widening its operations within the area of the Red Line. It created subsidiary companies, one for each territory to be explored. These companies would obtain from the sovereign power an exploration licence covering simple exploration over a defined geographical area, or a concession permitting exploration and the production of oil.

By 1948 IPC had 14 subsidiary companies with concessions or exploration licences.[10]

Typically, these subsidiaries shared personnel across the range of their territories and activities. A geologist such as Mike Morton would find himself being assigned to a number of different companies during the course of his career, though remaining subject to the overall direction of IPC.

Having gained the necessary concession or licence, a subsidiary company would send in exploration parties and either find oil or abandon the concession. Once oil arrived in commercial quantity, the wells, airstrip, pipelines, roads, camp and, eventually, the wives and children would follow.

The geologists came and went. They explored for oil, submitted reports to Company headquarters and moved on to the next area to investigate. In the Middle East, the exploration season was in the cooler months, October to April. The start of the season was usually heralded by the arrival of Company bigwigs on a plane from London, and its end by a repeat performance. In between, the geologists struggled in conditions of primitive hardship, living in tents, or 'ruddy fox-holes' as Mike's colleague René Wetzel used to call them, coping with vehicle breakdowns and dust storms, eking out the last drops of stale water from a long-abandoned well. And there were the politics to contend with, the niceties of observing government restrictions, the need to respect the customs and culture of a land, and to negotiate with its sheikhs. Local feuds or hostility to foreigners might unsettle their progress and, to protect themselves from the vagary of a stray bullet, the geologists were often accompanied by the military.

Occasionally, there was an element of detached amusement among the military towards the antics of the oilmen, who they called 'oily boys', much to the irritation of the geologists, drillers and the like.

The oily boys had to cease their activities at the beginning of World War II, which affected oil production in all the Company's areas; wells were plugged and drilling machinery removed.[11] At the conclusion of hostilities, however, when the scene was set for the resumption of operations, it was time for the geologists to return and explore the Middle East once more: the oily boys were back in town.

At this point in our story, in November 1945, a 21-year-old geologist named Mike Morton left Liverpool on an empty troopship bound for the port of Haifa in Palestine.

1   Shares of 23.75 per cent each were held by the Near East Development Corporation (representing American interests), the Compaigne Française des Pétroles, the Anglo-Saxon Petroleum Company, the D'Arcy Exploration Company and the remaining 5 per cent held by Participations and Investments Limited, representing C. S. Gulbenkian – thereafter known as 'Mister Five Per cent'.
2   *Oil in the Middle East* by S. H. Longrigg, 2nd Edition, page 70, by permission of Oxford University Press. Apart from in Saudi Arabia and Bahrain where ARAMCO and BAPCO respectively prevailed, IPC monopolized oil exploration inside the Red Line.
3   'The Story of a Famous Gusher', from the George Todd Library, author unknown, by permission of the IPC Society.
4   Ibid.
5   Ibid.
6   Ibid.
7   Ibid.
8   Ibid.
9   Ibid.
10 See Appendix 2, Middle East Oil Concessions.
11 In 1941 in Iraq, ten oil-producing wells and 38 observation and other wells were plugged in order to deny the enemy oil. Six thousand tons of drilling machinery was removed from Kirkuk to Basrah. In Qatar, three wells were destroyed in 1940 under military orders, with equipment removed, again as a measure designed to deny the enemy oil in time of war.

Baba Gurgur, Iraq, October 1927
© IPC Society Newsletter 1997

Baba Gurgur, Iraq,
October 1927
© IPC Society Newsletter

Chapter 2: Cold Wind Flowing

Huddersfield, 1924–November 1945

'The October evening wind flows coldly over the moor land'
Foundations, Percy Stock

The home that Mike left behind was in the textile town of Huddersfield, lying in the shadow of the brooding Yorkshire moors. It was a place to which Mike's thoughts often returned in his early days in the Middle East. Writing from the desert, he remembered the life he had enjoyed as a boy roaming the windswept moors above his home. 'How I wish I could tread the soft peaty moorland instead of the harsh, rocky desert,' he once wrote to Heather, his wife-to-be. Displaying a rare bout of homesickness, he went on to describe what he missed about the moorland. 'How I long for the rippling of iron-stained humus-laden streams, and their mossy, boggy sources; the coarse, friable Millstone Grit underfoot on Black Moss top, where ancient trees, which flourished in a long-gone age, protrude from the black acid soil.'

The contrast of the wild and yet abundant moors with the desert around Thalaitawat in the Trans-Jordan region could not have been more extreme. 'The camel scrub and tamarisk seem to mock me – they've been here for centuries, sucking the last drop of moisture from the sun-baked soil beneath the tarnished flints – they're strange to me, and not part of my Yorkshire heritage; they cling to life, when everything else has gone, and by their tenacity, seem to jeer at strangers who walk in their silent gardens.'

It was fitting that Mike should have such a strong affinity with the Yorkshire earth, for it was the reason that the Mortons first settled in the area. In 1558, Edmond de Morton and 'a numerous Scotch family',[1] fled from religious persecution in Scotland to find a home south of the border. They settled in a part of Huddersfield known as Salendine Nook. The family were potters, and the area attracted them because it was the source of a special type of very pure clay worked for the manufacture of earthenware pottery. Since that time the Mortons had branched out into other trades, while the pottery business continued. Mike's grandfather was a commission agent and his father Frank a woollen manufacturer's clerk.

On wet Sunday afternoons in winter, the front rooms of family houses, which were kept locked during the week, were opened up and relatives would gather round a warm fire, with tea sipped from the best china cups, to discuss the history of their ancestors. Amid a plethora of Edmunds, each generation having one son named so, the name of Michael Morton stood out, having registered his barn in October 1689 as a meeting house for Protestant dissenters and established the building as a religious site, which in time became a Baptist chapel that is still in use today.

At first, the small congregation found it difficult to adjust to this new-found freedom to worship:

The October evening wind flows coldly over the moorland. The houses are few and widely scattered. Lights shine here and there but one is more brilliant than the rest. Men and women are excitedly approaching the light. They are just plain folk, the women with shawls on their heads and clogs on their feet. The scene is in an ancient barn. The door opens and two men come through, one is old, the other of middle age. The old man rises and the service begins as he reads Isaiah Chapter 40 … Comfort Ye My People …The sermon has as its text 'Watchman, what of the night? The Morning cometh' and the speaker recounts the difficulties under which his followers have laboured. At this point he shows them a piece of paper – their licence – and dwells on what this means. The blessed morning has come. The big barn doors are open for public worship and, please God, the open door shall never be taken away again. Finally, he commends them for keeping alight the flame of the blessed Gospel in that place.

The meeting ended with the singing of the 124th Psalm – not very well rendered for this was the first time they had ever dared to sing together aloud.[2]

Perhaps the cold wind flowing over the moorland gave the most famous of all the Morton ancestors, John Morton, the idea of leaving Huddersfield to find his fortune in Canada in the mid-nineteenth century.

The story of John Morton would assume a particular significance for Mike. In Mike's younger days, however, it was simply a story to savour, an adventure straight from the pages of *Boy's Own* magazine. In 1862, John Morton, himself from a family of Huddersfield potters, arrived in the area that is modern-day Vancouver. He was interested in purchasing land, but his early efforts were not very successful. He visited a small island in the bay and was fascinated to find hundreds of cedar boxes perched in the upper branches of the trees. Going to touch one, he found it fragile and it crumbled easily, showering him with the bones of a long-deceased Indian. For these boxes contained the bones of Squamish Indians, and the island itself was the site of a fierce battle between rival Indian tribes during which some 200 tribesmen had been killed. John Morton's early foray into the property market stalled at that point, and he quickly changed his mind about buying the island.

With his cousin Samuel Brighouse and their friend William Hailstone, John Morton tried prospecting in the Caribou gold fields. They made two trips, walking a distance of some 2,250 kilometres. Although unsuccessful in their main endeavour, Morton chanced upon a profitable sideline in selling horseshoe nails. A blacksmith in the outlying territory had run out of nails, and Morton saved the day by producing 22 nails from his outfit and making the sum of 22 dollars in the process. The three friends returned to the small settlement of New Westminster to ponder their next move.

One day John Morton was passing by a shop window in the settlement when he saw a lump of coal for sale in the window and 'his interest was specially excited'. Coal was a rare commodity in those parts, the only available fuel being wood. But above all the sight had triggered his interest as a potter: he knew that a certain kind of clay used in pot-making was usually found near coal deposits. He entered the shop and asked the shopkeeper where the coal had come from.

'That Indian just disappearing down the road brought it,' said the shopkeeper. 'Ask him.'

Morton hurried after the Indian, caught up with him and made arrangements to visit the coal seam. He found little of value there: most of the coal seam and clay deposit had been washed away. But the site of the land, overlooking a natural deep-water harbour, so impressed Morton and his friends that they set about making enquiries with a view to purchasing it. They discovered that it had been neither staked nor surveyed, so they acquired 180 acres each, the maximum stake permissible under the law of the time. By Christmas 1862, they had cleared a small part of the land and built a log cabin, much to the derision of the local inhabitants who christened them 'The Three Greenhorns'.

A town grew up despite an early setback:

> On the night of June 13th, 1886, a bright glare appearing in the sky to the west was noticed by the people of Mission. It was the young settlement of Granville, recently incorporated as the city of Vancouver, burning to the ground. From the ashes of that little town of two thousand souls rose the new City of Vancouver.[3]

In 1886, Morton and his friends were persuaded to give one third of their land to the Canadian Pacific Railway as an incentive to develop the line into Vancouver where they had developed new property interests. But by the time the railway was developed The Three Greenhorns had gone their separate ways and felt they had been cheated. Not for long: by 1887 the lots began to sell and, within a couple of decades, the so-called West End had become the upmarket area of Vancouver. Morton, true to his roots, donated the first $1,000 towards the site for a new Baptist church in the city and, when he died in 1912, left an estate valued at approximately £154,000.

Today, Vancouver's art deco Marine Building marks the site of that little log cabin. At 22 stories and a height of 104 metres, the building overlooks the terminus of the Canadian Pacific Railway.

For Mike Morton growing up in Huddersfield, the story of John Morton was exciting and often told, surrounded as he was by numerous uncles and aunts. Mike lived in a close-knit community and his relatives liked to keep in touch, even after Mike had left Huddersfield for the Middle East. These well-meaning souls would write to him in some far-flung corner of the desert, where he was surrounded by a hostile environment and potentially hostile Bedouins, to advise him to 'be a good boy and choose the right friends'. And the Mortons had high moral standards, nurtured by the Methodist Chapel and their Baptist ways, a strict family with the Pot'oon Mortons the strictest of all.[4] Again in the Middle East, their strictures would come back to haunt a guilty Mike as he relived a night out in Aleppo: 'The Pot'oon Mortons will be turning in their graves,' he wrote to Heather, in a fit of post-alcoholic contrition.

But if the bones of his ancestors made only an occasional rattle in the cold wind flowing over the moorland, nothing would compare with what happened to Mike when he was seven years old. One can only imagine the scene that Saturday afternoon on 12 December 1931.

THIS WAS A very busy time, when the people of Huddersfield were crowding into town for shopping, football and theatre. Not that the town was ever quiet on a Saturday afternoon, but Christmas was looming fast. Tradesmen had little time to stand in doorways watching life passing by as mothers dragged children along crowded pavements into their stores packed with Christmas goods. 'Christmas Gifts – Let Khan Decide' proclaimed the frontage of one clothing store in Northumberland Street, but few shoppers took its advice, preferring instead to browse through the latest winter coats and *Hydroprufe* macs themselves. The few drivers who negotiated the Beast Market junction with buses and pedestrians were part of a familiar scene. There were Yorkshire men in dark coats and cloth caps, holding on to their sons and pushing on towards the Leeds Road Football Ground, while families formed a long but orderly queue outside the Palace Theatre waiting for the matinée show to begin. All this played out to the underlying rumble of trams and the tattered remains of the day before, a copy of the *Huddersfield Daily Examiner*, scuttling past in a momentary breeze only to fall into a gutter, its upturned page silently advertising to a distracted world:

WHERE TO DINE!
SOUP, FISH, JOINTS AND SWEETS
Served EVERY DAY in
Hobson's Café

And into this scene stepped Frank Morton, aged 47, his 73-year-old mother-in-law Mary a few paces ahead, and his seven-year-old son Michael walking along beside him. They rounded a corner and saw the object of their journey – the Palace Theatre – ahead of them. Perhaps as the box office came into view they could see it surrounded by a small crowd of adults and children. The waiting crowd would take the few seats left; the matinée was full. They turned tail and retraced their footsteps, heading up Silk Street towards Beast Market and Northgate where they would catch a bus back to their home in Sheepridge.

Mary could not remember anything once they got to the top of Silk Street, apart from falling to the ground and putting her hand up to her head and finding it was covered in blood. The Inquest would hear that a horn had sounded as a Buick taxi emerged from Silk Street into Beast Market, colliding with a Singer motor car and pushing it round. A witness said that Frank had tried to push the old lady out of the way of the car before it knocked him against the wall of a public convenience. The jury's verdict was that Frank was 'by misadventure killed'. Mary, although she appeared to have survived her injuries, died a few months later.

It fell on Mike's mother, Lucy, and his sister Freda, six years his senior, to support Mike through his school days, and it was a debt that Mike never forgot. Lucy was determined that her children should do well in life, despite the straightened financial situation they found themselves in. They saw Mike through school, technical college and university and, although some members of the extended family had other ideas about where Mike's future should lie, Lucy encouraged Mike in his ambition first to become a geologist and then to find employment with the Iraq Petroleum Company. When working abroad, Mike would send money home to Lucy, while planning for the time when she would be financially independent.

The story of John Morton took on a double importance in Mike's early life: from a young age it fired his imagination with the idea of making his fortune in mysterious foreign lands, and an inheritance under John Morton's will promised to provide Lucy with the financial security she needed.[5] In 1946 Mike received a letter from a relative telling him that the residue from John Morton's will was, after 20 years of haggling, to be shared out among the remaining relatives. The main asset of the estate was the Wainwright Block in Vancouver that was valued at $80,000 in 1939, and Lucy's share was to be one seventh of one twentieth of the proceeds of sale. As it happened, when the money did eventually come through, it amounted to little more than £30.

Mike met Heather at a dance in the early summer of 1943. Heather, a trainee schoolteacher from Barry, had been evacuated to Huddersfield because of the wartime bombing of her college in London, Avery Hill. In 1945, Heather returned to Barry for a while and then moved to London in September to teach at a school in Dagenham.

Mike's interest in geology began at Royd's Hall School in Huddersfield. A teacher sparked an interest in geography and chemistry and encouraged Mike to apply for a job with ICI. Mike then obtained a scholarship to study part-time for a degree in geology, which he started at Huddersfield Technical College and completed at the University of Leeds. He was granted a dispensation from working in the mines as 'Bevin boy' on account of his studies. As the war was ending and the Iraq Petroleum Company was keen to re-establish its operations in the Middle East, the Company advertised for geologists. Mike had his geology degree, applied for, and was appointed to, the post of field geologist in the autumn of 1945.

MIKE EXPLAINED THE role of a field geologist in a letter to Heather,[6] setting out the basic principles of geology of the time, long before tectonic-plate theory had taken hold:

> The formation of oil and gas is a natural process that occurs over millions of years. It begins with plant matter being washed by rivers into the sea where it mixes offshore with dead planktonic life. The debris is compacted by the weight of succeeding sediments and sinks deep into the earth to be transformed by subterranean pressure and heat into oil and gas which, being lighter than water, eventually rises upwards. Some is trapped beneath impervious rocks known as 'cap' rocks and held in porous rocks known as 'reservoir' rocks, while the remainder reaches the surface and simply evaporates or leaks away.
>
> It follows that the location of ancient shorelines, impervious and porous rocks, are important factors in the search for oil.

Mike drew cross-sections of two typical oil and gas traps: the anticline and the salt dome. The anticline is a convex fold in the rock strata, frequently in the form of an arch, where oil is trapped beneath a cap rock such as shale or shaly limestone.

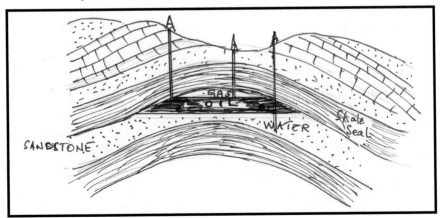

Structural traps 1: The anticline

The salt dome is a plug of rock salt which, because of its buoyancy, rises through the rock layers, arching them upwards and forming traps where oil and gas might accumulate.

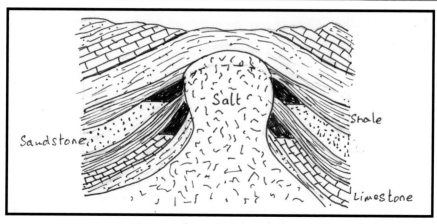

Structural traps 2: The salt dome

Geologists attempt to predict the presence of oil in the ground by surveying exposed rocks on the surface. A dried-up river bed, or wadi, where the water has sliced through the earth and exposed a cross-section of sedimentary rocks, is a good place to look. Wadis provide useful clues of what lies beneath the surface. Examination of several wadis can help a geologist build up a picture of the rock strata in between. In some places, the thickness of a bed can reveal where an ancient shoreline has been.

Fossils provide more clues. Oil was only found in rocks of a certain age, and palaeontologists would analyse fossils in order to determine the age and distribution of a particular rock bed. 'Thus you can tell where you are by the fossils, which bed you're in, what age, and what you're likely to find above and below,' explained Mike.

The role of the petroleum geologist was to bring all this information together in assessing the oil prospects of a particular area:

We measure sections of rocks in various areas, using wadis and exposed flanks of anticlines etc., trace the shorelines, map the structures, look for fossils and any indications of oil seepages, bitumen etc.

Mapping an anticline and working out the structure from the dips, faults and folds is a long complicated job, surveying being an important part. Measuring the thickness and dip and calculating the exact or approximate presence of a buried shoreline is also complicated as you'll understand.

But suitable rocks and good structures at the surface could not guarantee the presence of oil and gas – such was the promise and the disappointment of exploring for oil:

A beautiful structure does not mean that oil will be found there, and many wells that have been drilled after this business has been worked out do not yield oil. An anticline on the surface does not necessarily mean that the older buried rocks are also folded, so an extra test is made by geophysical means, by firing dynamite charges on the surface and measuring the reflected sound waves, which give the buried structure. Similarly there may be a buried anticline when the surface rocks are almost horizontal, as at

Moreton and Market Weighton, so geophysics can also help there. All these things combine in the search for oil.

MIKE'S FIRST POSTING was in Palestine. He was due to arrive in November 1945. He travelled down to London to spend time with Heather before his departure, and there was the small matter of inoculations to see to. Their last afternoon was spent together in Kew Gardens, London, when Mike's arm was still sore from the injections he had received. He then returned to Huddersfield to await news of his ship.

On 31 October 1945, Mike sent Heather a telegram: 'DON'T COME MAY SAIL SATURDAY LETTER FOLLOWING.' The letter following described his frustration at not being able to see Heather again before his departure, and told of the rush of last-minute preparations:

Disappointing isn't it, darling? I waited until the last possible moment and what do you think – they've sent me word to be ready to leave by Liverpool by Friday, probably to set sail on Saturday, having first to go to the Passport Office. So it's a damned unlucky happening, but I'm afraid it's no good coming up to Hudds, as from now on I'm haring around like a scalded cat … there's always the chance that I may not be going yet, as I've not had the name of my ship.

This was wishful thinking. On 8 November came the telegram that confirmed that Mike was definitely on his way: 'EMBARK TOMORROW CHICK ADIOS.'

As the troopship sailed out of Liverpool docks on 9 November, Mike could only imagine what the future held. No doubt he carried many uncertain images in his mind of the adventure that lay ahead, pictures of the people, the places and the terrain, but he could be confident of his relationship with Heather. The letters they exchanged over the next five years would sustain them both during Mike's prolonged absences abroad.

Perhaps the physical hardships of field exploration would at times test Mike's loyalty to the Company and his dedication to the work, but his relationship with Heather endured and strengthened. Home leave was allowed only once every two years, which meant long periods apart. In an age before email and reliable telephone links, letters and the occasional telegram were the only ways to communicate. Even during his darkest moments, Mike could not forget the happy times he had spent with Heather. In February 1948, recovering in Mukalla from a bout of malaria, he wrote to her:

It's funny but that afternoon I had decided to move my bed from the large one … to a pokey little one at the back of the house. I was delirious and knew it vaguely … I remember murmuring something like this … 'It was raining, and there was a mist on the mountain. The trees were all dripping and the rain was pattering on the car. And we wanted to climb the mountain, but it was raining too hard, and the road and the grass was all wet'… Could you identify that, darling? It was the day we went to Garth Smilog.

These memories, the rocks of the earth and the cold wind flowing over the moorland, would be with him always.

*Mike as a lad
growing up in Huddersfield*

*Mike and his mother Lucy
on holiday in Torquay, 1947*

1   Pastor John Stock, 'History of the Salendine Nook Chapel', 1874.
2   Percy Stock, *Foundations*, published by Edward Mortimer, Halifax, 1933.
3   *Huddersfield Daily Examiner* (date unknown).
4   The Potter Mortons, called Pot'oon Mortons because of the pot ovens they used to fire the clay.
5   Despite Mike's belief that money had been left by John Morton, the bequest was in fact made by Samuel Brighouse, the
     other Huddersfield Greenhorn.
6   Written on 9 January 1946, from a field camp in the Zerqa Valley, Jordan.

*Mike and Heather
on their wedding day, 1949*

Mike and Don Beydoun, c.1960

Chapter 3: Holy City

Palestine and Trans-Jordan, November 1945–December 1946

'Here is a place whose atmosphere is peace, where political and religious jealousies can be forgotten and international unity fostered and developed.'
Field Marshall Lord Allenby, 1933

The world of Palestine was a far cry from the cold, damp streets of Huddersfield town. The country was in a unique position as home to three major religions. It was an increasingly dangerous land, however, and Mike's arrival at the Palestinian port of Haifa coincided with a growing tension between the British, the Arabs and the Jews.

Haifa was a busy port, the terminus of IPC's southern pipeline. Here an invisible river of crude oil arrived from the mighty Kirkuk field to be pumped into tankers anchored offshore. In November 1945, Haifa was also the Company's headquarters for its Middle Eastern operations, the hub of an expanding exploration business. However, with civil unrest rising and the future of Palestine as an independent state increasingly uncertain, it would not be long before exploration headquarters were moved to the safer surrounds of Tripoli in Lebanon.

Mike's stay in Haifa was brief, and on 27 November he set off for Jerusalem which was to be his base for the next two years. He drove a Company 15 cwt. Chevrolet utility truck. 'It was like an armoured car,' wrote Mike, 'and about as comfortable as a tank.'

His home in Jerusalem was the YMCA in King David Street, reputed to be one of the most beautiful YMCAs in the world. In 1933 Field Marshall Lord Allenby, in opening the building, had remarked: 'Here is a place whose atmosphere is peace, where political and religious jealousies can be forgotten and international unity fostered and developed,' and these words were inscribed at the entrance to the building in Hebrew, English and Arabic. This message was also said to be reflected in the design of the building which was symbolic and peaceful, bringing together the different religious faiths of the region by reflecting early architectural styles of Judaism, Christianity and Islam.

Yet Jerusalem at this time was a place where gleaming symbolism ended and grim reality began. Conflicting messages had been given by the British Government about the use of Palestine as a prospective national home for the Jews. The Balfour Declaration set the ball rolling in 1918:

His Majesty's Government view will favour the establishment in Palestine of a National Home for the Jewish people, and will use their best endeavours to facilitate the achievement of this object, it being clearly understood that nothing shall be done which may prejudice the civil and religious rights of existing non-Jewish communities in Palestine, or the rights and political status enjoyed by Jews in any other country.

British forces had occupied Jerusalem shortly after this declaration was made and, since 1922, Palestine had been governed under a British mandate approved by the League of Nations.

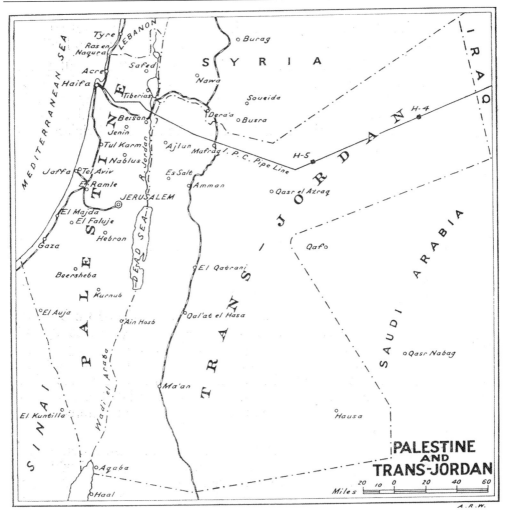

Palestine and Trans-Jordan in 1945
© *IraqPetroleum Company Limited*

The Jewish population began to rise, increasing from about 55,000 in 1917 to 650,000 by 1948. Various commissions, conferences and committees had come and gone, without achieving lasting consensus between Arabs and Jews. At the outbreak of World War II a truce was struck but did not hold for long; a terrorist Jewish faction carried out a number of violent incidents from 1942 on.

Nonetheless, to a young geologist on his first trip abroad, here was a new city to explore. He set out in search of the Palestine Museum, took a wrong turn, and ended up in the Old City. This was the real Arab Quarter, the true Bazaar, quite unlike anything Mike had experienced so far. It was 'a sticky business,' he wrote afterwards, 'negotiating through the narrow streets, so narrow in parts that I had to walk sideways through them.' There were low arches, making it dark and gloomy like a church crypt, and stretching over a wide area. When at last he emerged, momentarily startled by the glare of the midday sun, he quickly recovered his sense of direction.

In the afternoon, after lunch with Deputy Chief Geologist F. E. Wellings[1] and his wife, Mike completed his tour of the city by visiting the Mount of Olives, Rachel's Tomb, the Church of Nations, and the Church of the Nativity at Bethlehem. He bought some Christmas presents with his last 500 mils (10 shillings – 50p.), but these were stolen or swept up from his room by mistake the next day. 'I'm pretty mad about that,' he wrote, 'but it was my fault for leaving them lying in a scrap of paper among some old cigarette packets.'

Mike could be forgiven if his early days in the Middle East resembled the meanderings of a homesick tourist, for they were only letting him in gently for what was to come. His sightseeing complete, he was soon introduced to his colleagues in the IPC office on the outskirts of Jerusalem. There followed a number of familiarization trips, the first a guided tour of southern Palestine in the company of Norval E. Baker, the Chief Geologist, and Wellings. They made an amiable pair, Baker, the older man, was an American 'with a hell of a sense of humour'; Wellings was about 44 years old, plump, 'a very nice guy'. Both men were experts in the geology of the Middle East and highly respected for their work in the field.

The following day, the combined talents of Baker and Wellings were stretched by a more challenging task. They picked Mike up from the YMCA and set out to visit a Company camp at Kurnub, situated south-east of Beersheba, along the way taking a picture of him proudly wearing a new hat. About eight kilometres from Beersheba, along a bumpy track, they stopped for lunch and to examine a geological section, an exposed cliff, under which lay a pond, the only water around. An Arab was watering his horse in the muddy pool and the stench of camel dung permeated the air. As the geologists left the cliff, a gust of wind snatched Mike's hat away and deposited it 'plonk in the middle of the pond', where it capsized and sank. With the aid of a shovel, Wellings and Baker retrieved and presented the hat to Mike – a miserable, dripping object returned to a rookie geologist with a sagging sense of self-esteem.

Other aspects of a geologist's life – not documented in the text books – would be revealed. On one occasion, two geologists had carried out an impressive piece of research into a rock formation farther south, earning a bottle of whisky from an appreciative Wellings who christened the formation 'Whisky' Limestone. This was very much Wellings' style; a few weeks later, he would arrive at Mike's camp complete with bottle of cognac which, he claimed, was kept for 'snake bites'.

They retired for the night; the superior company tents and comfortable beds could offer no protection against the effect of the wilderness on the imagination of a 21-year-old geologist. Mike promptly fell asleep, only to half-wake in the early hours to find himself in pitch-darkness, without a sound anywhere, just a sixth-sense that someone was moving about inside his tent. He tried to speak, but was unable to utter a sound, nor even a croak; he tried to move but couldn't. Eventually, struggling against the weight of blackness that threatened to smother him, he uttered a low moan. 'That proved I was alive,' he wrote, 'but the stillness remained, and it was terrifying.'

Despite his degree in geology, Mike had much to learn about working in the field especially from his more experienced colleagues. Two geologists in particular would become major influences on his work. The first was Sami Nasr, an immaculate dresser for all occasions; a man who once visited a drilling site 'dressed more befitting a Royal Garden Party than an oil rig spattered in mud.'[2] The second was a geologist who first appeared at a party thrown by Sami on their return to Jerusalem, a 'Frenchman who looks like a German' called René Wetzel.

René was the scientific leader of Mike's first expedition. Mike's description of him was hardly surprising, since René came from a part of France with a strong German heritage: Alsace. He was born in Luxembourg in 1909 and had become a Company employee in 1937 when the firm he was working for was taken over by IPC. During World War II he had served in the geographic service of the French Army of the Levant before returning to work for IPC at the end of the war. The friendship René formed with Mike, 15 years his junior, would last until René's death in 1971. Mike was always eager to remind people of the debt he owed René in learning his trade. René was very much Mike's mentor in the early days.[3]

Mike wrote to Heather from Jerusalem, finishing in an upbeat mood, having enjoyed Sami's party and looking forward to his first proper expedition. 'Tomorrow I leave for Trans-Jordan for a few days,' he noted with anticipation.

THE RIFT VALLEY is the most remarkable geological feature of the region once known as Trans-Jordan. It marks the boundary between the African and the Arabian Plates, running from Lake Tiberias in the north through the Gulf of Aqaba to form the East African Rift Valley far to the south. The same processes that formed the Rift Valley created the Dead Sea, a depression filled with salt water. The Dead Sea is landlocked, with water flowing in from the River Jordan and other minor tributaries, but there is no outflow, and its surface lies some 400 metres below sea level.

Even the earliest explorers to the Dead Sea had been aware of gas and oil seepages and lumps of bitumen along its shore. The Romans named it *Lacus Asphaltitis* and collected bitumen from its surface. It occurred to the early geologists that the original source of the oil was to be found in the rocks buried beneath the sea. Several geologists carried out surveys of the region. These culminated in G. S. Blake's 1939 account of the geology of Trans-Jordan, together with the first geological map.

Like Palestine, Trans-Jordan was a mandated territory under British influence. After World War II, an IPC subsidiary company, Petroleum Development Trans-Jordan Limited, began a comprehensive study of the territory. In December 1945, René Wetzel was instructed by F. E. Wellings to study the eastern side of the Jordan Valley/Dead Sea rift and, together with Mike, began the work on 1 January 1946.

The routine of their lives for the next 18 months was quickly set as they camped at various sites in the eastern and southern parts of the territory. Sometimes a full team of geologists would work together as a single team while at other times they would pair up to explore different areas. At the start of the expedition they were provided with one chain man, two drivers, one cook, one mess servant and five labourers. Casual labourers were difficult to recruit in the area and their wages were consequently high, especially during the ploughing season.

Mike described the difficulties they experienced in those early days:

It was pay day in the camp and we had bags of trouble. Everyone wanted more than they were entitled to get, and consequently at about 6 p.m. the chain man came in with a message that the labourers and drivers wanted to quit. So right away René told him to get the names of those who were going in the morning and damn me, not one of them wanted to go then. The cook is the only one we want to get rid of, and he doesn't want to go, but he's going right enough.

The labourers had a way of bursting into song at the slightest excuse. They would seize on a phrase and sing it to rhythm in pitching monotone. One day, before moving a heavy box, some of them began talking about food. Suddenly, they burst out chanting: '*Lahme, lahme, lahme, mangaria mang–gar–ee–ah*!' – meaning 'meat, meat, meat, food, food.'

On another occasion, the men were handling long 'T' pieces of wood, about a metre long. As one passed it to the other, they chanted in Arabic, 'Shove it up your arse …'

Odeh was Mike's servant for a time. One day, Odeh cautiously approached Mike and asked: 'Please sir, what meaning bloody hell?'

Mike tried to explain in Arabic but could not get his point across. But Odeh persisted: 'Please sir, what meaning shit?'

'Odeh,' said Mike, who had recently treated him for stomach ache, 'what happens when I give you purge?'

'Nothing, sir, purge no good. I want 20 purge.'

Mike was at a loss to know how to reply to this, until he thought of another labourer, Toma, whom he'd purged earlier in the day.

'Odeh, why did Toma run into the wadi this morning?'

'Don't know sir, I not go with him.'

Mike had become camp doctor by default. He knew no medicine, of course; for headache – aspirin; for stomach – purge; for cuts – iodine. By some miracle his patients always seemed to recover and were very grateful. His reputation quickly spread. In Mafraq he often heard strangers say to their friends, or to his driver '*Wallah*, Mr Morton *quois*.'[4]

But there was no use in trying to explain the finer points to Odeh, and it was left to Toma to put him right.

THEY ESTABLISHED A series of flying camps, small encampments away from the main base. Although the presence of exposed outcrops at Zerqa Main saved tedious trench work, much time was spent on daily, tiring, climbing trips across scarps which had been described by an earlier traveller as being 'inaccessible even to well-trained monkeys'.

For the geologists, there were times when exploration was a miserable business. They slept in a small two-man tent, which René christened 'the ruddy fox-hole'. Lying on his camp bed after a hard day's work in the sodden countryside, Mike described the scene outside his small tent in the Zerqa Valley:

It rained cats and dogs last night and today, and I can hear the river rushing past, roaring and gurgling as it races over its rock-strewn bed.

During the winter months it could rain heavily for days, making transport difficult and restricting the area of their surveys. Tracks might be inaccessible to loaded transport for several days after the rain.

Working in these conditions was always going to be challenging, but transport problems began to dominate their lives. First, it was difficult to recruit decent drivers. Good drivers commanded a premium, an extra expense that the geologists were unable to meet. 'This is unbelievable but it is true,' they started in their monthly report, venting their frustrations at the driver of one of their Fordson trucks. This driver did not know where to find the air pump on his truck and, of course, he could not operate it. On a soft patch of ground, when he needed to use four-wheel drive, he was unable to operate the gear levers. But perhaps they were fortunate that he was driving a vehicle at all, since vehicle breakdowns were commonplace.

And then there was the cook, the one they had wanted to get rid of:

The cook is damn' awful. If I ever marry a woman who cooks like he does, I'll get a divorce on the grounds of cruelty or attempted murder. Today I took over, being Mess President, and I cooked a huge super pancake for René and myself. Then I made some delicious coffee, and played hell with the cook and our personal servant. The latter is the dumbest creature on God's earth, surely he's got less brain than a camel. ... If you can curse well enough, you don't need any Arabic.

There were some compensations, and a few creature comforts to be found in the camp. Writing to Heather from 'The Wilderness', Mike described a cosy domestic scene:

We've got a camp here, Chick. It's a nice camp too. I've got a tent, all of my own, a cute tent, 10' x 10' x 10', with a wee hidey-hole at the back too, where I can keep wine, women, and what have you. I've a petrol-pressure lamp which is quite as good as an electric lamp, a nice high camp bed, and there's a fine set of canvas pockets running along the bottom of the roof, where it begins to slant, so that I can put your photo in, and look up at you while I'm in bed, about 18" away. Oh, if only you didn't look like a schoolteacher!

New Year's Day 1946 was celebrated in true exploration style:

René returned after all last night and he brought two bottles of whisky and bottles of beer, so we had a New Year's Eve celebration. Just think, this is the first bottle of whisky that I've ever bought. Beer is scarce, because of the boycott on Jewish goods in these Arab countries, so is butter, jam and tea, consequently we may starve. Arab food is very poor, the bread is terrible, so we don't eat it. Our camp is in beautiful country. There are lots of green trees here, rolling hills, ploughed land, and many birds and sheep. Really Chick it's a fine life this, except for the lack of women.

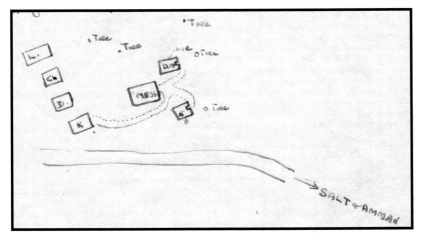

Mike's sketch of the camp in the Zerqa Valley

The work was arduous. Twice a day for six days they took off their socks and shoes, rolled up their trouser legs, and waded across the river Zerqa to look at geological sections on the other side and returned hours later. The rain continued to fall, leaving the slopes so sodden that on one occasion the ground gave way beneath Mike's feet and sent him crashing into a tangle of oleanders that lined the stream bed of the Wadi Hune.

With René in charge, Mike was finding it difficult at times 'living with one man all the time, especially if he's a foreigner and senior to you'. Matters came to a head one evening when Mike returned to camp to find René 'in hell of a temper' with Ahmed, the chain man. René had been doing the accounts all day and demanded an old bill from Mike who, already exhausted after a long drive, was in no mood to co-operate. René insisted on coming back to Mike's tent to watch him search through his belongings.

'Well, do you mind if I have my tea?' asked Mike.

René went into a rage.

Mike fumed:

He's the most meticulous and excitable man I know. A great fellow really but in those two points he differs from me. I'm not meticulous. I chuck my gear anywhere, cultivate a huge store of dirty washing, keep files with nothing in the right place and am generally lackadaisical. I never lose my temper outright with these people because, personally, I don't care two hoots for them. But René will poke his nose here and there, do things as soon as he thinks of them (usually too hasty) and wants everything done at once.

OCCASIONALLY, IN A brief escape from desert life, Mike and René would visit Amman for news and supplies, staying in the Hotel Philadelphia. 'There are some peculiar people in this lounge,' observed Mike:

Four doctors from here and Palestine, a tall dark sinister lookin' feller wearing a brown pin-stripe and navy blue shirt, a woman, probably English, a half-dwarf, and a fellow who looks like a gigolo. Then there's a most peculiar fat old man – like this:

Then there's the owner of the hotel, an old man who is gnarled and wrinkled but looks like Abdul the Damned[5] when young.

This damned hotel is bug-ridden and last night they got me. My arms and neck have come up in lumps and I caught one this morning. René was laughing as I told him about them tonight in the bar, and whatdyaknow, as I spoke I saw one crawling up his collar – last laugh [to me].

The waiter looks like Jerry Colonna[6] – you know – and he's just as funny.

THERE WAS A darker side, however. One day, not far from their camp on the Lisan Peninsula, the geologists were on a short recce when they saw three riders on horseback approaching: two Europeans and an Arab, their guide. Both Europeans carried revolvers strapped to their waists.

The geologists had good reason to be suspicious of the riders, armed Europeans on the Peninsula being a rare sight, and the Company being the sole concessionaire for the purpose of oil exploration. Nevertheless, as a matter of courtesy, Mike and his companion Chevenart invited the riders to dismount and join them in the camp mess for some tea.

The visitors presented a curious sight in the confines of the mess tent. Their leader, a small, red-haired man who, in Mike's words, had 'a nose that would have put any parrot in the shade', said he was Dutch. The other, 'a brute of a man, tall and heavily built with a very repulsive face' was a Pole. They said they were employed by the Palestinian Potash Company, working around the Dead Sea, otherwise they were tight-lipped about their activities. The geologists made polite conversation, discussing the trivialities of camp life, and this appeared to relax both parties, apart from the moment when the geologists mentioned that they had no radio, at which their visitors expressed some surprise. They parted company cordially enough, inviting the geologists to visit their potash plant at the southern end of the Dead Sea before riding away, leaving a trail of dust in their wake.

Two days later, a few kilometres away from camp, the geologists were surveying the Lisan Peninsula, 'a desolate, desert-like place where nothing grows'. On a hilltop, they had a panoramic view and caught sight of a party of men on horseback riding out from a narrow wadi, about 1.5 kilometres away. The riders saw them, and one galloped across to speak to the geologists. As he rode up the hillock, they could see that he was a Jew, and that he carried an automatic pistol. He arrived and introduced himself as Abraham. With the geologists wary and mindful of the fact that they were dealing with an armed stranger, their conversation was necessarily brief and Abraham gave nothing away. They exchanged brief pleasantries and the Jew departed, turning his horse and galloping away to join his companions.

Through binoculars, the shimmering outlines of the three riders came into focus. The geologists could see that they appeared to be carrying out survey work, but without instruments. Presently the riders disappeared and, once the geologists had completed their tasks, they moved to the other end of the Peninsula.

Again, they had company: the geologists were not the only ones interested in the far side of Lisan. The three riders were also there, gathered together on a disused wartime landing strip. As the geologists motored by, the riders ignored them completely, disregarding their uncertain waves. When the geologists reached their destination, they looked back and found – much to their surprise – that the riders had disappeared into the blue.

'All this made me wonder what they were at,' Mike recalled, 'because Jews are not welcome in Trans-Jordan and, at our camp, they'd remarked that they were expecting someone by boat.' All this seemed more intriguing when the geologists returned to town and saw the riders' tents, 'neatly hidden in the orchard of the best house in the district'. Next morning, as they drove past again, they noticed two radio masts protruding from the trees.

The geologists speculated about the purpose of this mysterious group. René thought that they might be prospecting and surveying, illicit activities since the IPC had exclusive exploration rights to these parts. Mike's ideas were more romantic. They were making a secret arms cache on the deserted and little-visited Lisan Peninsula – no one could possibly live there; or they were expecting illegal immigrants who might have obtained a plane through mass Jewish co-operation abroad and planned somehow to land on Lisan; or they were setting up a temporary broadcasting station of the illegal Jewish radio Vaad Lenim.

'However,' Mike concluded, 'we may never learn, or stumble on to something and get killed – one never knows.'

MOONLIGHT CAST HUGE shadows beyond the pale white tents of the Company camp and soothed the harsh landscape in a pallid glow. A breeze from the west gently caressed the canvas of the tents and the air felt warmer than it had done earlier in the evening. The view across the Dead Sea was as clear now as it had been at noon. From some distant village nearer the shore to the north the faint rhythmic beating of a drum and chanting of villagers rippled across the wadi. Yet it was not quite so idyllic as it seemed. As Mike walked to the camp perimeter to stand looking out towards the sea, he remembered half a kilometre to the west the thousands of mosquitoes breeding in a brackish, foetid swamp.

He looked across to the far shore of the Dead Sea sixteen kilometres away and saw the Palestinian mountains rising like a ghostly wall sheer out of the placid moon-bathed waters. As he later wrote:

In the soft, silvery moonlight, everything looks soft and beautiful.

There was no movement; there was no sound, except that of a cough from the tent behind him. He glanced round. A huge cliff – sharply incised by a narrow wadi – towered over the camp. Following the grey pillars of soft, dry mud, his gaze was brought back to the moonlight, the shadows and the night. All was peaceful now, but the riders they had seen on the Peninsula had been a chilling reminder of another world, of an unseen storm building on the other side of the Dead Sea, of troubles in the British Mandate of Palestine.

IN THE SUMMER of 1946 Mike returned to the YMCA in Jerusalem, a gleaming white structure with a tower that dominated the surrounding buildings. 'This is my home in Jerusalem,' he wrote. 'The tower is a carillon, or melodious peal of bells which plays hymns on Sunday afternoons, making a lovely sound as darkness falls.'

The King David Hotel stood directly opposite the YMCA. As well as being a bustling hotel in the centre of Jerusalem, the King David was the base for the Secretariat of the Government of Palestine and the Headquarters of the British Forces in Palestine. Just after noon on 22 July 1946, a small party of between 15 and 20 Jews, disguised as Arab workmen, gained entrance to the hotel basement without attracting attention. They brought with them several milk churns on a truck that they unloaded and placed in the basement, which was directly below the Secretariat offices. The churns contained 225 kilograms of explosives. A small diversionary bomb was exploded outside the hotel and curious onlookers gathered on balconies to see what was happening.

Mike was working in the Company office when the bombs exploded:

At about 12:15 p.m. on Monday July 22 I was in the office, a short distance from the city, when I heard a small explosion. This was followed by sirens and about ten minutes later the all-clear was sounded. At 12:37 there was hell of a crash which I took to be the boy fooling around with the metal map-cabinet, but when I realized by his face that he suspected I was also fooling about with something, I went outside. Slowly over the hill-top rolled a gigantic mushroom of grey-brown dust and smoke, and from the direction, and as was rather to be expected, we thought it was the King David. We had to wait before leaving, and as the car reached the hilltop we saw that the south west corner of the King David had been blown out in a neat square piece.

Mike struggled through traffic and diversions to reach his room at the YMCA, from where he witnessed the full scale of the devastation:

All the window hangings had been blown out, and my window was about 80 metres from the explosion, almost opposite. There was a huge pile of rubble, plaster, laths, and somehow, owing to the steel reinforcing, all the staircases and the top floor of the six storied building were still clinging to the wall, having swung flush against it. Swarms of soldiers and Arabs were working in the rubbish, and I saw two bloody corpses of Arab workmen, killed by blast and fragments where they stood across the road. Several slightly injured people were standing below, as the YMCA was a first aid post. Most of the King David's windows were broken, although the YMCA was undamaged.

In his letter to Heather, Mike recorded what had happened earlier in the day:

At noon, a party of Jews disguised as Arab kitchen boys entered the King David by the servants' entrance, walked along to the basement dining room and held up the staff. Then some returned and proceeded to drag milk-churns and buckets full of high explosive along to the kitchen. Passing the Signals Office, an officer of the RCS popped out at the noise, and they shot him twice in the stomach – he died yesterday. Then they proceeded to fuse the high explosive. Meanwhile, two diversionary hand grenades were set off outside, causing lots of people to crowd around windows and balconies, and covering the Jews. Then they set the fuses, dashed out, shot their way to the car, and escaped. Before an alarm could be given,[7] the explosion occurred, blowing out this section with twenty-five rooms, full of staff of the Secretariat. Also the two best bars and dining room in Jerusalem were destroyed, and the barber's shop. Debris landed all around, on buses and cars, and one poor chap was killed by a steel safe. A Swedish journalist I know was photoing [sic] the first grenade spot facing the King David and as a result got four snaps of the place going up and coming down – the perfect scoop.

Now, 60 hours after the explosion, the Sappers are still clearing the debris, and I saw two more bodies extracted this afternoon. There are still about 30 or more in there, and the poor soldiers are working their guts out. Last night a fellow called Thompson was pulled out alive and hardly injured although he's rather shocked now. Three others were found alive at the beginning, after falling 15 metres at least amid the remnants of the roof. There's no hope for the rest though, and I guess the dead will be over 100. The YMCA is now a closed area and the roads are blocked, almost a state of siege persisting.

The politics of accommodation could be supported no longer: the country's demographic balance had been stretched to breaking point. The Arab population was suspicious of a British Authority that promised to protect the civil and political integrity of their country while allowing the Jewish population to grow at an alarming rate. The Jews would become ever confident in their demands for an independent Jewish state. In the midst of this cauldron, the King David bombs had been ignited.

EXPLORATION LIFE COULD be a lonely business. Of course, there was the camaraderie of Mike's colleagues in the field, but returning to Jerusalem to write up field reports in the office and staying in the YMCA, despite its attractions, could be a solitary experience. A tour of duty lasted two years: he was not eligible for leave until mid-1947. His mother and sister were in Huddersfield, Heather was teaching in London and an endless stream of letters kept his only contact with them alive. Working a long-term relationship over a great distance could be difficult enough, since it could take weeks to receive a reply and then, like the proverbial London buses, several letters would arrive all at once. And there were always the small misunderstandings that could grow with each disjointed exchange: Mike replying to Heather's letter written before she had received his last three letters, and so on. There was no doubting the importance of mail in an age when international telephone calls were not a realistic option: expensive and of poor quality, the lines provided a daunting background of hissing and crackling sounds, as well as occasionally mimicking the human voice with a disconcerting double-echo effect.

'Jerusalem at Christmas is my next bright spot,' wrote Mike. 'Meanwhile, there's my work in the unexplored desert and my hunting and driving. Then the camp in Petra in spring – that wonderland of glorious sandstone.'

Mike had some hope of being fully knowledgeable of the geology of Trans-Jordan by the summer of 1947, which was not an impossible aspiration since he was learning from both René, who had done one half of the territory and Sami, who had done the other half.

But, as the year went on, it threatened to end in gloom. Approaching Christmas, Mike had not received any letters for two weeks and then, on travelling to Amman, he received letters that further dampened his spirits. He headed back to Jerusalem for a party, and arrived to find that his reservation at the YMCA had not been renewed, forcing him to move into a flea-bitten pension. He missed the party.

The combined effect of these events left Mike feeling at a low ebb again. He set out purposefully on a last-gasp mission to lift his spirits, and managed to do a round of parties over the holiday, including Christmas dinner at the Wellings' and culminating in dinner with the Haddads on Boxing Day.

They arrived too early at the Haddads' house, Mike dressed in checks and flannels and his Scottish friend Jock in a suit. A musical box dated 1880 provided a brief distraction and they amused themselves by humming 'Silent Night' to its creaking, brittle tune while waiting for the other guests to arrive.

The evening was memorable, though not exactly in the way the host would have intended. They sat around the dining table, a mixture of Arabs and Europeans:

The conversation was beyond me – off-colour jokes from the two Palestinian policemen, and anti-British talk from an Arab guest. These Arabs were Christians of course. Then this fellow and his wife left, and we had a very homely Christmas evening, with Mr and Mrs Haddad singing carols and listening to the gramophone, which gave us 'Die Stille Nacht' in German eight times, 'O du Fröhliche' twice, 'Art Thou Weary', 'Bluebirds Over the White Cliffs', 'Lili Marlene' and 'Onward Christian Soldiers'.

There was a wonderful Christmas tree there, with candles – it was more a German Christmas than anything.

Next morning he left for Mafraq.

1   Frank Ernest Wellings, known throughout the company as 'F. E.', gained a first-class honours degree at Cambridge before becoming a geologist with the Shell Company in Mexico. He met his wife 'L. C.' on a trip to Texas. In 1929 he joined IPC as senior geologist with responsibility for the early appraisal of drilling in the Kirkuk field. A full account of his contribution to the geological knowledge of the Middle East can be found in the *AAPG Trek of the Oil Finders: A History of Exploration for Petroleum*, 1975, written by E. W. Owen and published by the American Association of Petroleum Geologists.

2   Frank Gosling, *IPC Newsletter*, Issue 86, April 1995.

3   Their collaboration in Jordan was published later, in R. Wetzel, and D. M. Morton, *Contribution à la Geologie de la Trans-Jordanie: Notes et Memoirs sur le Moyen-Orient; Contributions à la Geologie de la Peninsule Arabique*, 1959, Mus. Nat. and Hist. Natur., Paris, France.

4   'By God, Mr Morton is good.'

5   Abdul the Damned was a 1935 film about a Sultan tormented by fear of assassination.

6   Jerry Colonna was an American comic who mimicked an operatic voice and admitted that by doing so he had 'destroyed many beautiful songs'.

7   Later accounts claimed that telephone warnings had been given by the terrorists.

Chapter 4: Recapitulation

Trans-Jordan, October 1946–July 1947

'De longue date, la vallé du Jourdain et la Mer Morte, la plus bassé depression terrestre, ont retenue l'attention des géologues'
Contribution à la Géologie de la Trans-Jordanie
René Wetzel and Mike Morton

His field reports of the time give no indication of the transformation that was taking place in Mike's understanding of the desert, its people and their culture. He teamed up with Sami Nasr at the end of August 1946, and they worked together for the next nine months. Between November 1946 and 23 January 1947, they made a survey of three geological structures: Arfa, Hasa and Sowan, previously discovered by F. E. Wellings. The reports they filed were factual, of course, accounting for their journeys, distances travelled, the stratigraphy of the region and any other items of note. What they did not – and could not – record were Mike's feelings and experiences during this time. These he kept to his letters to Heather which, despite their purple passages, tell us much about his growing attachment to the desert:

> Today I was standing on a steep scarp looking westwards, around noon. A panorama of rolling brown hills spread out in front, all low and of the same height, stretching out to the horizon until it merged into a dark, even line. No sign of life was visible, but ragged clouds were marching abreast towards me trailing tattered grey streamers that seemed like torn cloth flapping in the wind. A cold south-west wind was blowing, and odd patches of blue sky peeked out.

The moment briefly brought back memories of the life he had left behind in Huddersfield:

> I had that old feeling I used to get when I stood on the moors back home, and faced the fresh breeze that always blows across that moorland plateau. I turned as if to see Marsden on my right, or Pule Hill, and the Maltham Road behind me, but the warped, fractured face of the ugly Sowan dome, with its burnt out flints scarring the slopes, was all that met my eye.

With this panorama spread before him, Mike's mind began to wander, imagining the passage of time through this barren land:

> There is a strange silence in the desert too. I've often walked to the crest of some low mound, and standing perfectly still, gazed about me to the infinite vastness of the wide horizons. Not a sound can be heard. I listen and strain my ears, until I feel that

something is pressing in my eardrums: that the very air itself has been withdrawn and that my soul is completely detached from my body.

Then come the visions, sights that make my spine freeze, my blood chill, and a peculiar tearful sentimentality comes over me. I see the wandering Jews, with their patriarchal leaders, wearily driving their herds before them – lost in the desert, with the prospect of wandering from one scant pasture to another, as each local tribe may permit. I see the bearded Assyrians, with strange armour, riding on their mighty conquest, trampling down the camel thorns, and raising a mighty dust cloud. Then the thrifty Nabataeans, trekking from Petra to the Sirhan on their trade route to Syria, watering at Jaffar and Bair, where Abraham watered his flocks thousands of years ago. Then the columns of Rome clash by, short swords and shields, ancient Empire-builders with a lust for further conquest. From the south ride the Arabs, lean and tough, breaking into civilization to build another mighty Empire, and joining to make a unified nation, with a powerful religion. And still they ride, to join the distant clash of battle, with the Crusaders in the west – Englishmen, Frenchmen, who built their imposing fortresses on the desert's fringe.

Action in the desert, he observed, was momentous and short; the spirits of the desert walked hand-in-hand with the living of the day:

The tribes then ride, the long muskets crackle, and the roaring of stolen camels mingles with the acrid dust. And then, the tribes become united, this time with a mission and an English leader rides with their mighty chiefs. The thin-lipped, long-featured Lawrence passes by; lost in his thoughts of suffering, he rides like a warrior, a thief, and a man of might. And the roar of ghostly Rolls Royce engines, as they whine past Thalaitawat and through Bair, to drop down to the flat empty plain of Jaffar, brings me the vision of those other Englishmen who fought in the desert to kill the Turk.

It was perhaps inevitable that in this environment Mike would come to feel a close affinity with the Bedouin:

The Bedouin are unchanging and possess the magnificence of a people who have long dwelled on the earth. Their lore is their life, their religion is their power and though weak in body, their will to live their hard, unenviable way, gives them nobility, and respect – a true understanding of which is impossible by a man of civilized standards. Only a recapitulation of ten thousand years can bring out the greatness of these links with the past.

In his travels Mike collected fossils. He also found evidence from a more recent past: an ancient knife handle, lying where it fell in some *ghazzu* many years before; cartridge cases dating from 1874 clustered on hilltops, usually near the Mecca-pointing compass of a solitary grave; a piece of Roman pottery; a Byzantine fragment of an opaque glass; vertebrae; a sheep's skull; a camel ring; and an ancient ramrod, all telling of the comings and goings of people through the desert in time.

'You must allow for the fact that the whiskers are ginger, but the moustache is there, except it doesn't stretch quite that far, and the gazelle, somebody else probably killed that.'

'The Three Sisters'

One evening the geologists witnessed a spectacular sky and Mike recorded the joys of watching a winter sunset in the desert. 'Only in this season do the clouds gather, and the setting sun turns them golden in the west, while eastwards, rosy red cumulus hang like fat pigs in the blue loneliness.'

Writing in the moonlight shadow of Jebel Thalaitawat, Mike set down his impressions of the wilderness around him. 'It's cold here now,' he began, 'but under the shadow of three conical hills, the three sisters as the Arabs call them, the wind is not so bad. Outside, the moon is shining, and twinkling on the dewdrops that hang from the camel shrubs. There's a faint, aromatic smell of wormwood, mingling with the softness of tamarisk, and the chalk cliffs of Thalaitawat tower above our tents like snow-capped mountains.'

Lawrence had passed this way to attack the Turkish Army to the west. 'Next day,' wrote Lawrence, 'we passed to the left of Thalaitawat, the 'Three Sisters' whose clean white peaks were landmarks on their lofty watershed for a day's journey all about; and went down the soft rolling slopes beyond. The exquisite November morning had a softness in it like an English summer; but its beauty had to be fought off.'[1]

ONE DAY MIKE drove to Jaffar to see his Bedouin friends at the fort. He immediately fell into a conversation with the Sharwish while the time-honoured coffee and tea were brewing. They talked at first of the desert life, of gazelle shooting, hunting, then – after a brief discussion about beards and moustaches – of the government and women. They laughed at one poor legionnaire who was too young to have a wife, and they considered the merits of Arab and foreign women. Mike avoided the usual line about having three wives and six children and told the Sharwish that he had a bint back in England whom he was going to marry one day.

Mike had no need for an interpreter now: in fact he hadn't used an interpreter for months. His Arabic was good and he had worked hard to achieve the right inflections in his voice, making use of gestures as an aid to communication. He had watched with amused detachment as his Mafraq friends, using bad pronunciation with an English voice, tried to converse with the Arabs. It was a difficult language, of course, with no available books on the subject and no regularity about the verbs. 'However,' he reported, 'many words are derived from one root and if one gets that part of it, one can usually guess the sense by catching the tone, and the expression.'

The conversation suddenly became profound. 'If a man goes on a journey,' said the Sharwish, 'and returns from that journey, then it is by the will of God. He is in the hands of God, and so are we all, and whatever we make of our lives, it is God's doing, for we are His children.'

Mike said nothing at first, taking in the exquisiteness of the language and sentiment.

The Sharwish asked: 'Do people in England, and America, and the world think of God and his ways?'

'In the towns,' Mike replied, 'there is little time to think of God. There life is fast, and entangled with many little things so that the mind has no room for thoughts of working with God. There the people are many, and man has made so many things with which to occupy his brain that God is pushed aside, accepted, yet without devotion of mind. In the desert we have time to think of God. We feel that He is near us and that He watches over us. The desert is so wide and open that we cannot hide from Him, so we seek Him and understand Him for we realize that we are His followers, and that we are in His hands.'

'*Masbut*,' said the Sharwish: 'That is so.'

They talked about Christians and the difference between Greek Orthodox, Catholic and Protestant. Eventually the twinkle-eyed Sharwish asked, 'What kind of Christian are you?'

'I am not a worshipper of Jesus,' said Mike. 'Whatever I do, God will know, and whatever I do, that is the will of God. I do not see why I must be a Christian to be a believer in God, for surely there can be only one God in the world.

'I do not know God,' concluded Mike. Despite his experiences in the desert, this would never change and although the Bedu were Moslems, it would make no particular difference to their dealings with him; to them he would become known as Morton Bey.[2]

THESE WERE STRANGE times for Mike. In February 1947 he left the true desert, with its vast expanse of rolling, gentle, chalky hills and flat level flint-strewn plains, and spent a few weeks in Ma'an, the southernmost town in Trans-Jordan. Ma'an was a straggling mud-walled village, with a thousand ebony crows. 'And nightly,' he recounted, 'these crows gather on the tombs that climb the western hill, the cemetery, and here they seem to hold a funeral service for the dead.'

The street immediately below the hill is filled with coal-black Abyssinians, who peer out from behind snow-white robes. Higher up the street is the archetypal fat village butcher, and 'Shell', the benzene man, strokes his beard and spits into the dusty street. In the post office a Lugosian dwarf scrambles among the mail bags and chins himself on the counter to squint with evil ferocity at some solitary customer. The postmaster, in his neat suit and flowing headgear, blinks owlishly from behind his tortoiseshells – business is only one day a week, for the train comes Saturday and leaves on Sunday. In the street, a motley passel of zinc-ointment anointed brats mill and throng, sniffling their streaming noses and rubbing their red-rimmed ophthalmic eyes. The solid white-fronted shops and houses that line the main street belie the broken unfinished dereliction that lies behind this frontage. Round this corner, if you follow the huge crack in that adobe wall, you will come to the house of Mohammed Pasha Abu Tayi, the powerful Howeitat sheikh. While that whitewashed building on the hill is the Police Headquarters where Commandant Habbis Bey el Mojjali flashes a gold-toothed smile at his fellow legionnaires.

This was Ma'an, where the old caravanserai used to gather before leaving for the Hejaz via Jebel Tubeik, or Syrian Palmrya with its towering columns and the Damascus Suq via the Wadi Sirhan, or the descent of Wadi Arabah, the great Rift Valley *en route* for Palestine, Sinai and Egypt. Those were the days of Ma'an's greatness.

A kilometre or so from the village stood the Petra Hotel where Abu Yacob, an Armenian, squeezed the last drop of financial blood from the few travellers who crossed the desert to see the rosy Nabataean city from which he named his hotel.

Petra, with its silent sandstone tombs, was the real ancestor of Ma'an. The stronghold in Edom, the focus of old caravan routes, the customs house through which passed all the spices of Arabia, frankincense, myrrh, silks, gold and sandalwood, bought for Palestine's ports and Egypt's palaces. The milestones from Ma'an to Petra numbered the centuries that had passed since the ancient city flourished. An ancient civilization died there, and its history was buried with it.

Out in the desert, towards the rising sun, the tents of the Beni Howeitat were moving with their flocks. In December wet weather had come to the Tubeik and the Bedu had folded his tent in Jaffar and followed the rain. In the freshness of the thorny camel-scrub, the wormwood and dipping tamarisk, his flocks multiplied and his herds increased. And when the last black storm had spent its fury and sent its cannonades thundering among the sprawling quartzitic hills, the Arab grazed the last richness from the slopes, gathered his herds, and strapped his house to his camel.

When Auda Abu Tayi, Sheikh el Beni Howeitat, the 'Lone Wolf', father of Mike's friend Mohammed and one of Lawrence's chieftains, had set out from his rocky stronghold, there was joy among the tribe because, by the time he returned, some other tribe would be poorer by several herds. New blood feuds would soon empty a camel saddle or two. Basrah, Aden, Hadhramaut, and Syria were pillaged by the Lone Wolf, and yet his lair in the Tubeik was never plundered in revenge.

The spring of 1910 had seen a bloody battle when 300 men of the Howeitat and Beni Sakhr tribe died when Auda raided the latter's settlement near Amman, and rode hard to the south to escape his pursuers. A lonely grave near the tribal well at Bair held the bones of Auda's eldest son who had been ambushed by five feudal enemies.

Despite all this, Mike observed, the *ghazzu* was seen more as recreation than deliberate cruelty. Women and children were never harmed, tents and property were left intact, pack animals and water carriers were not stolen, prisoners were always returned, and a Bedu would never shoot at a burning light. The hospitality and courtesy of the Bedouin was supreme. By custom, he could not refuse to give food, shelter and transport to a traveller, neither could he profit by any such occasion.

Now the separation of the desert into nation-states had limited the nomadic life. In Trans-Jordan an Englishman named Glubb Pasha commanded the Arab Legion and had stopped the feuding by building strong forts at the few desert watering places. And so life in this part of the desert was peaceful:

> Petra, where I am camped now, is truly the gem of the whole country. The thousand mysterious tombs carved in the soft red and multi-coloured sandstone are but a hollow mockery to those who seek to unravel the history of this city. Castles perched on towering heights, temples of unbelievable beauty, a place of sacrifice, harsh and cruel, caps one hilltop, and the miles of broad steps, water channels and streets, tell of the progressiveness of the ancient race who built this desert city 2000 years ago. The architecture is well preserved, and the perfection of the whole is truly amazing. Even the pottery and coinage which litter the city centre is advanced, and the strategy which built this city, accessible only via a kilometre long narrow towering canyon, explains the reason for this being a trading centre, for protection could be given to all caravans, and security was absolute.
>
> So until my next letter, we leave this rose-red city while the flaming sun dips slowly in the west. Here, where our modern camera recorded scenes that have lasted throughout the centuries, as the waving oleanders crowded the valley floor: Petra, the rose-red city half as old as time, Petra, the magnificent.

'LOVER, YOU SHOULD hear it rain!' He was up in the hills at 6 a.m. with the sun rising in a clear blue sky. He was crouched in his shooting box near a well. As time passed by, Mike gazed about and, looking westwards, he saw puffy little clouds toppling down into the Wadi Arabah from the hazy hills of Palestine. 'Above these hills a paunchy cumulus was rising, with whirling thunderheads spiralling overhead. At about ten o'clock the first wisps reached Trans-Jordan, followed soon by clouds that looked like streamlined chariots with dirty under-carts.'

He travelled south to Negb Shtar and, looking back, he first saw islands, then continents of massive vapour shutting out the sun from the mountains of Petra. At Negb Shtar, there was the bitterest of cold winds blowing, and from 1,500 metres or more he could see the mountains near Akaba, 100 kilometres away, looking like molehills.

On his return, the wind blew strong and cold and the sun slanted down through murky dust clouds in the Arabah. When he reached his tent, a full gale was blowing, and suddenly the whole landscape was blotted out by a vast dust storm. It became dark as dusk and Jebel Haroun was invisible, yet there was a peculiar orange glow in the west. Then the dust passed and the first big raindrops fell, continuing intermittently for perhaps an hour; the thunder arrived, rolling and echoing across the Rift, crashing through the sandstone gorges of Petra; still the wind blew hard and furious and, by dinner time, the rain had increased to a downpour and half-minute flashes of purple lightning momentarily turned night into day.

THROUGHOUT 1946 THE papers were full of talk of conflict over the Middle East oil resources.

But Mike was pessimistic about finding oil in Trans-Jordan. As early as April 1946 he was writing, 'I'm convinced that there is or was no oil in the Jordan Valley.'

Near Mezra'a he had seen bitumen-soaked rocks, with a powerful oily smell. On the eastern shore of the Dead Sea between Zerqa Main and Mezra'a (Lisan) there were several oil seepages in the Wadi Mojil, and in the sea itself, and also gas seepages. After the last earthquake there in 1927 huge blocks of bitumen had been found floating on the sea, which was a strong indication of oil.

This, however, did not guarantee a large reservoir of oil in the ground. As a result of the rift and surrounding faults, the rock faces on either side of the Jordan Valley had been exposed, thus allowing any accumulations of oil to escape. Mike drew the structure like this:

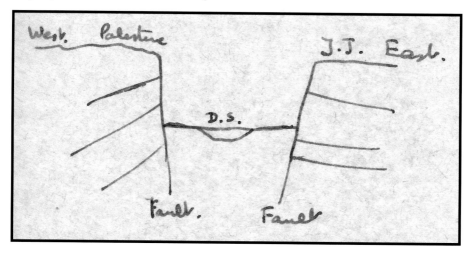

Sketch of Jordan Valley

Now you'll remember I told you that oil can escape along faults, and as these faults are very big and very old, the likelihood is that if there was any oil there, most of it will now have seeped out – so there's no point in trying.

At the end of the survey, Sami and Mike went their separate ways, Sami to stay on as the Divisional Geologist in Palestine and Trans-Jordan and marry Connie, a matron at the Jerusalem Hospital. Mike took his first spell of leave and returned to England. With Heather he made plans for their future; with his mother he went on holiday to Torquay. Then he returned to the Middle East, reporting to the Tripoli office for details of his next assignment: an expedition to southern Arabia with René Wetzel. They flew in a chartered plane from Lydda in Palestine, arriving in Aden on 30 October 1947.

---

1   T. E. Lawrence, *Seven Pillars of Wisdom*, by permission of the Trustees of the *Seven Pillars of Wisdom* Trust.
2   A sign of respect, derived from the Turkish for 'governor'.

Kurnub camp, 1 December 1945

L-R: Sami Nasr, F. E. Wellings, N. E. Baker, Mike Morton wearing 'the hat that fell in the pond'

Boxing Day 1945, Jerusalem

L-R Jim McGinty, Sami Nasr, Mrs 'L. C.' Wellings, Leo Damesin, René Wetzel, Mike Morton

***Mike's Identity Card, Haifa, August 1946*: colour section p. ii**

King David Hotel blown up 22 August 1946

A train on the Ma'an to Damascus line

'I'm writing this letter from a train. As the train stops for 30 minutes at each station, it should be quite a long letter by the time I reach Amman. I left Ma'an at eight this morning at this, the first station. It's a strange train, goods and passengers, and runs on a narrow 3'6" gauge. This is the railway that Lawrence tried to blow up. Damn, I think it's starting again.

'It's now 9:30 and we've stopped again. Actually, I'm travelling in a first class compartment on a second class ticket. Looking at the train, I could only see II and III class coaches, and as there is only one first class compartment, it's not surprising that I made the mistake. However, the guard was very nice and let me stay here without paying. Not that it really matters, as the Company pay all my expenses … .'

The approach to Petra

Chapter 5: Hadhramaut

East Aden Protectorate, November 1947

'The Hadhramaut is a land of opulence and indescribable poverty.'
Expedition to Southern Arabia
René Wetzel and Mike Morton

Any expedition, even a small one with an interest in geology rather than politics, was likely to be a dangerous catalyst in the prickly arena of southern Arabia. For the Hadhramaut was a fractured land, in both the geological and the political sense.

Aden was a British colony, first developed as a coaling station for ships passing to and from India. Its colonial status was in contrast to the surrounding territory, which was a loose confederation of tribes forming the Western and Eastern Aden Protectorates. The Hadhramaut was a long, wide river valley in the Eastern Protectorate, itself divided into the Qua'aiti and Kathiri states, each ruled by a Sultan. There was a small British political staff based in Mukalla who acted in an advisory capacity to the two rulers, and the military occasionally intervened in local affairs.

Its history had been one of tribal wars and blood feuds. Yet the efforts of British political officers, and one Harold Ingrams in particular, had brought a truce. Commencing in early 1937 and initially intended to last for three years, the so-called 'Ingrams' Peace' had been secured with 1,400 signatures from the warring tribesmen, as a result of which the country became relatively safe, roads were passable and agriculture and trade started to grow.

It still, however, required an occasional bombing by the Royal Air Force (RAF) to keep a few errant sheikhs in line. Bombing was often welcomed by both sides, being seen as a badge of honour for an ambitious sheikh, and a convenient way of ending a dispute without losing face. It was all so very orderly: warnings were issued to the offending tribe before punitive action was carried out, and bombing was used only as a last resort. But not everyone agreed with this policy – H. St. J. Philby, for instance, the famous Arabist, was critical, comparing it with the aerial bombardments carried out by Italy in the Abyssinian War of 1937.[1]

Whatever its merits, this policy brought about an interesting legacy for the geologists, as René Wetzel recorded:

> To stop some tribal disturbances the RAF bombed the Beihan area a few weeks ago.
>
> A salt mine which was hit by a bomb gave off an 'unpleasant and persistent smell' which was associated in the mind of the authorities concerned with a 'gusher' of oil.
>
> Major Seagar, the political adviser of the Western Aden Protectorates, was very keen to have this mine examined as regards the possibility of an oil field and proposed us a journey to Beihan by RAF plane.[2]

The Major's offer was carefully considered, and politely declined.

There was an established procedure for searching for oil in a foreign land. As we have seen, the Company would obtain an exploration licence, or a 'blanket' concession, which covered production as well as exploration rights.

Exploration was typically conducted in two phases. The first comprised surface geology carried out by mobile parties: the second, in cases where first indications were not entirely negative, would be geophysical research carried out by larger parties with highly specialized equipment.

The expedition to the Eastern Aden Protectorate fell into the first category. In the Aden Protectorates, a 'blanket' Exploration Permit had been obtained in 1938 by an IPC subsidiary, Petroleum Concessions Limited, and had since been renewed periodically.

In the late 1930s two geologists, R. W. Pike and H. R. Wofford, had carried out a preliminary geological survey of 220,000 square kilometres in the Eastern Aden Protectorate. It was conducted in a combined ground and aerial reconnaissance of six months' duration from 1 November 1937 to 30 April 1938. A Short Brothers' Scion Senior high-wing monoplane, chartered and maintained by Imperial Airways, was used to carry out the aerial work. Studies on the ground were both reconnaissance and detailed, and covered the line of the only existing auto road from the coast to the Hadhramaut valley; in the coastal zone east and west of Mukalla; and in the Hajar and Meifa valley, west of Mukalla and north of Ras al Khali.

Although the results had not been immediately encouraging, the Company believed that the area of the survey – the Wadi Hadhramaut and the Mahra country – held the key to the general oil possibilities of south-central Arabia. In technical language, the expedition was required to 'evaluate conclusively the oil possibilities of the sector of the basinal area flanking the basement core of central Arabia'.

The geologists would rely on their Political Liaison Officer, Tony Altounyan, to smooth the political way. Tony was a British subject, Armenian by birth, who came from a family well-known in the field of medicine in Aleppo. He had been educated in Aleppo, at the American University in Beirut and later at Emmanuel College, Cambridge. He had first joined the Company in 1932, holding various appointments in Syria, Lebanon and Palestine before leaving for war service in 1940. He returned to the Company in 1946, and was aged 42 when the expedition began.

The other members of the expedition were a Medical Officer, Doctor Mohammed Abdul Racheed Chaudri, a temporary employee of the Company who had arrived in Aden on a boat from Bombay and was promptly nicknamed 'Doc' and a wireless operator, Ahmed Hubaisly, 'a nice Palestinian *effendi* type', who was nicknamed 'Joe'.

It was in Aden that they met Wilfred Thesiger, the famous Arabian explorer. Later, in Dhofar, they would come across a number of Bedu who had travelled with the great man in his journeys across the Rub al Khali.

Mike wrote:

Thesiger is a tall gaunt man, over six feet, son of a Thesiger of the Colonial Office, and relative of Ernest Thesiger the actor. He's ex-Eton and Oxford, and during the war was on Special Service in the Western Desert shooting up the enemy behind his lines – playing a lone hand. In October 1945, he came to Dhofar on an anti-locust mission, again alone, and he did a remarkable, tough, journey of four months living with the Bedu as one of them. Then again in '46 he did a similar journey – accounts of these have been published in the *Q.J.G.S.*[3] Now he's on his own again, without Government backing, doing a mad scheme somewhere in the great sand desert north of here. He gave so many presents in previous years that it is rather difficult for us this time.

As we now know, Thesiger was in Aden at the start of his second crossing of the Rub al Khali, an arduous journey that ended with his arrival in Abu Dhabi on 15 March 1948. He was perhaps suspicious of the geologists in Aden; his deep understanding of the Bedouin led him to believe that the discovery of oil would have a profound effect on their lifestyle, and in time make it impossible for them to return to their old ways. Thesiger feared that the tribesmen, attracted by the relatively high wages the oil companies could offer, would start to gravitate towards the oilfields, eventually settling permanently in camps nearby. But that was for the future.

Thesiger left for Mukalla on 3 November, followed a week later by Mike and René.

At 3 a.m. on Monday 10 November 1947, Mike was roused from his slumbers and, together with the other party members, piled into a car to be transported to the aerodrome in readiness for their flight to Mukalla. Sheikh Othman field was a 'ghost-drome', an ex-USA air force ground used by private airlines, without staff and facilities apart from one tin shack.

He could see very little else as they waited for their aircraft to arrive. There was a flat, bleak stretch of sand and a windsock hanging limply in the raw light of dawn; and then he could hear the distant hum of aircraft engines, a speck coming out of the still-nocturnal African sky, and an Ethiopian Airlines Dakota touching down in the first light of day.

After refuelling was complete, the party boarded. The aircraft accelerated noisily down the airstrip, and lifted off turning towards the east. The flight would follow the southern coast of Arabia on its way to Riyan, an RAF air staging-post some 500 kilometres east of Aden, before dropping off the party and completing its run to Bombay.

Mike described a blood-red sun coming up from the eastern sea, bringing the first tints of colour to the mountains and sky to the north; these mountains, rising higher and higher inland, ran parallel with the coast and formed a formidable barrier to exploration. Long, thin lines of grey, smoky cloud were lying just under the crest of the foothills as peaks pierced the clear, cold pale blue sky. Mike followed the snaking lines of the wadis and looked down into the black crater of an extinct volcano. The narrow coastal plain was orange-brown, sandy, vividly contrasting with the blue of the Indian Ocean.

René's brief sounded simple enough: his party was required to make geological reconnaissances in three distinct geographical areas. First, to make a round trip of the Hadhramaut by motor transport, obtaining a wide and rapid introduction to the geology and various problems of the country; second, a camel-borne expedition to the Mahra, employing a dhow as a mobile base for stores while the expedition worked eastwards along the coast; and third, a further expedition by camel was planned to Dhofar.

Mike's thoughts were never far from Heather:

Do get a flat with all the accessories you mention. I'd like that very much and I'd even help with the washing-up too. We're going to have lots of fun, aren't we, although starving yourself to get thin for me must be quite hard. Darling, I'm thinking of you in a way that's not good for my desert morale …

THIS WAS THE Middle East, but not as Mike knew it. It was one of those moments when he felt 'electrified', when his senses were assailed by the sights, sounds and smells of a strange new land.

After landing at Riyan, they took a ride to Mukalla – a bumpy journey driven at speed over a stony track – and Mike had his first glimpse of the Bedouin of the Aden Protectorates. They were 'fierce-looking fellows', clad only in indigo-coloured loincloths and appearing to be very dark-skinned, as they also painted their hair and bodies with indigo to protect themselves from the sun and disease. Their hair was thick and tangled, but their teeth were perfect and their eyes clear. Around their necks they wore a single carnelian, regarded as a charm against bleeding. They were small but well muscled, and existed on a diet of fish and dates. As a result of Ingrams' Peace they carried no arms but, at their waists, each wore a huge, curved, dagger with finely-crafted silver handle.

As they careered along the track, they passed tiny, white stone structures, rather like shrines. These contained fountains, having been endowed by the wealthy Saiyids,[4] holy men and scholars, for travellers to use. They saw a small village at the head of a wadi, by some cliffs, with a flourishing date grove nearby. The houses were huddled together, white, and often three or four stories high. Winding through granite mountains, they came upon a wide valley leading towards Mukalla. At its western end, they could see a small watchtower built on an isolated high rock. Soon they were passing palm-branch huts where the road opened out on to a beach, and they saw gathered hundreds of sitting camels and 'wild Bedouin'. This was 'Camel Central', the camel terminus for trading caravans and the starting point for their return journey to the hinterland and beyond.

Dominating the scene was the high gate of Mukalla. They entered, reported to the Police post, and drove to their quarters, a house in the grounds of the British Residency that Freya Stark had visited in 1935:

> The Governor's Palace, the barracks, and various buildings are all behind it in a walled
> space where a few palm trees grow – the only green in Mukalla: in the same enclosure,
> and built on the city wall, is the guest house; a few Yafa'I soldiers, lounging and smoking
> in the guard house at the entrance, keep watch on all the compound.[5]

Little had changed by the time Mike arrived. The European population of the town comprised the Resident Adviser (Sheppard), a woman doctor and her husband (a scholar), a transport officer and, when back from leave, the Political Officer and his wife.

From his room, Mike peered out of his window to see the daily life of Mukalla passing by: over a high wall he could gaze upon the spectacle of the sugar-icing Palace of the Qua'aiti Sultan. Built on the shore, the blue and white building was 'perhaps the nicest building in Mukalla' and stood much as Freya Stark had seen it 12 years previously:

> The Sultan of Mukalla's Palace is at the west end of the town, near the battlemented
> gate by which all traffic, whether from Shihr or the north, must enter. The palace itself
> is on the sea, white and new, with coloured glass like a Brighton pavilion, and best seen
> by moonlight.[6]

The temptation to explore was irresistible, and Mike headed off into town. Mukalla was built between rocks and the sea, its high, white buildings occupying a narrow strip of land between a rocky mountain and a wide, sandy beach. The sea, brightly sparkling, was sparsely dotted with small boats, mainly fishing boats.

The coast of southern Arabia had been long known as the coast of the fish-eaters. There was an all-pervasive stench of fish in the town. Even camels and goats were fed on dried fish to supplement the scarcity of vegetation, and the strong smell of fish-laden caravans would leave a lasting impression on the field party in the months to come. All along the beach from the harbour to beyond the gate, rows and rows of fish lay drying in the sun. A number of the labourers, he discovered, could each eat 150 small fish with copious quantities of dates at one sitting.

Mike passed through crowds of savage-looking, well-built natives, a few Hadhramaut Bedouin Legionnaires and merchants dressed in Indian style, before reaching the part of town that straggled along the waterfront. Here were narrow streets with high, multi-storied buildings rising up like miniature sky-scrapers and the harbour, with dhows and fishing boats packed in close, all conveying a scene of bustling, malodorous, antiquity.

'WE EAGERLY AWAITED the arrival of our transport and main stores which had previously sailed with an Arab dhow from Aden,' wrote René.

The party's wireless sets were also awaited, perhaps most eagerly by Ahmed Hubaisly, alias Joe, the wireless operator. In Mike's eyes he was 'good-natured, selfish in some ways but not annoyingly so – it's rather a case of have, before someone else gets it'.

One wireless set was to be used by the party to maintain radio contact with Mukalla throughout their journey, the other on the dhow to track their progress along the coast. Joe knew that it would be an experiment taking a wireless into the wilderness, since the terrain presented physical obstacles to reception and made carrying the equipment difficult. The equipment itself was fairly bulky – four units, transmitter, receiver, accessory case and power unit (a pedal generator), all designed to be secured to two metal frames and carried on a man's back. Two aerials were included, a 5 metre portable tubular aerial and a 7.5 metre transportable mast.

It was this second aerial, difficult to assemble, that could be used as a tool for psychological domination. 'In places where you already got the people under your control,' Joe noted darkly, 'it is a very useful thing from a threatening point of view.'

They would soon discover that the wireless set had a powerful effect on the tribes; it had an almost mystical ability to subdue the most agitated men. At the close of the expedition, Joe was able to provide the Company with a full assessment, covering both technical capabilities of the set and its use in the wider context of human relations:

Apart from getting in touch with people far from us and apart from sending our news to headquarters, wireless was a very useful thing to have from the security point of view. I always tried to make people believe, by putting the set [on] and make [sic] them listen to Arabic stations, that I could get in touch with anybody and ask the help from anybody of our people outside their countries.[7]

By accident rather than design the wireless would become the expedition's secret weapon.

ON 18 NOVEMBER the dhow *Mukhlis* appeared out of the morning haze and anchored in the

Mukalla roadstead. For half an hour the small crowd on the quayside grew steadily in both size and volume, workers and fishermen jabbering excitedly as the dhow's cargo was landed, two shiny Jeeps and a Dodge four-wheel drive lorry, followed by equipment and stores of food. The mountains above the harbour echoed the commotion, while the fishing boats and dhows jostled gently on the swell. And while the geologists supervised the unloading and began the final preparations for their road journey, an escort of two soldiers arrived from the Hadhramaut Bedouin Legion (HBL).

This was a small military force, set up by Harold Ingrams in 1940 and modelled on the Trans-Jordan Arab Legion. By June 1944 it had forts in the significant Bedouin areas and an education system that included boarding schools for Bedouin boys and girls. A Bedouin from one of the local tribes would arrive at their military headquarters in Mukalla dressed in a short loin cloth or *fute*, black or dark blue, with hair and short beard heavily oiled; his body might be covered in indigo. Many had tribal scars on their faces, and most wore amulets round their necks and bracelets above their elbows, both made from silver and set with carnelian. If the recruit had his own rifle, it was likely to be an antiquated Martini Henry, possibly dating as far back as 1870.

As a private of the HBL, the recruit tended to retain his long hair and silver ornaments but otherwise would be transformed. Over shorts, he wore a khaki *qamis*, a calf-length one-piece garment with a shirt top. Round his waist was a leather ammunition belt under which he wore, on ceremonial occasions, a broad red webbing sash with long ends. On his head would be a khaki *kafiyah* with black head rope, or *iqal*, and the silver badge of HBL on the front. On being accepted, the recruit swore allegiance to HM King George VI and promised to obey his superior officers' orders. At the end of his first month, he received his pay of 22 rupees[8], this being the going rate for a private soldier. After their training, they would be posted to the interior to keep watch and deter any potential law-breakers or tribal raiders.

In the manner of a slow but inquisitive beast, the loaded convoy set out from Mukalla along the narrow track that wound steeply up the barren mountain slopes of the Jebel Kjarka. The beast lumbered along the route and stopped at regular intervals to examine its surroundings or, more accurately, to allow the geologists to investigate the geological outcrops, before continuing its ascent.

The journey was one of climactic changes, driving away from the hot and arid coast into the cool and temperate mountains. When they reached a Government guest house at Mula Mata, Mike looked back on their journey:

We've just stopped on a mountain about 7,500 feet [2,286 metres] up … After two-hours of steady climbing, we stopped and did a bit of rock-tapping, then had lunch and brewed some tea over a wood fire, with a couple of indigo Bedouins. Somehow the smell of wood smoke makes me feel that it's the best possible thing to live an outdoor life. Our lunch consisted of eggs and bully, with a banana to play with too.

We then continued our climb, winding up a steep mountainside with terrific bends and gradients, and passing long camel caravans at intervals.

The deeply cut wadis for the first 20 to 30 miles [30 to 50 kilometres] exposed the old granite core of the Arabian Shield. The road ran above this on a hard dolomite bed – a crude road, but soundly built in the bad places. Driving up wadi beds, we ran into rough going on the smooth, grey, round limestone pebbles, but still we managed.

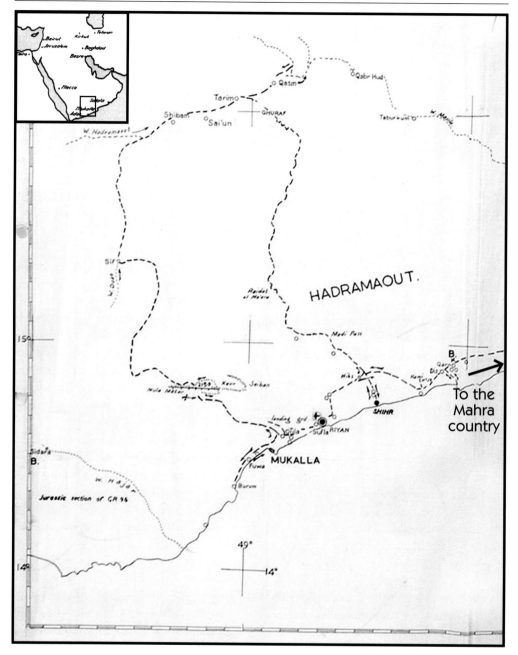

The Journey through the Hadhramaut Valley
© *Iraq Petroleum Company*

They had struggled on up the hill until they reached the top and saw their night stop ahead in the distance:

René and I were in one Jeep – self contained and lagging far behind the other Jeep and the Dodge three-tonner. After a particularly violent series of hairpin bends, we rolled over a crest, onto the flat, wind-swept *Jol* and saw the tiny guest house of Mula Mata in the distance. There we found calamity. The others had discovered that the kitchen materials had not been put on the truck – so there we were. We boiled water in an old biscuit tin, flashing our torches to look for a piece of spam or bully.

There were some aspects (crickets excepted) of his situation that must have been reminiscent of a night on the Yorkshire moors:

I'm trying to write this by aid of a small kerosene lamp and I'm straining my eyes. It's quite cold up here, Chick, and I'm wearing winter clothes and have blankets on the bed. There's a lovely crescent moon outside, crystal clear stars, and a distant chirping of crickets. It's very peaceful and very lovely.

The convoy continued its journey at dawn, heading across a brown stony plateau of scarce vegetation, consisting of scant summer acacias and aloes in the depressions.

Presently, they came to the edge of the *Jol* and looked down on the river valley below. A winding road of steep hairpins lay ahead, leading to the Wadi Do'an, a tributary of the mighty Wadi Hadhramaut. Freya Stark had once described the approach to the Wadi Do'an:

The wadi is a thousand yards [1,000 metres] wide and drops a thousand feet [300 metres] or so with sheer walls. On the rubble sides which hold the cliffs, little towns are clustered, built of earth like swallows' nests, so that only the sunlight shows them against the earth behind. Five or six are visible on the slopes as one looks down. Between them and their squared ploughed field on either side of a white stream bed, the wadi bottom is filled with palms. Their tops glitter there darkly, like a snake or a river, with scales or ripples shining in the sun.[9]

The geologists first glimpsed the wadi as the sun was low in the sky. They saw a vast chasm with villages and date palms on the valley floor. Eventually the difficult road levelled out on the broad alluvial valley floor and ran past tall mud-built houses of villages that sheltered beneath the sheer limestone valley sides. Here the romantic vision ended: projecting from the sides of the high buildings, between the windows of each floor, wooden boards were inclined, a primitive sewage system along which 'everything rolls down, or flows, as the case may be, on to the ground'.

The party camped beneath the stars near Do'an village, 'where they have the finest honey in the world'. The honey was produced twice a year, once in the summer when the *'ilb* trees were in blossom and once in winter from the *garmala* bushes. 'We had no cook but we ate honey,' Mike noted smugly before turning in at the end of the day.

The wadi joined the larger Wadi Hadhramaut on its 1000-kilometre journey across the Protectorate. Mike would have been aware of the land of Hadhramaut through history, said to be the land of Hazarmaveth mentioned in Genesis 10:26 and of Joktan the biblical Qahtan, from whom most Yemenis believed they were descended through the pre-Islamic prophet Hud. Caravans had travelled through this land for centuries, carrying incense along a trading route that ran from Dhofar to Shabwa and, ultimately, to Hejaz and the eastern Mediterranean.

But there was a far older land, a land of rocks and sediments, of fossils and land formations, a land before men and camels. It was this land whose voice Mike would have listened to, a voice that told a story of primeval seas drained, the earth ruptured and forests buried; it was a silent discourse shared between a geologist and the earth, alone.

THE LANDSCAPE NOW took on a medieval air. Early next morning, they drove deeper into the valley, passing kilometres of cultivated land irrigated by water drawn from wide, deep wells. Skin buckets attached to ropes were passed over wooden pulleys, and then harnessed to camels or cows which were driven back and forth in front of the well, hauling up the water-filled skins that were spilt out into an irrigation channel; the squeak of the wheel and the swish of water were familiar sounds in the countryside.

Amid this setting there was a hint of modernity: the most striking feature of the Wadi Hadhramaut and its tributaries was the distinctive architecture of its houses, tall mud houses constructed by skilled craftsmen. The windows were small and narrow, without glass, and interspersed with loopholes for rifles, relics of troubled times. Since peace had been imposed and the carrying of firearms prohibited, these loopholes had seen no recent use, and the farmers in the field no longer carried rifles.

They arrived at Shibam, an ancient trading centre, 'the New York of the Hadhramaut' as described by the few Westerners who had been there. This was another town with tightly huddled mud houses, or ancient 'skyscrapers', rising to seven or eight stories high. The tallest building was the blue and white palace of the Sultan of the Kathiri State. But the geologists did not stay long: the streets stank to high-heaven as a result of the primitive sanitation, and myriad flies drove them swatting and cursing from the town.

The convoy pressed on eastwards to the town of Sei'un, the administrative centre. Many date palms and cultivations lent a quiet air of prosperity to the town, the home of many rich men:

The Hadhramaut is a land of opulence and indescribable poverty. In this country, which grows insufficient food to support its population, there are unmistakable signs of wealth amid a predominantly near-starving population. Some fortunate families receive money from the many expatriate Hadhramis, who own rich plantations in Indonesia and Zanzibar. These plantations are handed down from father to son, the former returning to his native Hadhramaut to enjoy his accumulated wealth when the latter takes over. A favourite ambition of these men is thus realized when they build their own house at large expense. Unfortunately, the plain Hadhrami architecture becomes gradually spoiled by over-ornamented designs of foreign origin. We happened to stay in an ornate pillared bungalow in Sei'un, equipped with modern sanitation and electric light, and with a luxurious, though empty, swimming pool in the garden.[10]

It might have been said that the Saiyids had more money than sense. In the early 1930s, pilots flying on surveys from Aden had been astonished to find motor cars moving up and down a road some 300 kilometres from the coast. The Saiyids had built this road with the money made abroad, without linking it with the coast. As a result, motor cars arriving by sea would be dismantled and carried on camel to the Wadi Hadhramaut, where they were reassembled for use on the road.[11]

Venturing on to Tarim, a holy city to the east, the geologists found more signs of wealth in a mansion where their host enjoyed a comfortable life of 'pleasant religious simplicity'. Mike was a little more forthright in his letter to Heather:

> We spent the night in luxury – a wealthy Saiyid's house. The Saiyid looked worn out. As he sleeps with his wives each day, it's not surprising. Still he has to show he's a man.

THE SMALL PARTY made its way eastwards. Here Mike first glimpsed the point where the Wadi Hadhramaut becomes the Wadi Masila – as part of their next expedition, they planned to follow its lower reaches down to the sea. Although it is likely that Mike was becoming preoccupied by thoughts of the journey that awaited them in the Mahra country, there was still time to relax and take in the sights of this strange new world. Having visited the tomb of the Prophet Hud, they returned to Sei'un, and departed next day along the eastern limb of the Hadhramaut road circuit, along the road to the coast.

Everywhere they went they were greeted with warmth and hospitality. At the foot of the coastal range, they were met by wild-looking hill men selling armfuls of coconuts, which they bought for a few Maria Theresa dollars.[12] On reaching the plain, they settled in a date-palm plantation and, after a meal of tinned meat, tinned vegetables and tinned fruit, they slept under the trees.

There were reminders of a more violent past: driving across the narrow coastal plain to Mukalla the following day, they passed the picturesque towns of Shihr and Ghail Ba Wazir, where fortified walls told of past, but not entirely forgotten, tribal wars.

Finally, at the RAF station at Riyan, they slaked their thirst to mark the successful conclusion of their nine-day car journey through the Hadhramaut. They could look back on this stage of their expedition with a degree of satisfaction but look forward to the next stage with a certain apprehension. From now on, the going would get tougher: the transport arrangements were different, for a start. They would abandon the motor vehicle and take their chances with the camel.

---

1   See H. St. John Philby, Introduction to *Sheba's Daughter*.
2   Memorandum of April 1948.
3   *Quarterly Journal of The Geographical Society* – later a full account of his travels was published in his book *Arabian Sands*.
4   In origin, the Saiyids were emigrants from Hejaz who claimed descent from the Prophet and were much venerated. They had established themselves in positions of influence, such as teachers, traders and judges.
5   Freya Stark, *The Southern Gates of Arabia*, p. 30. Reproduced by permission of John Murray, Publishers.
6   Ibid.
7   'Report on South Arabia Expedition', A. R. Hubaisly, 15 May 1948.
8   £44 today.
9   Freya Stark, *The Southern Gates of Arabia*, p. 112. Reproduced by permission of John Murray, Publishers.
10   René Wetzel and Mike Morton, 'Expedition to Southern Arabia', *IPC Magazine*, August 1955.
11   Colonel Sir Hugh Boustead, *Wind of the Morning*, 1971.
12   These dollars (thalers) were first coined in Vienna during the reign of the Hapsburg Empress Maria Theresa. They became accepted currency throughout the Middle East and continued in use well into the twentieth century.

Chapter 6: The Land of Sun and Fire

Mahra, 29 November 1947–14 February 1948

'In cases of extreme necessity, and when the preservation of human life
depends on the obtainment of water, the supply to be found in the stomach
of a camel should not be overlooked or forgotten'
Shifts and Expedients of Camp Life, 1876
W. B. Lord and Thomas Baines

The Middle East has spawned many exceptional characters in its time: a glorious parade of intrepid individuals, men who could not live a dull life in the lands of their birth. Their manifestations have been various: some would 'go native' and – to the disdain of the British establishment – affect native dress and customs; others would negotiate their way through hostile territories with a side-step and a smile, surviving by dint of wit and guile; and still others less fortunate would end up running from a hail of hostile bullets. In the course of his travels, Mike would meet his fair share of these individuals – indeed at times he would display some of their traits himself – and a few of their number will figure in our story, but first to step forward is Tony Altounyan.

There was never any doubt about Tony's credentials to lead an expedition into the interior. Major Tony Altounyan was an expert in his field, with a great understanding of the Mahra tribes. As liaison officer, he was required to meet the political rulers of the areas to be visited, to arrange adequate protection and make all commercial arrangements with Besse and Company for supplying the expedition. He had advised the Company on the region, its people, conditions, diseases, rations required, the going rate for camel men, and so on. Over the course of the following few weeks, the party planned to travel 1,600 kilometres by camel – through many potentially hostile tribal areas – and the geologists would have to rely on Tony's expertise to get them through.

One detects here a source of tension with other members of the expedition, the difference between two worlds: the political world, a mercurial place of shifting alliances and tricky negotiations, and the world of the geologist, a scientific place of known facts and tested hypotheses. It was perhaps Tony's self-belief and the geologists' limited appreciation of the political nuances of his role, that perpetuated this divide.

Tony had cause to be proud of his achievements. He had already visited the Mahra country in late 1946. It was considered so dangerous, he reported, that 'one very old and expert resident of Aden went so far as to advise me to carry, hidden on my person, a small weapon or a phial of poison for use on myself to end the final agonies of torture!'[1] Rumours of savagery may have been sufficient to put off the faint-hearted, but not Tony Altounyan.

As he had discovered, tribal conditions offered some risk to the traveller, but in his opinion the region was on the whole quite safe for the survey contemplated. The political contacts he had made, and the friendships he had established, offered adequate protection for the safety of the party. 'Let commercial enterprise take its course!' he boldly declared.

THE GEOLOGISTS' IMMEDIATE future lay in the Mahra country, a ragged heap of mountains that tumbled down to the Arabian Sea. They were tasked to carry out a general reconnaissance of the southern coast and hinterland of Mahra towards the Dhofar frontier; they would rendezvous with the dhow *Mukhlis* at various points along the way, the dhow acting as a supply depot and bank for the plentiful supply of Maria Theresa dollars that were held in iron boxes on board.

The entertainment started at Raidut al Abdul Wadid, the eastern outpost of the Qua'aiti state. At first light in the trading town, the loading of the camels began. What else but the loading of a caravan could cause such uproar in these parts? Mike looked on with great trepidation at the performance which unfolded like a demented orchestra tuning up – the cursing, shouting and

The Journey Across the Mahra
© *Iraq Petroleum Company Limited*

hollering of men and the roaring, moaning and snarling of camels as the men struggled with the food-laden wicker hampers, camp beds and surveying instruments that were to be packed on to the camels' backs.

Once the transport camels were fully laden, the dust settled briefly, and then it came to the geologists' turn to mount their camels. The riding camels wore, for the first time in this part of the world, the expedition's two-poled Syrian saddles. The men mounted hastily, as each squatting camel waited its moment before lurching to its feet in the hope of catching its prospective rider off-balance and bringing him down.

The escorting camel riders belonged to the Bait Thayan, a tribe that subsisted by running transport caravans along the coast and to the Hadhramaut. They enhanced their appearance by wearing curved silver daggers, and cartridge belts and rifles, usually of an ancient vintage, slung over their shoulders.

The first day's journey took seven-and-a-half hours. The caravan was accompanied by a band of small boys on foot who tried to cadge cigarettes and sang tuneless songs. An old, very wizened *mugaddem* with a tiny voice and wearing a leather cap also tagged along. Their escorts chattered and shouted incessantly, discussing the latest feuds between the Manahil, Sahol and Zueidi tribes. The riders used umbrellas for shade as the caravan followed a barren sandy beach with dunes running parallel with the coast and hundreds of sea birds lining their route. The stench of rotting flesh was never far away as they passed piles of fish drying in the sun and camels carrying the dried product. 'Camels eat fish,' an escort informed them, 'to bring out fat worms from their noses.'

At some point next day the expedition crossed into Mahra. The mood of their escorts changed: the singing stopped, the cadgers fell away, and the escorts became quiet and subdued. The first Mahrani they saw was a boy standing outside a dwelling that resembled an air raid shelter. The first Mahra woman they came upon was standing at the side of the road, a ring through her nose, watching in silence as the caravan passed by.

Tony had a good idea of what the party could expect when they came across their first Mahra tribesmen:

> Noticeable everywhere, and particularly so in the interior, was the state of constant fear in which the scattered population lives. The sight of even a small party of mounted men was sufficient to send everyone scurrying to the cover of bushes and rocks from which they pointed rifles at the party until they were recognized as friends. Every man wears a rifle from which he is never separated.[2]

This behaviour, he concluded, was conditioned not by hostility to outsiders but by previous attacks from large armed raiding parties from the north and from Yemen. It certainly explained the growing tension among their escorts. The caravan stopped earlier than usual, having journeyed for only four-and-a-half hours, and made camp beside a well near Tamnum. The Bait Thayan tribesmen became edgy and fractious as the evening shadows lengthened – at one point they threatened to shoot Joe, Tony and Mike in a row over camel-loads and the distribution of cigarettes. The geologists got little sleep as a result, and the tribesmen kept a night-long vigil by the flickering fire of the camp, watching for raiders and holding an uneasy truce until dawn, when they moved on again.

'There were days,' wrote Mike later, 'when it was so hot that you were speechless during the noonday hours. Drinking water varied. There were times when it was good, mostly it was slightly off, and occasionally it was as salty as the sea, or as dirty as a canal, with camel droppings floating in it, like ripe plums.'

The camels lolloped lazily between the jebel and the bright, blinding sea. Mike could see nothing around him except the shimmering heat of the day, which lay before them like a furnace, its invisible door now opened wide, its heat unrelenting.

At various stages of their journey, the geologists would come upon traces of an ancient Mahra race, the Himyars. They were a pre-Islamic race, probably of mixed origins, with some degree of civilization. They had an alphabet and worshipped the sun and fire; the geologists found many sets of their ancient monuments, standing stones known as 'triliths',[3] along the dusty tracks they travelled.

THE FIRST SIGN of danger surfaced at their next destination, the town of Seihut, which they reached just as dusk was beginning to fall, their camels padding silently through the dark streets as fires burned, illuminating half-formed figures in shadowy passageways on either side of their path.

Although this part of the Mahra was nominally ruled by a Sultan, it was divided into tribal areas, with each tribe exercising complete hegemony over their own territory. Some were responsive to outsiders; others were not. All lived in fear of the Zueidi. In order to progress farther eastwards, it would be necessary for the expedition to negotiate with the Zueidi for safe passage through their land.

Ingrams had travelled through the Eastern Protectorate under the protection of the *siyarra* system, the recognized system of transit in Mahra. In practice, it meant taking with them a number of men from the territory they were passing through, the men acting as their 'passports' to guarantee passage through an otherwise unfriendly land. These Bedouin passports were not infallible, however, as Ingrams noted when his caravan was held up by armed Zueidis wanting to shoot him. '*Siyari* was never meant to apply to Christians,'[4] the Zueidi told him, perhaps with a glint in their eyes.

Over the course of the next day, Tony's negotiating skills came into play but, unusually, they were of no avail: 'You are denied permission to cross our land,' said the Zueidi *mugaddems* after lengthy discussion. They would not be persuaded either by Tony's smooth words or the Company's silver dollars; they were adamant that the caravan would not be allowed to cross their land to reach Qishn.

This created a dilemma for the geologists. They had hardly begun their expedition into the Mahra country and were now faced with the prospect of abandoning it or taking a different route around the Zueidi land to their following destination. The overland route would be impossibly long, both in distance and time: it would mean backtracking to Raidut and following a northerly route across the mountains before turning south again towards Ghaida. The alternative was to take the sea route, loading their possessions on the *Mukhlis* and skirting the Zueidi shore.

They had a discussion with Tony about the pros and cons. Despite the inconvenience of unpacking and re-packing their gear, taking the sea route appeared to be the only realistic option. So they took the decision to travel to Qishn on the *Mukhlis*, and set sail that same evening, arriving at the roadstead off Qishn just as day was breaking.

The landing was not without difficulty. At first, the geologists stared anxiously across a rough sea at the outline of a town partially visible in the distance, then they clambered as best they could on to narrow canoes that were bobbing alongside the dhow. Looking ahead, through gaps in the surf, they glimpsed a thin, sandy shoreline and the mountains beyond. As their canoes lurched alarmingly towards the beach, one capsized, spilling a member of the party into the ocean rollers and forcing him to swim his way to the shore.

Never entirely at ease on a small boat, Mike was greatly relieved to reach the shore without suffering the same fate. Qishn, a few square mud-bricked buildings, some with crumbling walled enclosures, gathered along the coast, was unremarkable but safe. He could see the horns of the jebel known as Al Gurn to the west, with twin peaks that seemed to puncture an overcast sky, and the Zueidi lands they had left behind; the Zueidi were no threat in these parts.

The Treaty Sultan of Mahra, who ruled Qishn, spent most of his time on the island of Socotra, leaving the town in the capable hands of his cousin Sultan Ahmed bin Abdullah bin Issa bin Afrir. The Sultans eagerly welcomed the promise of oil wealth, for their people were in dire straits. Everyone in the Mahra country, including Sultan Ahmed, was desperately poor, and any killing of sheep from their precious flocks to do honour to the visitor was a great sacrifice. The party was anxious not to become a burden to them inadvertently, Altounyan having advised the Company to bring gifts: 'Generous lengths of black tweed or Kashmir cloth suitable for making dress robes for each of Sultan Ahmed and Sultan Khalifa. Cotton piece goods, plain or checked, and cut into three-yard [-metre] lengths are acceptable little gifts, and are used as turbans or *futahs* as required.'[5]

ONCE THEY WERE back on the Mahra trail, tensions surfaced again as trouble brewed in the caravan, among both tribesmen and camels. One evening, Mike noted: 'Bin Kalshat made hell of a noise during the night – blood feud digging up.' The geologists tried to carry on their work as best they could, despite the attentions of a lone sniper who took pot-shots at René one day while he was surveying in the mountains.[6]

On the shore near Tobut they came across a pile of granite pebbles, some 800 kilometres from the nearest source. At first the pebbles were thought to be ballast from a wrecked dhow but the mystery deepened a year later when Wilfred Thesiger arrived at Expedition HQ in Tripoli with a similar pile of stones from the Liwa Oasis, again far from their source. Mike then realized that they must have come from Dhofar and had been used for cinching camel-loads, being deposited once the journey was over.

As they approached the town of Ghaida on Christmas Eve, feelings were still running high: 'The Kalshat tribesmen were troublesome and said they would not make Ghaida that night,' wrote Mike. Deprived of the whisky that was stored on the dhow anchored somewhere off Ghaida, the geologists shared a tin of sardines and a Christmas pudding around the camp fire and crawled exhausted into their bedrolls.

The camels played their part in the general unrest. Waking to find a camel nibbling the foot of his bedroll, Mike shooed the beast away. He turned over, adjusted his bedding, and was drifting off again when he was suddenly disturbed by the snorting of a camel nearby. He sat bolt upright: facing him were four camels. He raised both arms to shoo them away but the result was not exactly as he had intended: one of the indignant camels – with forefeet hobbled – bounded angrily across the moonlit sand towards him. In the nick of time, Mike managed to extract himself from his bedding and pull himself on to his feet, avoiding the first lunge of the camel's frothing, vengeful teeth. But there was no time to stand on ceremony. Clad only in his red-striped pyjamas, the luckless geologist fled in terror as the roaring beast turned and gave chase into the night. It was a dishevelled-looking figure that re-emerged from the darkness when the camel had quietened down. By the dying embers of the camp fire, Mike climbed back into his bed, exhausted but ever-watchful.

AHMED HUBAISLY, alias Joe the wireless operator, employee of the Iraq Petroleum Company, had come in peace. He was a peaceful man.

Joe was the expedition's advance party, arriving in Ghaida on 23 December, not knowing quite what to expect. After Seihut, Ghaida was the largest of the Mahra towns, 'a cultivation on Jiza's floor', situated at the mouth of the Wadi Jiza which swept down from the mountains and drained into the Indian Ocean. It was believed that a Sultan had ordered Ghaida to be set back from the sea to prevent it being raided by pirates.

He reached the shore and unpacked his wireless set. He radioed the *Mukhlis*, but the wireless operator on board seemed to have difficulty in hearing Joe's requests for stores and equipment.

Now, alone and facing a potentially hostile reception, Joe was concerned. Despite his efforts to communicate with the dhow, there was no sign of a response. 'The dhow operator did not answer me,' complained Joe, 'while I used to hear him perfectly.'

Eventually the message got through and the stores were duly unloaded on to the deserted beach. It was only when Joe set about packing up his equipment before moving on to the village that he noticed a group of tribesmen approaching from that direction. There was much excitement among the crowd, with arms being waved in the air and several men carrying rifles which they pointed upwards as if to shoot at the sky. 'We do not want *Nasrani* in our village,' they hollered. 'They will not live if they enter our village,' one proclaimed. 'We are having a big shooting party when the *Nasrani* arrive,' another told him. 'It will not be safe to be in village, especially for *Nasrani*.'

Perhaps this was the moment when Joe found his true vocation. Motioning to the partly packed wireless set, he addressed the gathered crowd:

> With this machine I can summon up more than fifty aeroplanes to bomb your village, if you men are thinking of attacking us. See here, I can talk to others who are waiting beyond the mountains. Come with me and greet my companions and I shall call off the planes.[7]

The wireless was unknown in these parts. The tribesmen crowded round as Joe gave a demonstration of its – his – powers. He left them in no doubt that the wireless was the door to another world of cars, aeroplanes and … bombs.

As it happened, when the caravan entered Ghaida two days later on Christmas Day the inhabitants' fears of a *Nasrani* invasion had been subdued, and the expedition received a peaceful welcome at Sheikh Abdullah's house. The result of Joe's divine powers, perhaps? As Mike recorded:

> Ahmed the wireless operator, has been very useful politically on this trip and even

ended up by being a Saiyid – a Holy Man, respected by all tribesmen, who come to kiss his hand.

'Calling Aden' became a byword for summoning up the spirits of the outer-world, spirits that were sometimes benign, sometimes malign, but always under the direction and control of one Ahmed Hubaisly, W/O, of the Iraq Petroleum Company.

At Ghaida, the party rested in Abdullah's house over Christmas before continuing the next leg of their journey.

THERE WAS NO sign of trouble on their next excursion to Damkaut, apart from a half-hearted attempt at a hold-up by half-a-dozen bandits on the shore: these were men of the Amarjit tribe, whose reputation had preceded them. Thesiger and his companions had been held up by Amarjit the year before while travelling further to the north.

But when the party returned to Ghaida a few days later, it quickly became apparent that there was a problem. Tony was conducting *siyarra* negotiations with the Kalshat sheikhs for the next stage of their journey, and on the evening of 3 January he explained the nature of their predicament to the geologists:

> Our host [Abdullah] belonged to a tribe which owned half the town, the other half being occupied by another tribe, the Bin Kalshat. Our [next] journey lay through Kalshat territory and, as our long stay with our present host had offended the Kalshat sheikhs, we were requested to spend a similar number of days as their guests.[8]

The party could not afford to spend too much time with the Kalshat sheikhs without seriously disrupting their plans. But they were in a cleft stick: if they stayed any longer in Abdullah's house, the greater the offence caused to the Kalshat sheikhs; if they left early, offence would be caused to both sides. The visitors were anxious to leave town for reasons of their own, for 'to spend one night in the interior of a house would be sufficient to become infested with body lice and fleas'.[9]

The official account of what happened is sketchy. Apart from referring to a 'complicated situation' and 'troublesome negotiations', it gives little away. There are many reasons why a writer in these circumstances might wish to be circumspect. For the geologists, it was the sensitivities of the time that caused them to be so, avoiding controversy and embarrassment for the Company in the conduct of its business in the Middle East. Mike's journal and correspondence, however, hint at a darker undercurrent of suspicion and hostility that pervaded the town in early January 1948.

The geologists were packing, ready to leave. Tony had been to-ing and fro-ing over the previous two days between one part of the town and the other, walking a diplomatic tight-rope between the hospitality of their host and the sensitivities of the Kalshat sheikhs. At some point the negotiations developed – or deteriorated – into what Mike described as a 'tribal war', in which Mike and Doc were taken hostage:

> Doc and I were held hostage in a tiny room for half a day by two Sultans, hiding in one town, wanted for murder by the Sultans of the land.

Mike's account with its reference to murder is puzzling. The Kelshat tribe would be required by law to put the two local Sultans to death as murderers. If this did not happen, the ancient rules of Mahrani justice allowed the deceased's tribe to intervene. He wrote:

The murderer is put to death by his own tribe, and, if they fail to do so, it is recognition on their part that the offended tribe may take revenge. But once a man is declared a murderer by the Muqaddam he is outlawed and may not be greeted by his people. There is an appeal from the Bin 'Ali Muqaddam to the Bin Afrar Sultan.

Later in the day, news came of a breakthrough. Perhaps because of the murder implication, the Bin Kalshat Sultans were in a precarious position and tempered their discussions accordingly. Whatever their logic, it was agreed that, if the members of the geological party stayed with the Kalshat sheikhs for one night, honour would be satisfied. Mike and Doc were released, the baggage was delivered to Ahmed the Kalshat merchant's house, where the party spent the night; and thus they were allowed to depart Ghaida without further ado the following day.

MIKE WAS MESMERIZED by the 21 figures, by the sing-song voice of the *muezzin* and by the mass-like chant of men at prayer. He did not know how long it had been going on, as he had only just arrived. But time didn't seem to matter here. Quietly, he had slipped on to the bank of the wadi, just below where the worshippers had gathered on their knees to face Mecca. The thin blade of a new moon was hanging low on the tinted orange horizon, which merged upwards with a pale blue sky and darker heavens above; the evening star was shining. The silhouettes of the men stood out with those of the hills and the tamarisk-like trees against two thin streaks of orange cloud.

He let the moment sink in for a while and then, despite his curiosity, slipped away feeling as if he were intruding on their privacy. But he had hardly turned his back when the meeting broke up and the men started coming down the bank to return to the camp in the Wadi Jiza.

Back in camp, two men arrived on camels. 'Amarjit,' someone said. A number of Balchit men surrounded the riders and began to engage in an animated conversation with them. Suddenly the Balchit were shouting and firing their rifles in the air, not in a warlike manner but in a *feu de joie* to welcome the tribesmen to their fold. It transpired that the Amarjit men had just been released from prison. More worryingly, they brought rumours of a tribal raid involving 300 men, making the northern route a more dangerous proposition than before. A *mugaddem* from Murait arrived, an old man with flowing hair and sharp eyes, and the party spent the rest of the evening discussing this news and taking his advice about the next move.

'The decision is up to you,' said the *mugaddem* helpfully.

At that time of year, the temperature during the day was as hot as on a summer's day in the Syrian desert. After sunset, it would fall rapidly and, in the hills, become quite cold with heavy falls of dew. A chilly night would follow, and they would wake to an even colder morning, with visibility poor and hazy.

They re-lit the fire and considered their situation again over breakfast, René, Mike and Tony talking quietly together. It was true that the Bedu fed on stories about camel raids, but it was unlikely that the raiders – even if they existed – would choose to attack the caravan, except perhaps to take their camels, and this was a risk that a few silver dollars would, it was hoped, avoid. So they ran through the options for a last time: turn back, carry on, or try another route.

Each time they came back to only one option: there was to be no turning back, and no change of route. They finished their breakfast and cleared up the camp site. The caravan was ready to depart at nine o'clock.

The impact of the rumours was less apparent among the Bin Kalshat men who were still providing good *siyarra* for the caravan. At 12 noon they sighted Murait, a green oasis in a wadi, with palms, grass fields, and with goats and cattle grazing. When they set down beneath the palms to the south of the village, the tribesmen started bartering for new *siyarra*, demanding to stay with the caravan, initiating negotiations that lasted through the night and into the following day, delaying their departure until 12.30 p.m.

It was time for Joe to work his magic on the Bin Kalshat men. 'We stopped all the troubles by putting on the wireless and made them believe that we are asking our people [Hadhramaut Government] to send us motor transport to go back to Raidut,' he wrote. 'Everything was settled up and they asked to be paid off in order to leave a good name.'[10]

21 JANUARY SAW them on the Wadi Masila (the 'Stream of Floods'). This wadi, which comprised the lower reaches of the Wadi Hadhramaut, had a strong perennial flow of waters in parts and although the river disappeared underground before reaching the sea, the expedition's water supply problems were solved for the rest of the journey.

But there were other problems, as Mike described:

We eventually reached running water and had to dismount. The vegetation was prolific near the water's edge with large trees, mud, swamps and many fish. We lunched under a large cliff near the water beside a deep, still lagoon. I washed and felt like a new man.

The people were very lazy. I walked along a cliff after lunch and saw a large tree beside a Bedu cave - no people, just an *abba* and a bleating kid. We arrived at a junction with a large wadi from the south-east and people stopped and refused to go farther owing to fear of malaria and blood feuds with the Zueidi. The Sahol were adamant and sat down beneath a poplar-like tree and waited. After argument, several agreed to go – there was a split in party, resulting in the loss of half a day for us.

I pottered around for a short while then prepared for the night. The situation appeared better, but the Sahol were still out, including Sheikh Mohammed. Fear of the Masila seemed prevalent and unanimous among all and stories of people dying from smelling the water were circulated.

People lived in the Masila valley, but none by choice, apart from ex-slaves of Negroid stock who cultivated land along the river bank. Otherwise, the vegetation of the valley was dense. Steep cliffs, towering to 500 metres in places, though picturesque, prevented the heat of the day from escaping. Added to this, humidity made working conditions difficult as the geologists struggled to scale the cliffs, often daily, to examine geological sections; and as soon as their work was completed, they were back in the saddle again. The trail sometimes crossed thick jungle and swamps, and was often lost in the complicated irrigation network of the cultivations. Tony's camel slipped while crossing the river and fell, pulling a tendon, and had to be left behind. On one occasion a party of baboons crossed their path: they were fairly common in that part of Arabia.

The caravan changed its composition again: they had one Sahol tribesman, five Kumsait, two Obthani, three Amarjit and one Manahil. After lunching beneath a tamarisk tree, the caravan went to traverse the river again but the water deepened and they crossed with some difficulty to the other side. 'The doctor is the man who goes in front to see how deep the water is,' became a kind of battle cry as Doc headed the caravan across the deeper stretches.

Mike and René went ahead of the caravan to look for more geological sections. They came to a village where they were the 'object of the eyes of all the villagers'. These people were small and Bantu-like, well-proportioned, living in houses of thatched branches. Mike took off his hat and talked with them for awhile. 'They were a friendly, peaceful people,' recorded Mike, 'obviously slaves, working perhaps for a Saiyid.'

The geologists made their reconnaissance and found a sandstone section near Bin Qora. The fields on the left bank of the wadi were quite wide with date palms, shade and women working in the fields.

One day, Mike set out with Kennedy one of the camel men and 'another odd sod' to climb to the top of a jebel and get a panoramic view:

We proceeded along the top of the Eocene to look down on the famous bend [in the river]. There was emerald green and blue water in a gorge 1.5 kilometres wide. Cliffs stood like huge buttresses from the landslides; and great pieces of cliff leaned drunkenly on scree slopes. A narrow green band of vegetation and water lay 400 metres below. Trees lined the banks, and the adjoining wadis had dry, yellow, sandy mouths. The base of the cliffs is purple, brown and orange with tiny green squares of irrigated, cultivated land. There is a cluster of branched houses.

The *Jol* has a flat top with Oligocene hillocks and steep cascading dry wadis plunging down a vertical Eocene cliff. Tiny goat tracks are traced like salty wrinkles on a brown chin.

So much for the evil of the Wadi Masila! Perhaps it was at moments like this that Mike forgot the mosquito bites that itched incessantly on his skin, the temperamental camels and the Zueidi lurking in the wadis and memorized only the beauty he saw from this place high among the rocks.

ON 25 JANUARY 1948, picking up a Saiyid on the way, they travelled to Moqrat, situated on a 'volcanic island hill through extensive date groves, surrounded by a palisade of palm trunks'.[11] They found a village of thatched houses and palm-frond huts. The people were black-skinned and kept their women and children well hidden. The ground lay black around the dwellings, partly basalt, partly filth, dung, straw, rough stones and a fine, loose dust.

The Saiyid's house was a Hadhrami-style mud structure built near the rocks. The geologists dismounted and were shown to a small square hut which served as a reception room. It was time for lunch. They went through to a room with fan-shaped windows. A dish of fermented dates, slightly alcoholic, was served, followed by more dates, these ones dry and hard. The Saiyid, dressed in a mess-style white jacket with a white *futah* in a green turban, sat at the head of the table, a pinched, unshaven face but smiling and genial towards his guests. A small boy, the Saiyid's son, entered the room. He wore a coloured 'flower-pot' hat and sat to one side, silently watching the geologists as they consumed the last of the dates.

They left the Saiyid's house in good spirits and continued their journey, the camels padding softly along the left bank, across fields where men and women were working, past small shelters where cattle and goats rested in the shade. Aqueducts built from mud and branches irrigated the fields.

Within a couple of hours, with the heat of the day beginning to subside, they found a camp site on the alluvial delta of a dried-up wadi. Here they rested, the shaded cliffs on one side and the parched river-bed on the other. The monotony of rock and shale was broken by thorny trees dotted about the terrain and the overlying silence broken by the faint squeak of a pedal wheel turning, the wash of the empty airwaves and the twitch of radio dials, as Joe vainly tried to connect with the outside world.

MIKE'S ADVENTURES ON this leg of the journey were mainly with the camel. Mike had never taken to the camel, and he was riding the mother of all she-camels. He had first seen her in Ghaida, standing upright, her shape looming large, the Mahra sun casting her large shadow across bumpy ground. She had roared loudly, her huge lopsided hump seeming to inflate and straighten with each angry lungful of breath.

'A camel,' wrote Mike, 'is far more comfortable to ride than a horse. I must say, though, that although being thankful for a large bottom, there were times when I wished it somewhere else.'

A man could survive almost anything in the desert with a reliable camel. In the arid heat the camel would press on regardless, only complaining at the stops and starts of a fractious journey. A man could fall in love with his camel, whisper sweet nothings in its ear and be rewarded with the unquestioning devotion of a principled beast; a man would ignore these small entreaties at his peril as Mike had already discovered.

As the caravan continued on its way, Mike would sustain himself by reciting – in hushed tones so as not to agitate his camel – an increasingly realistic piece of doggerel:

Take me back to my camel,
Let me ride that trail once more,
Till my arse is red and sore.
Let me wander across the desert,
I shall see the Bedouin smiles,
I shall feel the painful piles.

Later, when the caravan joined the Wadi Massila, Mike witnessed the exorcism of his camel:

Six or seven men stood around the camel's head and laid hands on her (one holding the mouth). Rhythmically, they swung down on the head, chanting loudly in the ears:

'Hay thobah! Hay – Hay thobah hay!'

After a while they stopped, one spoke a few words, then spat in the mouth, several times during the exorcism. Again, more chanting and finally a vicious spitting bout in the eyes, ears, nose and mouth. The chant is of repentance.

There was an added complication: the presence of two bull camels in the caravan. The wisdom of this arrangement had been a matter of much debate among the camel men. The sex-drive of the bull camel was legendary: one introduced to the caravan on an earlier occasion had rogered each and every female camel, culminating with a virgin camel that was brought in by the Bedouin especially for the occasion. This camel had stayed with the caravan and was known as Roger in acknowledgement of his sexual prowess. But Roger II had joined them at Murait and the scene was set for a showdown.

The camel men's fears seemed to be realized as the bull camels slogged it out in a series of unearthly roars that they exchanged as the caravan made its way southwards down the wadi, with Mike's camel, along with the other females, being the focus of their rivalry.

It all added to the general anxiety. One camel man – Tawi – was becoming increasingly agitated and, when the caravan came to rest, he was unable to sit still, pacing up and down and neurotically tapping his thigh with his camel stick. They were at the edge of Sahol territory and Tawi would not cross onto Zueidi land; Kennedy explained Tawi's finely balanced predicament like this: 'The Zueidi will cut his throat.' And so they bade farewell to Tawi, whose camel kicked up a cloud of dust and pulled away with a snort.

They pushed on. Although the bull camels were quiet now, and Roger II muzzled, Mike rode a safe distance from Roger II just in case the presence of his she-camel with her outsized hump should re-ignite the bull camel's passion.

It was hot now. Mike kept a loose grip on the camel bridle, and pulled his hat to one side to protect his face from the sun as he looked out for any interesting outcrops or formations on the way.

Next day, Mike rode halfway along the caravan between an Amarjit man in front and a Sahol man behind – Tawi had returned to the caravan in the night, his fear of a slit throat having apparently evaporated. They passed through Tehair, and dropped down to the wadi bed, where the vegetation became denser. They had to cross and re-cross the wadi several times again, and they found this hazardous as they encountered numerous deep pools in places where the wadi had been dammed with palm branches. It was during one of these crossings that Mike's camel slipped and deposited him on the bank. He washed himself in a pool and, still smelling of mud and dripping wet, tentatively remounted the beast. Together, they continued their journey through tamarisk groves until they reached Miraga, a village on a basalt flow, where they settled down for the night.

Their journey was almost complete but it is likely Mike's grip on his camel's reins was tighter in those last few days than it had ever been before.

ONE CAN IMAGINE the scene on 2 February when the geologists emerged from the Mahra country at Raidut al Abdul Wadid, bleary-eyed, sun-burnt, saddle-sore and hungry, to find their motor transport waiting. They had covered a total distance of 960 kilometres in 65 days, crossing 16 tribal territories and changing the entire convoy eight times.

Their return from the wilderness was duly reported in the Company's newsletter:

An RAF doctor ... gave us news of our intrepid explorers, René Wetzel and 'Mahra' Morton ... the Doc had poured out some mosquito larvae from a gin bottle for Morton who walked in on him straight from Masila, and scared the scalpel off him. He confirmed that the camels were so tired that they flopped their long heads out on to the ground and wouldn't even eat the 'Exploration News'.

Our boys were hungry though.

After weeks of strenuous riding and climbing on iron rations and rice without any fresh food, Morton surprised and gratified a coastal Sultan by consuming a whole sheep, including picking the bones.[12]

Not all their meals were so eagerly consumed; and the geologists had become accustomed to eating fish and dates in dirty conditions. Mike would conceal unpalatable food, usually rotting fish, in the palm of his hand and pretend to fill his mouth while stuffing it inside the neck of his shirt, waiting until the end of the meal to slip away and quietly discard the stinking mess in some dusty corner.

On a more serious note, Tony wrote:

No part of the interior was denied to the party on security grounds, and at no time was the party subjected to any real danger.[13]

He could rightly feel proud of this achievement, but it is unlikely that the geologists shared his view entirely. 'I've never been as dirty in my life,' wrote Mike, 'never been bitten by so many pests, but thank God I didn't get lousy ...'

The Mahra people were riven by tribal and personal feuds: they lived in constant fear of raiding parties from the north and of outsiders generally. It was a testament to their fear that the expedition had been allowed to pass through the territory relatively unhindered.

But there was something else troubling Mike. A new drug called Paludrine, which was better than Quinine, Atelrine and Mepacrine, being a prophylactic and not merely repressive, had become available shortly before their departure from Mukalla. The Resident Adviser had issued supplies to the expedition but the Paludrine had run out in the Wadi Masila, the most highly malarial area.

This thought weighed heavily on Mike's mind as he rolled up his sleeve to inspect his mosquito bites. He could see a few tell-tale pock-marks, red and swollen, dotted randomly up his arm. Whatever happened, the malarial die was cast. It would take 15 days from incubation for the parasites to hatch in the blood stream.

Although the expedition had emerged safely from the Mahra, Mike would chunter all the same: twelve days later he went down with malaria.

Riding along the Mahra shore

1   Memorandum from T. Altounyan to the General Manager, PCL, 14 January 1947, IPC 119 PC/44 Part 3 (270), BP Archive.
2   T. Altounyan, 'A Report on the Mahra', IPC 119 PC/44, Part 3 (274), BP Archive.
3   Triliths are monuments dating back to pre-Islamic times and distributed across southern Arabia from the Wadi Hadhramaut to the interior of Oman. Their alignments vary but usually follow the course of a wadi or track. Although their exact purpose is unknown, many now believe they were built to commemorate the death of a man of importance rather than being tombs. (See 'Excavation and Survey in the Sharqiyah, Oman, 1976', by B. de Cardi, D. B. Doe and S. P. Roskams.)
4   From *Arabia and the Isles*, by H. Ingrams, p. 229. Reproduced by permission of John Murray, Publishers.
5   T. Altounyan, 'A Report on the Mahra', IPC 119 PC/44 Part 3 (274), BP Archive.
6   Ibid.
7   'Report on South Arabia Expedition', A. R. Hubaisly, 15 May 1948.
8   René Wetzel and Mike Morton, 'Expedition to Southern Arabia', *IPC Magazine*, September 1955.
9   T. Altounyan, 'A Report on the Mahra', ibid.
10 'Report on South Arabia Expedition', A. R. Hubaisly, 15 May 1948.
11 From H. Ingrams, *Arabia and the Isles*, p. 225. Reproduced by permission of John Murray, Publishers.
12 'Exploration News', Volume 1 No. 5, May 1948.
13 Memorandum dated 1 June 1948, IPC 119 PC/44, part 4 (24), BP Archive.

Ancient Himyaritic writings

Men of the Bin Kalshat tribe

René taking a compass bearing

An ornamental gate at Ghaida

Wadi Masila

Expedition members at Murait L-R: Tony, Doc, Joe, René

Men removing worms from a camel's nose

The power of the airwaves: tribesmen gathered around Joe and the wireless set

René and Mike on camels at the end of the Mahra expedition:
note the body language of Mike's camel

Chapter 7: A Province Favoured by Providence

Dhofar, 21 February–11 April 1948 and beyond

'A mountainous country, hard to cross, wrapped in thick clouds and fog.'
Periplus of the Erythrean Sea, first century AD[1]

L ike a derelict house on the edge of town, Dhofar stood neglected by the oil companies for many years. In the early 1930s, when IPC was ready to expand its operations from Iraq, the far province of Dhofar was low on its list of priorities. Its range of coastal mountains made access difficult, and its tribes were largely unknown. Major Frank Holmes, a representative of Petroleum Concessions Ltd., the IPC subsidiary, eventually set out from Bahrain in 1936, making agreements with a disparate collection of local sheikhs along the Trucial Coast. He reached Muscat to find a Sultan who was 'glad to relieve his financial straits by granting concessions or options for concessions for the main block of Oman'[2] and, separately, for his province of Dhofar in the south. The Dhofar Oil Agreement was signed in June 1937.

Precious little happened after that. The Trucial Coast sheikhs were happy to receive their annual payments and carry on their little wars. There was nothing much to keep the geologists interested in Dhofar. Initial hopes that it held good possibilities for oil were soon dampened by aerial reconnaissance and a brief survey around Murbat, which proved negative, together with the difficulties of exploring the rugged interior. Then along came World War II, and the Company's entire exploration programme was shelved.

After the war, while the Sultan was keen to further his plans to find oil in Dhofar, the Company was decidedly lukewarm, preferring instead to sit on the concession as other ventures were developed elsewhere. It was only when news reached the Company that the Sultan was thinking of allocating the oil concession to another company, possibly American, that it was galvanized into action. Tony Altounyan was dispatched to meet the Sultan in Salalah in December 1946. The official purpose of his visit was to discuss oil exploration prospects and the possibility of an expedition in the 1947/48 season, but unofficially to head off any challenge for the oil concession from a rival company.

A draft agreement was reached: the Company would mount a survey, for which the Sultan would provide security. The terrain determined that the expedition should be mostly camel-borne. The Sultan promised to pay the escorts at the rate of four Maria Theresa dollars per man/camel per day,[3] and any tribal difficulties would be overcome by including a representative from every tribe in the caravan.

Altounyan returned to London, reporting to his superiors in IPC that Dhofar presented no exceptional difficulties for an expedition and recommending that the Company should proceed with its plans. The Company agreed.

And so, on 21 February 1948, geologists Wetzel and Morton appeared on the scene, refreshed and revived after their journey through the Mahra country, Mike having recovered from malaria, both alighting on the airstrip of RAF Salalah after their flight from Riyan in a converted Wellington bomber.

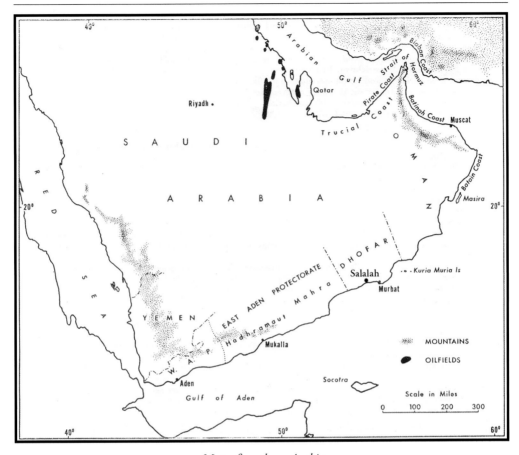

Map of southern Arabia
from D. M. Morton, 'The Geology of Oman', Proc. 5ᵗʰ World Petroleum Congress, 1959

IN REALITY, DHOFAR was blessed in many ways. In the words of Bertram Thomas, it was 'a province favoured by Providence':

> It owes its unique climate to the 'Indian' south-west monsoon, which here makes a preliminary call and during the summer months sprinkles these mountains with a drizzling rain so that the region flows with milk and honey. Just over the mountain divide flourish the famous frankincense groves of Arabia.[4]

Dhofar was very much the Sultan's personal domain. Although it had been connected with Oman since the nineteenth century, historically it tended to look west, having strong trading links with the Hadhramaut through the frankincense trade. The coastal strip around the capital Salalah was fertile and the Qara mountains provided grazing for cattle, goats and camels even in the drier months. The Sultan spent most of his time here, passing whole summers in his palace in Salalah in preference to the barren rocky outcrops of Muscat.

The Sultan's Palace was a large, white fort, square, with red shutters, set in a coconut grove overlooking the ocean. The red flag of the Sultan of Muscat fluttered half-heartedly in a faint sea breeze. The Palace dominated Salalah, a small town on the shore, a place of palms and ocean rollers, marked by the stench of drying fish.

It was late in the day, around 5 p.m., when the party comprising René, Mike and Tony Altounyan swept through a narrow guarded archway in the Sultan's American limousine, arriving in a gravelled courtyard for their appointment with the Sultan. They entered the Palace by a long hallway lined with the Sultan's bodyguard – fine-looking Bedu in uniform – and rifles hanging on the walls. They went up a flight of marble steps to a landing guarded by more armed men and entered a large European style drawing room. Here they came upon the Sultan, a small, plump man with round, olive-coloured features and a thick black beard with a white flash on the left side of his chin. He was dressed in a long white gown covered with a blue, gold-trimmed cloak, and wore a large white turban on his head. His name was Said bin Taimur, and he had been Sultan since 1932.

Tea was served in silver teapots and cakes served on plates covered with lace squares trimmed with glass beads; each cover had a different colour bead and the beads gave a musical tinkle as the covers were lifted. The conversation wandered around the subjects of minerals, oil and world affairs and – perhaps in desperation at the failure to find oil in the province so far – other ways of raising revenue such as issuing postage stamps. They found the Sultan charming, polite and well informed. The meeting was cordial and ended on friendly terms: the Sultan confirmed that all the arrangements regarding their caravan, escort and security were completed and they could leave the next day. The Sultan wished them well and the geologists retraced their steps, returning to the RAF camp for the evening.

The question of how many tribesmen – and thus the number of camels – in their convoy remained a concern. As Thesiger had discovered on a visit to the province in 1945, there would be no shortage of volunteers. An expedition provided the local tribesman with a 'heaven-sent opportunity to enrich himself'. Thesiger's convoy numbered 45 camels, and it was anyone's guess how large the IPC caravan would turn out to be.

They rose early next morning and went out to the billet to watch the main event unfold, Mike looking on as the number of camels seemed to multiply with each passing moment – first 20, then 30, 40 – eventually 76. Men were arriving all the time, fine-looking men, not as quarrelsome as those in the Mahra, but the chaos of camel loading was much the same: the general belly-aching and confusion, roaring, bellowing, shouting and shoving. Soldiers of the Sultan's bodyguard – slaves rather than local tribesmen – looked on. Their complement included 19 sheikhs of the Bait Kathir under their paramount leader, Sheikh Ahmed. Next came the Sultan's man, an adviser attached to the party who controlled the six Negro servants who were to act as the geologists' 'constant batmen'.

Order was imposed by the appearance of a small, dumpy man, smooth-skinned, with a bushy beard. This was Saif, the Sultan's man. He swiftly imposed himself on the men through a series of crisp commands issued in the manner of an efficient sergeant major. 'The sheikhs of the various tribes also are under his command, yet preserve their own rights and dignity,' wrote Mike.

The caravan set off, the geologists taking a short motor journey to Ain Gunzis where they would rejoin the caravan for their trip into the interior.

AT THE TIME of their survey, detailed knowledge of the Dhofar hinterland was sparse, relying on the reports of travellers such as Bertram Thomas and Wilfred Thesiger, and on the brief

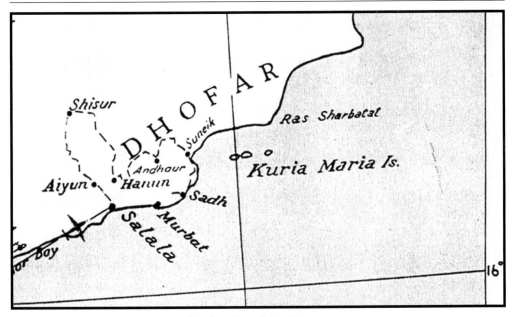

Dhofar: Expedition Itinerary

surveys of geologists such as Basil Lermitte and Sir Cyril Fox. Despite the latter surveying the coastal regions and reporting a 'petroleum residue', there was no conclusive evidence of oil being present in the rocks below.

Although comparisons with the oil-rich territories of the Persian Gulf were unfavourable, Dhofar was not an entirely hopeless case. The expedition was to be a local survey with regional implications. As defined by their order of work, René and Mike's task was two-fold: first, to gain enough knowledge of the stratigraphy and structure of the area in order to evaluate the local oil possibilities, and second, to form a broader view of conditions in the region as a whole.

The geological relationship between Dhofar, its neighbouring regions, and the mighty Arabian Shield had intrigued geologists for a long time. As S. H. Longrigg observed:

> The territories of the three states which form south-western, southern and south-eastern Arabia – Yemen, the Aden Protectorate and Oman – all represent a fringe of the continent, deeply sedimented by the transgression of the sea over it, all slope inwards towards the heart of Arabia, and all terminate southwards in a faulting system related to a depression which forms the Gulf of Aden.[5]

The fact that an ancient sea had once lapped its shorelines made these southern fringes of the Arabian Shield worth exploring. The sedimentary rocks of the Hadhramaut – possible reservoirs of oil – carried over into Dhofar. What the geologists needed to establish, before formulating a view about the likely presence of oil, was the order and thickness of the strata.

Of course, their analysis was never going to be a simple matter: the pressures of the Earth, moving continents, and periods of uplift and erosion, had left behind a confusing puzzle of folded and missing strata, which the geologists were attempting to unravel – much as others are doing today.

AFTER INVESTIGATING THE terrain around Ain Gunzis, the geologists returned to the shaded valley where the caravan was resting and patiently waited for the camels to rise; but by evening they hadn't moved an inch. The huge caravan split into little groups, with the camel men busying themselves with various mundane tasks – repairing ropes, grinding coffee, tending the camels – all overseen by Saif. His title was *Akit*, the equivalent of *Muqaddam* in the Mahra. Incongruously, Mike noted, some of the tribesmen had wrist-watches and 'it seemed absurd to see one fellow writing in a note book. But their clothes were clean and they showed more intelligence than the Mahra'.

An early start the next day surprised them, as the camels were ready to leave half an hour after dawn. This was the first time in three weeks that the geologists had ridden camels, and most of their energies were devoted simply to staying in the saddle – these camels were more powerful than those of the Mahra country, and they were unaccustomed to the geologists' Syrian saddles. René fared worse on this occasion, falling from his camel three or four times as they made their way up the Wadi Gunzis.

'The huge caravan was never all in sight,' Mike wrote, 'and riding was dangerous as the trees overhung the path.' Riding up the wadi in a morning shower, the men in the convoy showed little interest in their surroundings. Many days' riding lay ahead of them; they knew this country well and were content to chatter amongst themselves.

Later, after a dinner of venison, Mike and René got to know their travelling companions. They strolled between several camp fires, stopping every so often to talk with one of the 19 sheikhs of the caravan. Out of deference they went first to Ahmed, the most important sheikh, paramount of the Bait Kathir. The processes by which a man became the leader of their tribe had often intrigued Mike. Foremost among his peers by dint of wit, respect and judgement, and elected by them, it was important for such a man not to lose face in front of his tribe.

They moved on to the next flickering fire where they found Salem Tanitim, Sheikh al Bait Ghuass, with his retainers. They stayed awhile to listen to the songs and gossip, and to sip another coffee. Salem was an old stager, active, pleasant, grey-bearded and wrinkled. He wore a brown smock and a faded brown turban, and was over 80 years old, although he claimed to be over 100.

'One time the number one trouble-maker for the Sultan in Salalah', as Mike had heard the next sheikh, Said bin Ahmed bin Katmin bin Arsi bin Maram, described. He presented a tough, wiry, lean man, dressed in black with a dark turban that seemed to impart a metallic shine in the moonlight.

Then there was Musellim bin Gharajib, Sheikh el Bait Hamar – another pleasant old greybeard who, despite his age, was 'a great hunter, shooting gazelle with extraordinary regularity'. Like the fire that brightly burned beside him, Musellim was warm and glowing, plump and cheerful, his eyes flaming with reflected firelight, his face often breaking into a wide, engaging smile.

Around another fire sat Mohammed bin Ahmed bin Hamar and Bin Zaoud bin Wasad, Sheikh el Bait el Hiza, the long and the short of an assorted group of tribesmen crowded around a pile of smoking, hissing branches.

Finally they came upon the steady burning fire of Sheikh Mabkhout and his men. Mabkhout was the most impressive of them all: a proud and handsome Bedu. His piercing eyes, Semitic nose, black beard and moustache, curling around a firm-set mouth, were typical of the true Bedu, and he wore a simple purple turban and white smock. His voice, too, was clear and firm – in Mike's view 'his every gesture shows his good Arab breeding'.

The geologists slept in the bottom of a ravine, illuminated by a thin shaft of bright moon-light, with a small patch of night sky visible with grey clouds scudding across.

TEN PACES, 20 paces, 30 paces, 41: counting camel strides was a good way of passing the time. Their camel strides averaged 41 per minute, which meant an average speed of approximately five kilometres per hour. A difference of three, or possibly four, paces a minute would be important to a man who counted them to measure his progress, since it meant a difference of days in the overall journey time – but the counting might have sent him a little mad if there hadn't been other distractions along the way.

These camels were larger and stronger than those of the Mahra, which walked an average of 37 to 38 paces in a similar terrain. The Dhofar camels were mostly Omani in origin, a breed that was famous for its qualities as a strong, swift beast. In the words of an Arab proverb: 'Do not ride an Omani she-camel and do not marry a girl from the Za'ab tribe. The first will upset the pace of the army, the second will upset your wives.'

And so, as the caravan lumbered onwards at a regulation 41 paces for the next few days, the geologists took in a changing landscape. They passed through Aiyun and reached Ma Shedid, where they rested and watered the camels for three days, then proceeded northwards along the Wadi Ghudun. The appearance of the wadi altered from a valley filled with small clumps of dwarf Phoenix palms and *triall*, a green plant with a small, daisy-like yellow flower, to a harsher aspect; the wadi bed was uneven and covered with drifting sand and pebbles, with cliffs of rubbly chalky limestone on either side rising to nine metres. *Kifi* – thorny bushes with small, violet flowers – were spread around. They travelled along a flat, gravelled terrace, cutting off a curve in the wadi, which they rejoined at its junction with the Wadi Gharzah. A flat, stony gravel-strewn desert, slightly undulating, and with a few smooth hillocks protruding from the plains, strewn with black, shiny flints, lay ahead. The meagre vegetation, *harmel* – a leafy, light-green shrub that grew in clumps – was disregarded by the camels slouching past.

Earlier in the day, René's camel man, Ahmed, had found what he called a '*dhab*' (sometimes pronounced '*dhlab*'), a large, scaly lizard about 30 centimetres long from its head to the base of its trunk. They had seen this reptile's hand-like prints on the ground the day before. At lunchtime, Ahmed skinned the *dhab* and gave René the skin. 'The meat is eaten by the Bedu, who roast it,' noted Mike. 'The body was about five inches [13 centimetres] across and one-and-a-half inches [four centimetres] thick, providing quite a substantial piece of meat. The skin was very pretty and large and the armoured tail quite belied the harmlessness of the timid, slow creature.'

LATER, THEY CAME upon a boy lying under a tree, moaning. They gathered round him, while Mike asked him what was wrong. Pains in the stomach and a headache, he said. 'I thought it was the incapacitating colic, to which Bedu are particularly prone,' noted Mike, 'but our learned doctor pronounced malaria (rather unlikely) and gave him quinine. He is a good doctor but lacking in practice.'

When the doctor's remedy failed to work, it was time to try a more traditional approach. The following night, when it appeared that there had been no improvement, the Bedu carried out an exorcism of the boy. After much chanting, spitting and exhorting the devil to leave the body, they helped the boy to his feet and brought him into the firelight. His eyes were dull and he seemed to be hypnotized, mechanically rubbing his sleeve slowly across his wet face. His pulse rate after his 'cure' was 120.

Next day the boy appeared to be quite well. Mike was mindful of him for a while, but his interest began to wane in a battle with the rising heat, as the sun became very hot and gave off a 'frightening glare'. They were riding towards the water hole at Shisur, along the Wadi Ghudun, which was now between one and two kilometres wide. At eleven o'clock they split up, and each man sought shade among a patch of thorny acacias. They lay there until four o'clock. Then they set off again, following the wadi until it made a sharp turn to the north-east, when they carried on straight ahead, climbing a small ridge and crossing undulating country until a white cliff appeared in the distance. This was their destination: Shisur.

They took in the moment and then urged their camels on.

EIGHTEEN YEARS EARLIER, in 1930, the explorer Bertram Thomas had been approaching the southern edge of the Rub al Khali. It was Thomas's ambition to be the first European to cross the great sands but, as he began his camel journey, he was given a timely reminder of the dangerous land that lay ahead: he was told of a lost city whose wicked people had attracted the wrath of God and had been destroyed. In that barren, desiccated land, he would find few remnants of ancient civilizations. The Bedouin forefathers, perhaps by virtue of their nomadic ways, not seeking immortality on earth, had left little in the way of monuments behind them.

The story of a lost city in the sands had become an explorer's fascination; a few wrote accounts of their travels that perpetrated the myth. T. E. Lawrence planned to search for the location of a lost city somewhere in the sands, telling a fellow traveller that he was convinced that the remains of an Arab civilization were to be found in the desert. He had been told that the Bedu had seen the ruins of the castles of King Ad in the region of Wabar. In his view the best way to explore the sands was by airship, but his plans never came to fruition.

Bertram Thomas would also gaze longingly in the direction of the sands. His guide pointed to wide tracks between the dunes and said: 'Look, Sahib, there is the way to Ubar. It was great in treasure, with date gardens and a fort of red silver. It now lies beneath the sands of the Ramlat Shu'ait.'[6] 175 kilometres to the south-east lay the well at Shisur with an unremarkable ruin, which Thomas dismissed as a 'rude' fort and took to be only a few hundred years old.

St John Philby, anxious not to be outdone, went in search of the lost city of Wabar to the north and came across an extinct volcano half-buried in the sands. The trail went cold, but many years after René and Mike arrived in these parts, it was the rude fort at Shisur that attracted the attention of archaeologists. Here, it was said, was the site of Ubar, the famed lost city of the sands.

When the geologists arrived at Shisur on 4 March, the damp clouds of the coast were a distant memory. The heat was mind-numbing. All around stretched a barren, flat, brown expanse, like an enormous airfield. 'The Bedu say that there has been no rain here for twenty years,' wrote Mike, 'and some of the goat droppings were ten years old.' But far to the north a cluster of dark green indicated some grazing for the camels and wood for the camp fires they would light in the evening.

The white cliff they had seen rising out of the plain marked the location of the well at Shisur. As they drew closer, it became apparent that the cliff was in fact a ruined fort, built above a large quarry-like cave, which was screened by a drifting sand dune. The fort had been built from the same white rock as the overhanging cliff, and gave the impression of being part of it. Mike noted:

'There are no houses, tents or people here: only the tumble-down ruin of this pre-Islamic fort.'

Later explorers would discover a large octagonal fortress dating back some 2,000 years beneath the crumbling fort at Shisur, and a vast limestone table lying beneath the main gate which had collapsed into a massive sinkhole around the main well. But the geologists of 1948 would probably have cast a sceptical eye over the notion of a fabled city lying amid the ruins of the pre-Islamic fort. At the time, there was no evidence that this was Ubar; but in the early centuries BC, Shisur had been at the hub of caravan routes carrying frankincense from Dhofar to the north and the west.

For the geologists, Shisur, like Ma Shedid before, was a 'difficult water'. Just how difficult was described by Mike in his notebook:

The approach is as follows: the camel track runs alongside the low hill on which the fort stands and turns around it until facing the quarry cliff. Then on foot, one must 'slide' down fifty feet [fifteen metres] of sand dune, which has drifted by the wind into this natural and partly man-made quarry. The last fifteen feet [4.5 metres] are under the low overhang of the cliff with barely room to stand up, narrowing until a tiny hole is reached, the diameter of a slim, small man. Squirming along the narrow passage, towards the foul mud-choked water, the smell of hydrogen sulphide, like rotten eggs, is almost overpowering. It is pitch dark, hot, stuffy and tomb-like, and difficult to fill a water skin from the narrow funnel-like aperture near the water.

Camel droppings, an inevitable result of the way the Bedu watered their camels, caused the smell: the camels collected on a ledge at the base of the sand dunes and their droppings would roll down the slope into the water hole:

The water fresh from the well is black, with a high content of evil sulphurous mud, which gives off the strong bad smell. We boil it, strain it through lint, and then it is quite palatable and has no mineral taste, although it has the annoying property of coagulating soap.

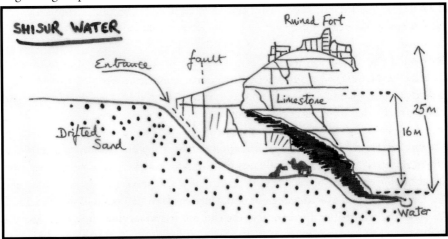

Shisur water sketch

The geologists put their beds on the sandy flat near the mouth of the water hole. The sun was still extremely hot at 5 p.m. and Mike was completely exhausted, feeling dried-up and aching in every joint. This was to be their stopping place for three days, being the time it would take to water 76 camels. There was nothing to do for the rest of the day except relax and wait for the evening coolness.

Mike passed a restless night, tossing and turning with stomach ache brought on – no doubt – by sampling the dung-flavoured water. Awakening in a red-and-gold dawn, he got up as the sun was rising above a thin membrane of cloud and sat with René in the shade of the cliffs, watching the spectacle of camel watering taking place.

A chain of tribesmen first took out pans of sand and camel dung from the choked entrance to the hole, chanting ancient work songs as they worked through the morning. Much as Thesiger had found when he had stopped here with his companions to water their camels on their way to the Rub al Khali, the Bedu had to work hard to extract water from the well. Several camels would be brought down to the ledge to drink from water-skins carried up from the water hole in the darkness below:

> In turn they scrambled up the slope out of the dark depths of the cave, the quaking water-skins heavy on their shoulders. Moisture ran down their bodies, plastering their loin-cloths to their slender limbs; their hair, thick with sand, fell about their strained faces.[7]

There was no class distinction among the Bedu – the 19 sheikhs worked just as hard as their men. Each camel would drink three water skins and, with each skin holding just over four litres and taking ten minutes to make a round trip, it was a mammoth task to water 76 camels. A camel would settle at first near the well and then, despite the ministrations of its owners, might have other ideas:

> Every now and again one of them rose jerkily to her feet, anxious to wander off, and her owner ran across a gravel stream-bed to bring her back, shouting her name Farha (joy), Matara (rain), Ghazala (gazelle), Safra (the yellow one), or some other name which in battle might be his war-cry.[8]

And so the party settled down for their last night at Shisur, waited on at dinner by the Sultan's black slaves. When René and Mike went down into the cave to sleep, they were joined by the slaves who lit up a fire and, curling up nearby, drifted off to sleep, having no dreams of the ruined lost city that lay undiscovered in the earth around them.

NEXT MORNING WAS cool in the cave, and it was a long time before the sun gilded the cliff top above them. After sorting their rations, there was little to do but wait until watering was complete. It was not until 3 p.m. that the camels were ready and, for the first time that day, the geologists emerged from the cave and mounted their camels, departing from Shisur an hour later.

Over the next four days, they would ride east and then south-east to the Wadi Dauka, across the Hanfit hills to the Wadi Rabkut, and then due south to the water hole at Hanun. The scenery was varied: at first they rode across a wide, level sand flat, El Haili, which had a long line of camel scrub and thorn bushes. Running almost parallel with their route was a camel pasture for those using Shisur water. They came to a low, rounded, limestone ridge on their eastern flank where there were a few isolated thorn trees, with wind-blown sand piled around the roots. Here they stopped for the night, eating cold venison for dinner.

Eventually the sand flat gave way to a low, undulating gravelly terrain. They crossed into the Wadi Hauf (Valley of Danger) and proceeded east-south-east to the Wadi Dauka, one of the long wadis that flowed northwards from the Qara mountains and disappeared into the Rub al Khali. They fixed up shade from the sun, under a small thorny tree, and lay there in the heat of the day.

THE WORLD WAS disappearing, the stillness sucked away. Sand was carried across the sky, blurring the sun, melding heaven with earth, until all became a stinging, swirling mass around them. Racing through the wadi, the sandstorm was reaching its climax. The whole river-bed was alive with darting trailers of sand.

It had begun in mid-afternoon, when they were about to set off again. A strong breeze blew up, carrying fine particles of sand into their shelter. Soon everything was covered with a thin film of sand, as well as their faces. The breeze became stronger and eddies of swirling sand ran down the wadi. By the time the camels were ready the hot, stinging wind was almost unbearable. As Mike struggled to wrap his headcloth around his face, René's umbrella was whipped from his grasp. The wind carried it away at high speed, rolling, bouncing, over and over, until a Bedu on a fast camel stopped it about three kilometres away.

They mounted and left at 4.30 p.m., riding directly into what had become a fully-fledged sandstorm. The sand drilled into them, stinging their exposed hands and faces. Soon everyone in the caravan was riding with thick headcloths drawn across their faces, covering even their eyes.

Now and then Mike peered through a gap in his ragged shield. The sun, like a silver sphere, gleamed faintly through a solid mist. Most of the time the eyes of the camel men remained tightly closed and the direction of travel was left to the camels. Mike tried looking around for his companions – contact with other parts of the caravan was easily lost – but this was of no real concern, he reminded himself, since their direction of travel lay along the wadi. Mike burrowed his chin into his chest and again wrapped up his eyes against the storm.

At 6.15 p.m. they stopped near a low mound, which stood some two metres above the dried-up wadi, providing some respite from the sand streaming across its bed. Here they dumped their kit, and sat in the lee of four rolled-up beds waiting for the wind to drop. By 7 p.m. there was not so much sand coming down, so the geologists put up their beds, ate a quick dinner and retired early with a strong, cold wind still blowing.

They woke before dawn and using a mug full of water washed the sand from their faces: the sand was everywhere, even in their food, which they chewed with little enthusiasm. The lack of water was – as ever – a problem: extracting water from the wells at Ma Shedid and Shisur had been difficult enough, and water was always precious. At least the wind had dropped and the desert world – scoured but intact – had reappeared.

Herein lay the scenes of their journey: first they saw four oryx, white animals larger than gazelle, at a great distance from the caravan. A shooting party went after them, but returned empty-handed, unable to get within range. Then the caravan unexpectedly changed direction. Their guide Sheikh M'Zaoud – a tall, thin, emaciated old man with a high-pitched quavering voice – began leading the camels off course. 'Probably wanting to make the journey last longer, and also to reach a wadi with camel food earlier,' grumbled Mike. The caravan slid away to their left, going eastwards, making a feeble curve of rising dust.

Tony and the geologists set off on a south-south-west bearing, hoping that the caravan would change its course. Sure enough, the caravan soon began veering back towards them. The unmistakable shape of M'Zaoud came riding back towards them, his high-pitched voice sounding over the plain. Soon the caravan was whole again, re-united with the exploration party, with the tribesmen chattering as before.

They came upon a large wadi and stopped for lunch, continuing their journey in the afternoon:

> Soon after riding along this wadi, we forked right along a shallow valley with *samr*, acacias, dwarf (phoenix) palms and '*rakh*', a green flashy, vine-like plant, which the camels enjoy. We stopped for the night near a small isolated hill. The pleasant scent of aromatic wood-smoke drifted across the camp from the many fires.

Next day, across the far shivers of a hazy horizon, the northern flanks of the Qara mountains could be seen, gently sloping down to join the barren gravel plain. The way ahead was dotted with green wadis. They rode past many Himyaritic remains, their camels padding softly as if trying not to disturb the spirits of those who built them. They paused at a small pool of salty, dirty water in a narrow wadi with steep limestone cliffs. They watered the camels, rode on for one-and-a-half hours, and arrived at Hanun Pool.

This was a natural catchment, a permanent pool of run-off water trapped in a massive pot-hole, situated between sheer white dolomitic cliffs which had eroded at the base to form a long open cave running along both sides of the wadi. On the walls of the cave were crude drawings of men and camels, 'probably Bedouin', painted with a tar-like substance. Above the cliffs, on the east bank of the narrow wadi, lay more Himyaritic remains: two long tombs with circles arranged along long axes running from north to south.

René and Mike went to work on a geological survey south-west of the water hole. On the way, they passed more Himyaritic remains and saw a crude stairway running up a hill with old, stone fortifications on top. Everywhere lay reminders that this was a land with an ancient history: on the way back, by a different route, they entered a valley with many tombs along it, with a large cave at its head. Frankincense trees with twisted trunks and crinkled leaves grew sporadically in all the wadis on the northern slopes, and it seemed that the cave had been used as a temporary storehouse for their resin. A peculiar stone structure with a wooden door like a house stood inside the cave. Mike noted:

> The tombs must have had some connection with the frankincense working; perhaps the large circles nearby, suggestive of the fireplaces of the Bedu today, were part of some harvest ceremony. A blue limestone found in most of these circles, and smelling faintly of some tarry substance, yet which is not found in the surrounding strata, may be ordinary limestone impregnated by the aromatic wood when burned, in some manner.

By the time the geologists returned to the camp it was late in the day. All around the narrow gorge were long strings of raw meat dripping and drying in the dying sun, the remnants of two bullocks that the Bedu had slaughtered earlier in the day. They feasted 'royally' that night, gathered with the sheikhs in groups around the roasting fires.

THEIR JOURNEY THROUGH south-eastern Arabia was now coming to an end. On reaching Obet they travelled to the large oasis at Andhaur, turned south, and dropped sharply down the rugged slopes from the plateau to the sea. On 29 March, after much exhausting work and hard riding, fighting high temperatures and enervating humidity, their hardships were over:

> We were eventually met by the Sultan's cars and were driven to Murbat to stay with the Wali. Our hardest work was now complete and the scarcity of water, which had been a major problem *en route*, no longer existed.

At Murbat, they investigated reports of oil seepage:

> The so-called oil seepage of Murbat was visited and it was made sure that this seepage, if it has existed, was no longer active. The sample of sandstone from where the oil is supposed to seep is yellow by oxidation which would not be the case in the presence of hydrocarbons.

René noted afterwards:

> We were told by an RAF officer in Salalah that barrels of petrol and kerosene for consumption in Dhofar were generally floated ashore and that frequently there are lost barrels which may give rise to false oil seepage when buried in the sands of the shore.

The expedition's tired camels had carried them 600 kilometres through Dhofar, and they had been away from Salalah for about six weeks. A motor road ran from Murbat to Salalah, so their homeward journey was in comfort. Aden, 800 kilometres away, was their next goal. Here, after five months of hard living and sleeping in the open, the exploration party would disband.

'NOT TOO ENCOURAGING is it?' said the Sultan.[9]

It was the spring of 1951, and the Sultan was considering his options. After the Dhofar expedition, the geologists' conclusions had confirmed what the Company had long suspected:

> Dhofar is devoid of suitable structures under impervious cap rock beds for oil accumulation. In the absence of direct evidence in favour of the existence of stratigraphic traps, these are too remote a chance to justify consideration. Dhofar can therefore be rejected as a possible oilfield.[10]

The IPC subsidiary company had served notice of abandonment of the concession in the autumn of 1950, at the same time dropping 'Dhofar' from its title to become Petroleum Development (Oman) Ltd.

Now, in the course of a discussion between the Sultan and a young American by the name of Wendell Phillips, events took an unexpected turn. When Wendell Phillips expressed some surprise at the Sultan's 'delight' on hearing the news of IPC's withdrawal, thinking that the Sultan might miss the Company's annual payments, the Sultan explained:

> Yes, that is true, but we need oil in Dhofar, not annual payments. And by the Will of God we shall have oil, for I am granting *you* the oil concession for Dhofar.

It took a little time for Wendell Phillips – an archaeologist with no experience of the oil business – to recover from the shock. His arrival in Dhofar had been by accident in the first place, chased from Yemen by the authorities who suspected his party of smuggling out ancient artefacts. The Sultan had taken him under his wing and was now offering him an oil concession the size of Indiana – no wonder he had been taken by surprise.

In some ways, this was a huge gamble. But in other ways, the Sultan's choice was a canny one. Since conventional wisdom had ruled out the prospect of finding oil in Dhofar, it was time for an unconventional approach. 'Wendell,' the Sultan used to say, 'just think what I can do for my people when we have oil.'[11]

Over the next few days Phillips hammered out with the Sultan an oil-concession agreement, which the Sultan himself, an expert in international law, typed out. Phillips then set about arranging finance, but still the obstacles were formidable: IPC had ruled out the possibility of oil being found, Dhofar was 'remote from American thinking', and there were no port facilities, so that all equipment would have to be flown or floated in. Undaunted, Phillips pressed on with his plans and in January 1953, with the Sultan's agreement, the Dhofar concession was assigned to Dhofar-Cites Service Petroleum. Phillips, taking a leaf out of Gulbenkian's book, retained a two-and-a-half per cent share.

All the while, IPC looked on. In May 1953 it was suggested that the Company might re-acquire the concession, but this was dismissed. The real interest of the Company lay along the eastern boundary of the concession area, where it adjoined its own concession in central Oman. To date the Sultan had not defined the eastern boundary of the province, but this area showed the most promise.[12]

The Company had eyes and ears in strategic locations. 'I gathered that they expected to start drilling at Dhofar early in January 1955,' wrote a representative of Petroleum Concessions Ltd from Aden. Two months later he observed: 'There appears to have been quite a bit of activity by Cites Service employees here in Aden during the past week.' Eleven days later: 'Yesterday, the *SS Mohammed Ali el Kabir* was at Aden bound for Solala [*sic*] with equipment for the drilling to be carried out in Dhofar. The ship had been chartered for the journey, and we understand that two landing-craft have also been chartered for the unloading.'[13]

Cites Services set up their headquarters in a palm grove near a beach to the west of Salalah, and a number of aerial reconnaissances were flown over the territory. The Sultan built a 50-kilometre road from Salalah into the Qara mountains to allow huge Kenilworth trucks to transport collapsible derricks into the interior. Exploration camps grew up overnight, and millions of dollars were spent.

The stage was set for drilling to begin. On 15 April 1955, filled with optimism and the excitement of a new challenge, the Americans spudded-in their first test-well at Dauka. This was followed by the middle two wells at Marmul in 1957 and 1958.

At first the signs were encouraging, but these early signs did not last. The oil flow from Marmul declined on testing and the oil was too heavy to exploit commercially.[14] Further disappointments followed, with low oil-prices and the problem of loading crude on the coast during the monsoon season (June-September) only adding to the difficulties. In 1967, after an expenditure of $40 to $50 million, and 29 wells sunk, the Americans relinquished the concession.

Dhofar was a province favoured by Providence in many ways but not in oil resources, it seemed.

A collection of Dhofar sheikhs

1   A navigational guide to the Red Sea and Indian Ocean, written by an anonymous Alexandrian sea captain.

2   S. H. Longrigg, *Oil in the Middle East*, 2nd Edition, p. 115. By permission of Oxford University Press.

3   Approximately £44 in today's money.

4   From Bertram Thomas, *Arabia Felix*, p. 8, Jonathan Cape. Reprinted by permission of Random House.

5   S. H. Longrigg, *Oil in the Middle East*, 2nd Edition, p. 8. Reproduced by permission of Oxford University Press.

6   From Bertram Thomas, *Arabia Felix*, p. 161, published by Jonathan Cape. Reprinted by permission of Random House.

7   Wilfred Thesiger, *Arabian Sands*, p. 100, with permission of Curtis Brown on behalf of the Wilfred Thesiger Estate Copyright © Wilfred Thesiger Estate 1959.

8   Ibid., p. 100.

9   Wendell Phillips, *Unknown Oman*, p. 241.

10   R. Wetzel and D. M. Morton, Geological Report 198-199, with permission of PD(O) Ltd.

11   Wendell Phillips, *Unknown Oman*, p. 247.

12   R. E. R. Bird, 'Oman and Dhofar', paper dated 1 May 1953, PC/27 (222), BP Archive.

13   Correspondence, 28 September, 18 December, 29 December, 1954, PC27B, Part 1 (63, 71, 74), BP Archive.

14   Hal Knudsen, email of 12 June 2004 to Alan Heward: 'The low gravity crude, reservoir conditions and the existing world crude prices were overwhelming negatives.'

Ahmed with a dhab - 'lunch is served'

Leaving Hanun with 76 camels and still counting ....

Mike at the end of the Dhofar expedition, April 1948

Chapter 8: Aleppo

Syria, July–December 1948

'To all in Alep and the man in Amman
If it's oil you want with a rush
Just bury those slide-rules, and burn all your maps
Get out there and drill by that bush'

Mike Morton

In 1914, T. E. Lawrence stayed at the Baron's Hotel in the city of Aleppo, Syria. He stayed for six nights, spending hours pacing up and down the terrace. At the end of his stay, he subtracted from his bill the price of a bottle of Cordon Rouge supplied but not consumed, for Lawrence never drank alcohol, preferring nothing stronger than lemon juice. Later, in the 1960s, the British double agent Kim Philby[1] stayed in the same hotel and attempted to make up for Lawrence's omission, trying hard to drink the bar dry on his visits from Beirut where he was stationed when working for the *Observer*. It was amazing, the hotel manager would later remark, that despite his legendary consumption, Philby never gave the game away. But Philby need not have tried so hard to drink the bar dry, for there was a dedicated group of IPC employees based at the hotel in the late 1940s who had already made a pretty good job of making up for Lawrence's lack of interest in beverages of the alcoholic kind.

Today, Baron's Hotel lives on its memories of better days. The famous unpaid bill of Lawrence is still on display, but there is a feeling that the prices are too high and that the hotel seeks to exploit its reputation as the most famous refuelling stop in the Middle East. It is still a grand building, but one of faded charm.

Mike arrived in Aleppo in the summer of 1948. Aleppo was being used as the forward base for the operations of the Company and those of its associates which were involved in drilling operations at Baflun and Dola'a and exploration up to the north-west frontier.

On 13 July he took charge of his first field-team and was detailed to carry out a survey of the mountains of north-western Syria. Dick Browne had already carried out stratigraphic investigation in the early part of the year. Mike, assisted by a geologist named E. H. Rumsey, was now tasked to map part of the territory to the north-west of the Aafrine River.

Mike arrived with a memento of his desert days. A colleague was startled to find a dusty old camel saddle in the company staff quarters; on enquiring about its ownership and purpose, he was told that the saddle belonged to Mike Morton 'just back' from the Hadhramaut who was using it as a makeshift armchair.

The social life of Aleppo was legendary, with Baron's Hotel being used as an improvised mess for Company personnel and two high-class night-clubs with cabaret shows in the town; there were also several good restaurants, and an exclusive country club.[2] The Company had a camp at Minakh, some 25 to 30 kilometres north of Aleppo. A party was hosted at the camp every Saturday night, attended by guests from town, where there was dancing, imported food and plenty of drink, including the occasional bottle of Scotch whisky.

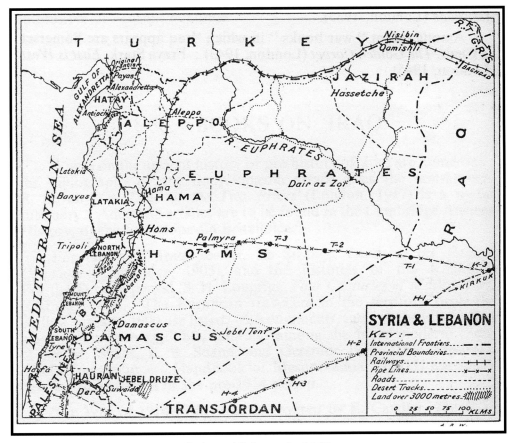

Syria and Lebanon in 1948
© *Iraq Petroleum Company Limited*

Historically, Aleppo was situated at the junction of many ancient caravan routes, with the result that a wealthy merchant-class existed in the town. A number of girls from the wealthier families would attend the Company social functions – Zuzu, Lucy and 'Big' Rosie among others – and enjoy themselves. They were at the very centre of the Company social scene – destined to marry within their own social circle but, until that moment arrived, determined to have a good time. They were witty, intelligent and able to converse in several languages. They made a big impression on the young men of the Company with whom they spent many a happy hour, dancing, sharing jokes and occasionally playing strip poker – chaperoned by the Company wives and stopping strictly at undergarments.

Mike enjoyed this social life for a while, but the novelty wore off, as he focused on his career and new responsibilities. This was his first time in charge of a field party and he found the work tiring at times, as he described in a letter to Heather from Aleppo:

I'm sorry that I've been unable to write for two weeks, but I'm working very hard. Out with Dubertret, averaging 13 hours a day in the summer is no joke. It's very interesting geology here, though, but very thirsty work.

There have been two more parties since I last wrote. Same pattern, same girls – and very heavy going. It's really an anti-climax here after Tripoli. I haven't once reached a minor inebriate phase which, however, is probably a good thing. Driving about in a car makes me awfully sleepy too – probably because I'm always tired, and as I'm geologist-in-charge now, I've lots more work than when I was merely an assistant. Brain – and office – work I find is also fatiguing.

REGARDING SYRIA, 'THE most striking result of the work,' wrote E. J. Daniel[3] 'was to establish the occurrence of Jurassic limestone in the region … the application of this work is more towards an understanding of the general geology of north-west Syria; and some useful information regarding the origin of the basic igneous rocks of the district, and also in respect of faulting, has been collected.'

Mike worked in the Kurd-Dagh mountains where the border between Syria and Turkey lay. Maps were not entirely reliable at the time. For example, maps of Syria seemed to have a Jebel 'Hada' at every point of the compass. As Mike discovered, this was the result of an attempt by a senior geologist to map the region, his only Arabic phrase being: 'What's the name of that jebel?' The guide would inevitably answer: 'jebel hada?' and point towards the jebel in question, meaning 'this jebel?' But the geologist, taking the guide's answer as final, would record yet another Jebel Hada on the map.

In one letter, Mike described the problems of working in an area where the frontier lines between countries sometimes became blurred.

Mike and Dubertret were looking towards a hilltop, a vantage point from which to view an interesting valley. Mike waited for Dubertret as the senior geologist to make the first move.

There was a certain irony about their situation, considering they were in a land that was not officially recognized on the maps – Kurdistan, land of the dispossessed. However, the map indicated that the border with Turkey ran across the hilltop, and they would have to cross it in order to view the valley below. In the field, the lure of an interesting rock formation could exert a powerful hold on a geologist's mind and herein lay their predicament: what should a geologist do when an interesting feature beckoned him to cross a border?

Dubertret set off, but it was a short-lived excursion. 'We were all arrested by a Turkish frontier patrol,' wrote Mike. 'We were about ten yards inside Turkey when we heard whistles. A couple of Turkish soldiers dashed up with rifles ready.'

Their misdemeanour was settled with a handshake and a smile, the geologists explaining that they were only looking at rock formations. And that would have been an end to the matter, had not Dubertret decided to take matters into his own hands again the very next day:

Did I tell you that Dubertret got himself arrested and almost shot by the Kurds in the mountains here? They took him (as all foreigners) for a Jew (beard, bald head, nose, language, etc.) and almost forty armed men chased him across the mountain, caught him, and dragged him off to the village to see the Mukhtar. He didn't get back until 10.30 p.m.

There would be future temptations. In the southern reaches of Oman where interesting features known as the 'J' and 'K' Alphabeticals lay on the edge of an oil concession area that was ill-defined and unguarded, Mike would venture forth. But on the Yemeni frontier where their very presence was likely to attract a salvo of shells, Mike was more cautious. He was careful not to get arrested again.

MIKE'S LETTER WENT on to tell of a new arrival. A 23-year-old geologist by the name of Ziad ('Don') Beydoun had joined the party. Don came from a distinguished family, his father having been the Mutasarrif of Haifa in the last days of the Ottoman Empire, and his mother of Turkish lineage. Brought up in Palestine, he retained a remarkably forgiving attitude towards the British after they abandoned the country in May 1948. Mike had a very high regard for his work, as well as becoming a close personal friend. Over the succeeding years, their paths crossed many times. Don Beydoun went on to become a leading authority on the geology of the Middle East. Highly respected among his colleagues, he was awarded the William Smith Medal of the Geological Society of London in 1994 and the Order of the Cedars in 1995, joking that it was good to receive it while he was still alive. He was godfather to Mike's eldest son, Peter.

In concluding his letter, Mike wrote:

> Went into Aleppo last night, and saw a terrible film, 'The Lost Moment', with Robert Cummins and Susan Hayward. The only bright moment was when Paul got up to spend a penny, and fell down the tier of steps – the whole cinema heard and whistled and shouted. Dick Browne, the Divisional Geologist, was with us, but he wouldn't go cabaret-ing afterwards.

Such was life in Aleppo in 1948.

A sketch from Mike's notebook of the Kara Su Valley, North West Syria: colour section p. ii.

---

1   Son of the Arabian explorer St. John Philby.
2   Mike Gardiner, *IPC Newsletter*, July 2000, p. 17.
3   IPC 266 'Syria – Report on the Search for Oil 1947-1950' by E. J. Daniel, page 20, BP Archive.

Chapter 9: The Trek to Buraimi

Qatar and Oman, December 1948–August 1949

'The scenery compelled us to stop'

Mike Morton

Mike's assignment in north-west Syria came to an end in December 1948, when he was posted to Qatar. In contrast to the Kurd-Dagh mountains, Mike found the sheikhdom of Qatar to be an unprepossessing place – a barren, waterless desert, almost completely devoid of life. At this time, the population was scant and wretchedly poor, with the Company's operations being almost the sole source of wealth in the territory. Doha was the Sheikh's capital and the only sizeable village.

The long, low swell of the main Peninsula; the narrow pronounced hills of the Dukhan anticline; the groups of mesa-like hills of the horizontal Miocene rocks in the south; the sand dunes of the south-east, varying from ten to twenty metres in height; the so-called 'singing sands', where the action of the wind on the grains of sand made them vibrate, emitting an eerie humming sound – these were some of the features that made up Qatar. Apart from the irrigated areas, which were few, most of the Peninsula was barren, dotted with a meagre spread of camel thorn and stunted acacia trees. There was no soil mantle to speak of, only alluvial deposits in the depressions. After exceptionally heavy rains, these depressions would flood and hold water for a long time.

In the 1930s, geologists of the Californian Company were hard at work prospecting for oil a few kilometres across the border in Saudi Arabia, finding their first promising structure at Jebel Dhahran. A permanent camp was set up, and in April 1935 the first well was spudded-in. IPC watched this development with great interest, since there were believed to be close geological connections between the Dhahran structure and those existing in Bahrain and Qatar.

Petroleum exploration in Qatar had begun in the early 1930s. The presence of an anticline (the Dukhan anticline) in the west of the Peninsula was recorded, and predicted to be a good oil prospect. An associated company of IPC, Petroleum Development (Qatar) Ltd., was granted a concession on 17 May 1935 for a period of 75 years, and drilling began in October 1938. After more than a year of drilling difficulties, the drill shaft penetrated a limestone of middle Jurassic age at a depth of 1,700 metres and revealed the presence of oil.

A mariner's message from Qatar's domain,
Brought the Company rushing to toil.
He said 'There's n'owt 'ere but earth, sea and sky,
And it's 'ot, so there ought to be oil.'[1]

Drilling operations were suspended for the duration of World War II, with wells being plugged to deny the enemy – the Japanese – and field equipment removed to Basrah and Bombay. Once hostilities had ceased, there was much work to be done to restore the operation to its pre-war level. When activities could be resumed in early 1947, an aerial survey was made of the Qatar Peninsula and more detailed geological mapping of the anticline was carried out. Drilling did not recommence until late 1947, and exports were not secured until late 1949, following completion of a pipeline across the Peninsula.[2]

On his tour of duty, Mike was put in charge of a field party carrying out structure mapping around Dukhan. An oil camp had taken root in the shadow of Jebel Dukhan and, when not staying in the field, Mike lived in bachelor quarters. Dukhan would be Mike's base for future expeditions to Oman and eventually become home to Heather and his children.

There was a flavour of the Wild West about Qatar at this time. On New Year's day, travelling from Dukhan to Umm Said, Mike arrived at the Company camp at midday to find it apparently deserted: everyone was still in bed. Mike approached a sleeping colleague and gently rousing him asked 'What's happened to everyone?'

'They're all drunk,' the man replied, before slumping back to sleep.

Beauty is in the eye of the beholder and, whatever the outward appearance of the terrain, it presented an attractive prospect to the geologist. Although the work of exploration in the Qatar Peninsula was ongoing, however, Mike soon discovered that the Company's exploration compass was pointing firmly towards the south, in the direction of the Sultanate of Oman and the oasis of Buraimi, and that was where his next adventure lay.

BEFORE THE ARRIVAL of the oil company with its men and machines, life on the south-eastern rim of the Arabian Peninsula had remained unchanged for centuries. It will be remembered that there had been invaders in the past: the Persians, followed by the Portuguese, and then the British. But for most tribesmen, life had carried on in much the same way. However, the post-war development of substantial oil fields in Saudi Arabia and Qatar had attracted a new interest in the curious backwater that was conveniently defined by western politicians as the independent Sultanate of Muscat and Oman.

Tourist brochures, if they had existed for this part of the world at the time, would probably have described the country in the following terms:

The area of the Sultanate has been estimated at about 82,000 square miles [212,000 square kilometres]: the population of over half a million is mainly composed of Arabs, but there is a strong infusion of Negro blood, especially along the coast. There is a fertile strip along the shores of the Gulf of Oman in the Batinah district, north-west of Muscat, which is prosperous and noted for its dates. Inland are hills and plateaux; but, with the exception of the oases, there is little or no cultivation in the latter. Muscat, one of the two chief towns, which has a population of 5,500, still shows signs of its Portuguese occupation in the sixteenth and seventeenth centuries.[3]

The Omani tribes were fiercely independent. Quite often fully bearded and wearing sandals or going barefoot, the tribesman's dress was traditional: a thickly wrapped headdress, plain long shirt (*thawb*), and highly ornamental bandoleer. They carried a curved dagger (*khanjar*), sheathed

95

in a silver scabbard and supplemented by an inevitably ancient rifle, usually a Martini Henry lever action single shot, using cartridges with heavy slugs that could cause grievous wounds. The *accoutrements* of the desert life – a flint and steel, a used cartridge case for carrying kohl to apply under the eyelids to alleviate the sun's glare – were tucked away in the folds of the headdress.[4]

The independence of the tribesman was reinforced by his right to carry arms:

> Throughout the Arabian Peninsula, and certainly in Oman, it is essential for a man to be armed. A man who does not carry a weapon is not a man. His virility is in question. A boy at puberty is circumcised and given a rifle or *khanjar*, both acts being important badges of manhood.[5]

It was not always easy to define what constituted a tribe. Not residence in the same place, since although most Omani tribes could be traced to a particular geographical area, they would be widely scattered across it; not blood relationship nor common occupation or interest. The defining thread was 'the consciousness of a common tradition; they are born and they die conscious members of the Beni Shamal or Albu Junub.'[6]

Much depended on the personality of the sheikh. Each tribe was ruled by a sheikh, who was elected by the tribe and only remained leader for so long as his followers still respected him. Loss of face among his followers was a serious blow to a sheikh's authority. This could make it difficult for the Company in its negotiations with the sheikhs, since they could be reluctant to back down or be flexible in their discussions. Not surprisingly, the sheikhs usually preferred to acquire money rather than an understanding of the oil business and the process of extracting oil from the ground.

THE DUNES OF the Persian Gulf hinterland were stark and featureless, with no vegetation to protect travellers from the remorseless desert sun. The interesting geology lay inland: the mountain called Jebel Hafit in an area known as Buraimi, around the western flanks of the Hajar mountains in the east of Oman, the mid-Cretaceous jebels of the centre and the Haushi-Hugf scarp in the south.

Buraimi was an oasis village, in a cluster of seven villages around Jebel Hafit. To desert travellers, it came as a refreshing contrast to the arid surroundings: here there was clear, clean water that flowed through an ancient irrigation system of aqueducts known as *falaj*, a legacy of an earlier period of Persian occupation, and *barasti* villages that rested quietly in the shade of date groves in the lee of the mighty mountain.

Buraimi was rumoured to be floating on a sea of oil, according to the popular press of the time, but there was no hard evidence to back up the rumour. In some ways it was a convenient rumour for the Company, for it enabled their geologists to explore the region around Buraimi without revealing their prime area of interest, which lay in the area to the south-east. What had really excited the Company's interest in Oman was the discovery of good oil prospects during a series of aerial surveys undertaken in the late 1940s.

The Deputy Chief Geologist, F. E. Wellings, and his colleagues, were thrilled at the sight of two anticlines, to be known as Fahud and Natih, lying within a few kilometres of each other. Jebel Fahud in particular showed all the signs of a classic oil-bearing structure, 'a beautiful anticline, an absolute natural'.[7] Wellings had first seen these structures on a reconnaissance flight between the Sharjah and Masirah airfields on 17 March 1948. Further flights followed, one being jauntily described in the February 1949 edition of the Company's in-house magazine, 'Exploration News':

> Following the trail blazed two years ago by W. Thesiger,[8] we spotted two new structures which made F. E. Wellings scrape the head off his new vaccination 'take' on the toilet-

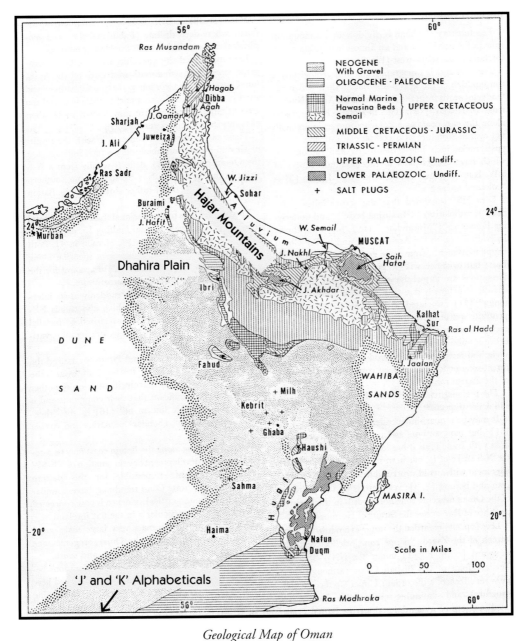

Geological Map of Oman
from D. M. Morton, 1959, The Geology of Oman, Proc. 5th World Petroleum Congress, p. 3

roll holder. Altogether we four geologists took nearly 250 photographs which the Deputy Chief Geologist had to unscramble after developing and printing in Beirut.

If we can only get in on the ground, we have aerial anticlines and stratigraphy galore to work on.

The anticlines were indeed a tantalizing prospect, but ground survey work was essential before their oil-bearing promise could be confirmed. With the tribal situation uncertain and the terrain difficult, 'getting in on the ground' would be harder than first appeared.

As we have noted, the sheikhs wanted a share of the riches that the oil company would surely bring, and those around Buraimi were no exception. Company representatives faced a dilemma when dealing with the sheikhs: should they barter with the head of each tribe or deal exclusively with Sultan Said bin Taimur? The Sultan spent most of his time in Dhofar province and rarely ventured into the interior of his lands. His grasp over these tribes was, at best, tenuous and further weakened by the existence of an Imam to whom a number of tribes had given their allegiance in preference to the Sultan.

The tribes were everywhere. Between Buraimi and central Oman lay the Dhahira plain, populated by three tribes: the Beni Kaab, the Al bu Shams and the Naim. These tribes had agreed to the paramountcy of one sheikh, Saqr al Naim, the Sheikh of Buraimi, otherwise known as the 'Old Fox'. If the Company were to succeed in its ambition to approach Jebel Fahud from the north, it had to first gain permission to access the Dhahira plain: Dhahira was untamed, with central government control almost non-existent. In this situation, the attitude of the local tribes – now purportedly united under Sheikh Saqr – was crucial.

To understand the delicacy of the situation, one needs to step back in time. Earlier attempts to access Oman had been fraught with difficulty. When the geologists Hotchkiss and Thomson attempted a survey in the 1938/39 winter season, they experienced a variety of hostile receptions. The reaction of Sheikh Saqr was typical – he 'sent out a messenger in advance of our caravan to notify the people of Al Hail that we were coming and that it would be a wonderful opportunity for a first-class hold-up.'[9]

Although operations were suspended on the outbreak of World War II, the Company recognized where its future interests lay by signing a full concession to the territory in May 1944.

In the 1947/48 season, the Company's representative, Dick Bird, managed to sign individual agreements for three-year concession rights with the three tribes in the area. But these agreements angered the Sultan who saw them as usurping his authority. He forbade substantial payments to be made to the local sheikhs, lest it be seen that that the oil belonged to them, rather than to himself. The Company recognized the difficulties that might arise if the Sultan's authority were undermined, and thus deferred to the Sultan. Discussions were left hanging in the air until the following field season.

Bird's actions, however, had a galvanizing effect on the Sultan, who sent out invitations to the local sheikhs to meet him and then proceeded to distribute considerable largesse (by his standards) to all those who responded. Sheikh Saqr refused to travel to meet the Sultan, but exchanged letters with him instead, declaring his loyalty to the Sultan in return for appropriate recompense. In the autumn of 1948, the Sultan had made it known to the Company that the three tribes of the Dhahira had united under Sheikh Saqr and would now receive the Company's representatives without requiring any further payments. But Saqr's sway over the local tribes was uncertain: he was unpopular, it was said, with a 'reputation for toughness'.[10]

Into this scenario, in October 1948, a new Company liaison officer arrived. Edward Henderson had first come to the Middle East with the British Army in 1941, spending two years in the Arab Legion in Jordan and Palestine before returning to London and joining the Company in 1946. Henderson was in the mould of a career diplomat, public-school educated, a tall man who always seemed able to dress immaculately whatever the desert conditions. He developed a strong rapport with the tribes, and with Sheikh Zayed of Abu Dhabi in particular. His efforts in smoothing the political way were to be crucial for the development of Company operations in the region over the next few years.

Initially based in Dubai, Henderson arranged to travel with Dick Bird the 190 kilometres south to Buraimi to renew negotiations with Sheikh Saqr. There was no airstrip in Buraimi and his party had to make the difficult motor journey across the dunes.

A few days after their arrival Henderson went to visit the Old Fox at Buraimi fort:

We motored over the light-coloured sand in front of al-Buraimi fort and up to its gloomy portal. Sabir had to knock many times before a small shutter opened and part of a face showed itself which proved to be that of Saqr himself.[11]

After the sheikh had unbolted the gate and let them in, he offered them cold coffee but little else in the way of comfort:

He was a small man, rather stout; he sat and waited for us to talk after he had, with apparent reluctance, shown us into a tiny and very dark room close to the fort's entrance, with a plain rush mat on the floor and nothing else to grace it.[12]

Their next visit, arranged for two weeks later after much obfuscation, included the sheikhs of the other tribes of the area, and appeared to go reasonably well until the conversation came to the nub: the sheikhs wanted money. Despite the agreement Henderson had been told about, that the sheikhs would accept the Company's presence without requiring any payment, it became quite clear that the sheikhs were expecting something. Eventually, after visiting each sheikh separately, small amounts were passed and agreements appeared to have been brokered.

The Company could now pursue its plans to enter the Dhahira plain. Of particular interest was the Wadi Jizzi, which linked the Batinah coast with Buraimi and the plain. In the summer of 1948, the Chief Geologist Norval E. Baker had noted its strategic importance:

We would point out that if the Wadi Jizzi and other similar wadis can make the western mountain front accessible from the Batinah coast a tremendous economic and political asset would be established. The transportation of development materials through Wadi Jizzi to Hafit or other favourable structure (which some day may be drilled), with the possibility of shipping oil out (if found) would eliminate a long haul around the tip of the Oman Peninsula where living conditions are better (though not good) and political security is greater.[13]

In mid-February 1949, Henderson returned to Dubai to meet Dick Bird, surveyor Nick Fallon and geologists Dick Browne and Mike, who had flown in from Qatar. The next stage in the plan was discussed and agreed: they would test the new arrangements by approaching the Dhahira plain from the east, through the Hajar mountains. They would leave from Sohar, on the Batinah coast of Oman, drive through the Wadi Jizzi and cross the Dhahira plain to reach Buraimi:

> *You've heard of the coast called*
> *Batinah and P. D. (Oman and Dhofar),*
> *You should know of the trek to Buraimi*
> *That started one day in Sohar*[14]

They reached Sohar without incident, and the convoy divided: Henderson to travel to Muscat for more discussions with the Sultan, the geologists to remain in Sohar. On his return, despite having received assurances from the Sultan, Henderson was apprehensive about the trip, sceptical about the Sultan's ability to deliver or his promise of safe passage through the interior. He brought with him the Sultan's representatives, Sheikh Ya'qub, a man of unknown ability and experience, and Sheikh Ghusan bin Salim.

They set off again in convoy – five pick-ups, two Dodge Power Wagons and two GMC lorries – at 5 a.m., travelling west. Their drive to the entrance to the Wadi Jizzi seemed innocuous enough, a verdant screen of plantations overseen by the serrated grey mountains of the Hajar range. The absence of any tyre tracks on the rocky plain confirmed the fact that no one had attempted a vehicle crossing of the mountains by this route before. 'Explorers before were on camels', Mike wrote. Dr Lees had carried out camel-borne expeditions through the wadis of the western Hajar in the late 1920s, but nothing significant had happened since then.

Near Wasit, one of the GMC lorries broke a wheel and the convoy was delayed for an hour to change it. While this was going on, a large group of Shawami people gathered round, friendly but curious, and the party had great difficulty in keeping them away from the vehicles. Ya'qub was insistent that a number of Shawami should accompany them up the wadi, to assist with the work of clearing boulders from the track that lay ahead. Bird in his account described being followed by a number of Bedu running up the wadi, while Henderson mentioned a dozen being taken on board the convoy. Whatever happened, the convoy lumbered onwards, taking the course of the wadi on its way upwards, accompanied by men of the Shawami tribe.

Just east of Hail and Rabi' the vehicles descended to the wadi floor. There was some greenery in the wadi, small bushes growing out of the gravel-lined river-bed. They had been assured that a track would be prepared by the local villagers along the way, but there was precious little evidence of it. The villagers they met farther along were helpful enough, pointing to where a track had been cleared, but it soon became obvious that they had little conception of the width of the vehicles coming through, and the tracks they had made were too narrow. Furthermore, it had rained in the past few days: such track as existed was blocked in places by watery pools, many of uncertain depth. Although with some they took the risk and ploughed straight on through, with others they guessed to be too deep to navigate they went around clearing a path to one side, getting out and using crowbars to remove any large boulders that stood in the way.

At one point, Bird's vehicle got stuck in water in the middle of the wadi, while the others crossed at different points, some getting stuck, others getting over. 'At that crucial moment,' noted Bird, 'a crowd of Bedu started shooting at us from a cliff over the wadi at a range of about two hundred metres'.[15] Confusion ensued, one youth shooting as fast as he could reload his musket, general uproar, men and women from villages on both sides of the wadi running out and yodelling.

It was a 'nasty moment', recalled Bird. Sheikh Ya'qub was 'prodded into reluctant activity and dismounted under duress from my car'. Mike's first reaction on hearing gunfire can only be imagined: if it was to reach for a rifle he would have been quickly disappointed, for there were no rifles to hand – everyone decamped from the vehicles and hid behind the tail boards. Ahead of them the leading truck was submerged in water and the Shawami workmen were also crouching in the water or hiding behind the vehicles. According to Bird's account, about 200 Bedu collected around the party as a furious dispute unfolded:

> One old man waving a stick and cursing the Shawamis and the other one hundred and
> ninety-nine all shouting at the top of their voices. In the general melee I had my beard
> pulled which was disconcerting![16]

Eventually, Ya'qub went to parley with the shouting men, edging forward and shouting back as he went, their combined voices echoing around the canyon. He returned a short while later and reported that the villagers had known about their visit all along, having been told by the Sultan's men to expect it; and they would be pleased to let the convoy through:

> But, why had we picked up those beastly Shawamis? Everyone knew, but not us and
> certainly not Ya'qub, that Shawamis were not allowed on the territory of these two
> villages, and their plan to come as part of our party was just a trick to get them over
> forbidden ground.[17]

After more negotiation, and much to the displeasure of the Shawami, it was agreed to let them go and take men from the next village instead: members of the Beni Ghaith. Coffee and dates were offered and consumed, and the convoy continued on its way.

When they reached the watershed, it was apparent that the worst of the journey was over and, indeed, the descent towards the Dhahira plain was considerably easier. They emerged at dusk on to the Dhahira plain, reaching their destination of Buraimi well after dark, a journey of eleven hours:

> *And so to the peace of Buraimi*
> *Where above the soft sand palm trees loom,*
> *On a health resort basis,*
> *I could stick the oasis*
> *And the Jizzi as well – if there's room.*[18]

IT WAS THE most that could have been achieved in the circumstances: the trek to Buraimi was a success, within its own limited terms of reference. Bird's beard was intact, the geologists had survived to tell the tale, and the way had been opened through a strategic wadi. Henderson returned to the wadi four days later with representatives of the tribes and did the journey – a round trip – in around five hours each way.

But the geologists had only penetrated a part of the Dhahira, and permission to visit places farther south such as Ibri was still withheld by the Sultan. So negotiations with the local sheikhs resumed but deadlock remained: the sheikhs wanted money; the Sultan forbade the Company to pay them. The Sultan's Minister was fetched from Muscat to try to break the deadlock, but the Minister's visit was a public relations disaster, ending with 14 sheikhs shouting him down.

It was – literally at times – an uphill struggle. Edward Henderson organized a field trip for the benefit of Sheikh Saqr. Together with Dick Bird and a small group of geologists, they came to a small hill outside Buraimi and the geologists set to work. They busied themselves collecting rock samples, packing them into bags that were then loaded on to a truck. At this point, the Old Fox interrupted them:

'What are you doing with those?' Dick explained that they would be sorted out, examined and cut into fine pieces for microscopic examination, the most interesting ones being sent to London for further tests. The Sheikh said he thought that if they were worth sending to London, they must be worth a lot of money. He would keep these samples, and as for the future an 'arrangement' would have to be made.[19]

The Company adopted a 'wait and see' policy, and this might have succeeded if Saudi Arabia had not intervened. Rumours of oil around Buraimi proved too much of a temptation for a state already awash – but perhaps insatiable for – oil. In April 1949 the Saudis lodged a claim to part of Abu Dhabi, the Buraimi oasis, and areas occupied by the Dhahira tribes. In March 1952, IPC officials were banned by the British Government from exploring any of the areas within the Saudi claim. Approaching Jebel Fahud from the north became an unrealistic option, and the Buraimi project was shelved.

It was a bleak picture for the Company. Yet Oman was too promising to be forgotten: the geologists had been given a tantalizing glimpse of what was on offer. A visit to Seih Hatat near Muscat confirmed what the geologists had long suspected:

There the plutonic rock pushing up through the sedimentary [beds] has raised the latter and broken it leaving exposed cliffs where one can see on the cliff side the same geological succession as a drilling log in any well at Dhahran would show. The strata are all there in the same succession, wider or narrower perhaps, but basically the same.[20]

MEANWHILE, THE SHEIKHDOM of Qatar hardly stirred from its slumbers. The most exciting business that year was the Company's purchase for £15,000 of an 18-metre yacht as a gift for the ageing Sheikh Abdullah. A Company official reported:

I was delighted by the yacht as she actually exists. The lines are very good looking, construction appears sound, decoration artistic, and the internal planning is extremely good … so, on the whole, I think the old man should be extremely pleased. It is certainly the best present the Company has ever given to anybody.[21]

Upon delivery, the old man was indeed pleased to receive his yacht but when he abdicated a month or two later in favour of his son, Ali, Company officials were mortified to discover that he had given the yacht away.

Qatar's awakening as a serious oil producer was heralded by two developments. The first overt sign was the construction of a new pipeline from Dukhan to Doha that opened up exports of crude oil to the outside world. The second, and more sinister, turn came in the form of surreptitious encroachments by ARAMCO survey parties into the southerly reaches of the sheikhdom: Qatar's burgeoning oil resources were also attracting the attention of Saudi Arabia.

Unscathed by his encounter with the Beni Ghaith in the Wadi Jizzi, Mike returned to his post in Qatar. At the end of the season, he returned to the UK for his leave and married Heather at All Saints Church, Barry, on 10 August 1949. After honeymooning in France, it was back to the Middle East for Mike, but Heather did not follow straight away. They had difficulty in getting married accommodation, and it was not until the spring of 1950 that Heather left to join Mike in Tripoli in Lebanon.

The Company's immediate plans clearly did not have the newly-weds' happiness in mind: Mike was directed back to the Hadhramaut again.

1   From a cartoon by Mike Morton (see Appendix 4).

2   Stephen Longrigg, *Oil in the Middle East: Its Discovery and Development*, 1954.

3   *Illustrated London News*, 7 January 1956.

4   George Laurance 'The Oman – before Oil', *IPC Society Newsletter Issue 102*, April 1999, with permission of the IPC Society.

5   John Townsend, *The Making of Oman*, Croom Helm, 1977, p. 147.

6   *IPC Handbook*, 1948, p. 30.

7   D. M. Morton, 'The Geology of Oman', Proc. 5th World Petroleum Congress, 1959, p. 293.

8   Wilfred Thesiger in his map in the *Geographical Journal* of March 1951 was the first person to give these features a name, based upon what the Bedouin called them: Fahud and Natih.

9   Lester S. Thomson, 'Progress Report', dated 10 December 1938, PC/27A (84), BP Archive.

10   Edward Henderson, *A Strange Eventful History*, 1988, p. 52 (expanded and republished in 1999 as *Arabian Destiny – The Complete Autobiography* – for publisher details, please refer to 'Acknowledgements' p. 258.

11   Ibid., p. 59.

12   Ibid., p. 59.

13   N. E. Baker to W. Kitchin, letter dated 13 July 1948, from PC/27 Part 4 (3), BP Archive.

14   Mike recorded their exploits in a cartoon: see Appendix 3.

15   R. E. R. Bird, Report of 22 March 1949, IPC/27 Part 5 (5), BP Archive.

16   Ibid..

17   Henderson, Ibid., p. 65.

18   The trek to Buraimi, cartoon by Mike Morton (see Appendix 3).

19   Henderson, Ibid., p. 69.

20   Ibid., p. 86.

21   S. H. Longrigg to B. H. Lermitte, letter dated 31 May 1949, PC/30 (275), BP Archive.

Chapter 10: They Have No Beards

Western Hadhramaut, 15 October–25 December 1949

The old man looked at him with alarm, the first white man he had seen.
'They have no beards!' he exclaimed

The Kingdom of Melchior,
Master of Belhaven[1]

Images of the frankincense trade, with its dusty caravans, staging-posts and ancient trails through the barren wilderness, were never far from the mind. The great cities of the Hadhramaut had sprung up to protect the frankincense routes. To the west, where raiders roamed the desert at will, Shabwa became the place where large caravans mustered, where traders gained safety in numbers before embarking on the dangerous journey across the sands.

The interest of the oil companies in the Western Protectorate was aroused by the travels of St. John Philby, who visited the region in 1936. At the age of 36, Philby was an experienced, if somewhat irascible, explorer of the Arabian Peninsula. Apart from Bertram Thomas, no foreigner at that time knew the southern desert better than Philby.

In his role as adviser to Ibn Saud, King of Saudi Arabia, on the pretext of mapping the Saudi/Yemeni border, Philby had travelled by car to Shabwa. Although his ambition to be the first Westerner to visit Shabwa was pre-empted by the visit of Hans Helfritz in 1934, his enthusiasm for exploration was undimmed: he pressed forward with a detachment of Saudi troops towards the romantic land of Sheba. The Yemenis already had territorial claims in the area, the British were the dominant power, and the appearance of Philby with a detachment of Saudi soldiers did little to dispel the notion of Saudi claims.

When the axle on his pick-up broke, Philby was forced to leave his troops in the Hadhramaut and seek supplies in Mukalla, where he was cold-shouldered by the British authorities. Eventually he withdrew declaring his 'occupation' at an end and returning to Saudi Arabia.

The most significant legacy of Philby's exploration, so far as the oil companies were concerned, was his detailed description of the geology of the area, and a good map. Indirectly, he provided the oil companies with exactly what they were looking for: strong indications of oil-bearing strata.

The first general geological reconnaissance of the area by Pike and Wofford was not able to penetrate the Shabwa country owing to 'local objections'. Their examination was thus confined to aerial observation and they found little of petroleum interest.

As well as the writings of Philby, the geologists would have been aware of the travels of the Dutch explorer Van der Meulen, and a recently published book written by Lieutenant-Colonel Hamilton. In 1938, in response to a growing military threat from the Imam of Yemen, Colonel Hamilton had arrived at Shabwa with aeroplanes and a contingent of British troops:

We dropped down on Shabwa from a burning pale blue sky in June in four old Vickers

Vincent aircraft, lurching and bumping over the unprepared sand.[2]

There to greet them was an old Karabi Sheikh, Ahmad bin Qateiyan, who 'met us doubtfully and gave the aircraft a distrustful look'. The sheikh reassured his visitors that his tribe would offer the Yemenis no assistance. His main cause for concern was the appearance of the foreigners:

Air Commodore McCloughry was introduced to him as our commander, and held out his hand. The old man looked at him with alarm. 'They have no beards!' he exclaimed.[3]

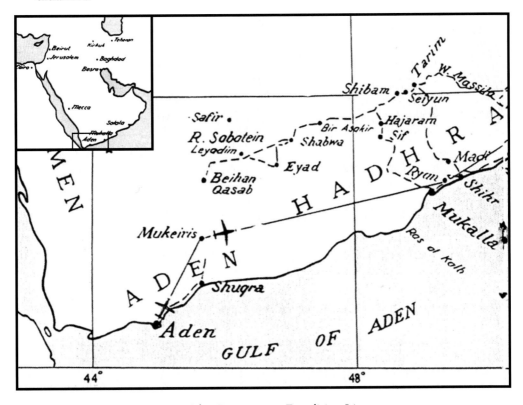

Western Aden Protectorate: Expedition Itinerary

MIKE WOULD HAVE tossed many thoughts over in his mind: Philby's report of bituminous matter in surface rocks was an encouraging, but not conclusive, sign of oil reserves beneath the ground. It might simply mean that oil once present had simply risen to the surface through porous rocks and evaporated.

By 30 October 1949 Mike, René and Tony Altounyan were back in Mukalla. Since their last expedition, there had been a subtle shift in the dynamics of the partnership. René now had experience of south-west Arabia, and Mike had more experience altogether, making it a balanced party, which Tony appeared to accept. Certainly there was no indication of the tension that had existed between them in the past.

There were other changes, too. A new Resident had recently taken up his post. Colonel

Boustead was another one of those larger-than-life figures that populated the Middle East. 'He was quite a character,' wrote Mike. 'Ex Everest climber, Sudan Political service after the regular army, then commanded a brigade in Eritrea and Abyssinia during the war. Bachelor, fifty-five years old, and a little eccentric.'[4] Perhaps eager to make the most of the social opportunities presented by the arrival of three Westerners in town, Boustead arranged for them to take all their meals in the Residency with him. At dinner, the geologists would discover that Boustead had an unusual system of communicating with his staff: one blast of a whistle for the batman, two blasts for the waiter, three blasts for the cook, four blasts for the gardener and five blasts for the house boy. Some whistle blasts later, the geologists were dismissed to their quarters.

Extensive discussions about the security arrangements hinged on the competing claims of the political representatives of the Western Aden Protectorate (WAP) and the Eastern Aden Protectorate (EAP). In the end it was agreed that Government Guards (controlled by WAP officials) would take over from the HBL guards (controlled by EAP officials) in the vicinity of Beihan.

The party departed Mukalla at dawn on 7 November, accompanied by a Liaison Officer, Rais Abdullah Sleiman. Fifteen men of the Hadhramaut Bedouin Legion dispersed amongst the transport of two jeeps, two Dodge Power Wagons and a Bedford Three Ton Truck, which were all loaded to capacity. They retraced their 1947 route towards the Wadi Do'an, then turned westwards towards the HBL fort at Bir Asakir.

Bir Asakir lay under the high cliff of the Wadi Hadhramaut and was surrounded on three sides by a flat, sandy plain, a part of the desert known as the Ramlat Sabatein. The surface was covered mostly by loose, coarse, yellow sand, with occasional patches of gravel. Vegetation was scarce, and water absent. It was, however, a reasonable surface for motor transport, although – when heavily loaded – the cars tended to drag a little in the sand.

After resting at the fort overnight, the party set out for Shabwa on 11 November, driving across a wide plain, keeping parallel with the wadi cliffs and heading westwards. At one point, they were distracted by a herd of gazelle crossing their path, and the convoy struck off the track in hot pursuit. Mike found no pleasure in the sport: their guides shot three of the animals. 'It is rather sickening to see a game little beast running on two good legs and two stumps – I think it's a cruel sport,' wrote Mike. 'On finally downing the beast, a Bedu will immediately leap out of the car and cut its throat (a religious observance).'

After about 50 kilometres, the cliffs of the wadi to the south opened out and the expedition turned southward.

Twelve kilometres from Shabwa, a black rugged mass rose out of the plain. This was the salt dome Milh M'gah, one kilometre in diameter. Then, from a prominent yellowish hill at the debouchment of the Wadi Irma, they got their first view of Shabwa. It was a scene of desolation.

The ruined town was perched on several clay hills, presenting a ramshackle, derelict collection of mud houses, partly roofless with many broken walls. On approaching the town they came upon a crowd of thin, hungry-looking, unhappy people standing around a large whitewashed grave, adding to the overall sense of wretchedness and decay. These were men of the Kurab tribe, fierce, wild and dirty. At this point the convoy stalled and Rais Abdullah went to sound them out.

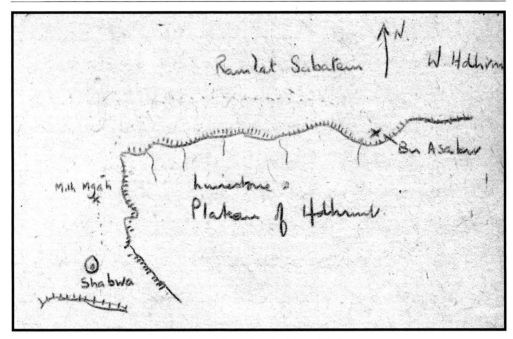

The Route from Bir Asakir to Shabwa

As the tribesmen explained to the party:

The night before they had been raided by a party of the powerful Yemen tribe called Dahm. These robbers had stolen nineteen camels and vanished into the sands before dawn. This was a great financial loss to all concerned – they were too weak to pursue the Dahm, and they were poor and undernourished owing to the recent famine.

The geologists were signalled to approach. HBL guards had now taken up defensive positions all around the settlement. The people of Shabwa were divided into two factions and lived apart from each other in separate clusters of houses. Keeping apart, the factions closed in on the party in separate halves of a semi-circle. The geologists went round and shook hands with each tribesman in turn, making a smacking handclasp to which the tribesmen responded with a tiny kissing noise.

As a result of the famine there was no feast in the offing, but the geologists offered what they could to the tribesmen: some dates and a gazelle to each of the factions. 'This pleased the tribesmen immensely, and we continued our recce,' wrote Mike. Hajar, the main village of Shabwa, was built on the eastern ridge; and the ruined site of the ancient capital, Sabota, occupied a sandstone spur and a strip of low hills immediately to the north of it. A fort, Husn el Ma, dominated two wells in the wadi bed immediately below – the Hiswa well, which contained sweet water in quantities hardly sufficient for the needs of the village, and the Dihan well which produced a strongly brackish water used only for the animals. Although they set up camp between the two wells, for the next few days they would have to rely on a supply of water carried over from the fort at Bir Asakir.

They walked around the hills of Shabwa, each hill now protected by an armed HBL guard. Ruined sluice gates and abandoned irrigation channels suggested extensive cultivation in the past, but only small patches were currently cultivated for millet and barley.

They found the ruins of an ancient kingdom, 'to whichever one Shabwa belonged'. Mike remained unimpressed:

These were rather disappointing, although the well-trimmed blocks of masonry indicated an ancient populace of higher intelligence and knowledge than the present. All that remained were basement foundations of burial places and a few scattered stones with chiselled inscriptions.

At the time of Mike's visit, salt production was the main – maybe only – industry of the region. On the outskirts of town, the Rashid mine consisted of two pits connected by a small hole leading from the bottom of one to the other. A second mine had been abandoned after the roof had caved in and a third was no longer worked.

The working of the salt was the prerogative of the Mudhahs, freed slaves of Bin Bureik. It was back-breaking work. They used a pick, about half a kilogram in weight, to dig out the salt. The larger fragments were crushed into pieces the size of a walnut and gathered into heaps ready for packing in bags for transportation by camel. A camel load usually consisted of two bags, each weighing about 68 kilograms. The slaves received one Maria Theresa dollar for every load of camel salt removed from the mine, with a cut of one-quarter going to the Kurab tribe for offering protection. A miner generally quarried four to five camel-loads a day. Shabwa exported about 200 to 500 camel-loads a month, mostly to Hadhramaut and some to Nejran. Caravans usually comprised 10 to 30 camels, with a camel load fetching as much as six to eight dollars.

One evening, the Kurab sheikhs discussed the origin of the Queen of Sheba. Their history mentioned Bilthgen – a woman ruling the area at the time of King Solomon – but there was no proven connection between her and the mythical Queen. The firelight stuttered: the legend of Sheba tiptoed softly back into the void.

Next day, the party returned to Bir Asakir. On their arrival at the gate it was almost dark: Mike could see two figures approaching in the gloom. One he recognized as Lt. Col. Naif and the other was a stranger. Stepping forward to shake their hands, Naif welcomed the geologists and then introduced his companion, Captain El Khalidi, with a smile.

Who could have predicted their meeting a man like El Khalidi in the whitewashed surrounds of the Bir Asakir Fort? To meet a Famine Control Officer in the employ of the British Political staff was not in itself particularly remarkable, for the region had a history of recurrent famine; but there was another side to Captain El Khalidi, DSO, MBE, which emerged during the long evenings at the fort and implied that there was more to this man than first met the traveller's eye.

El Khalidi spoke of cold, dark days in wartime England. He described the treacherous politics of the post-war Middle East, as if anyone could speak of politics in that part of the world where decisions were inexorably reached by force of arms. He told of how he had straddled the great Arab-Jew divide, how he had fought alongside Jews in the Palestine Regiment – with controversy following only a short step behind.

The tales of El Khalidi conjured up visions of an outer world. Events flashed into view, briefly illuminating the imagination of his audience. Otherwise the darkness was almost complete: a pressure lamp, hanging on crude hooks suspended from the ceiling, lit the room in a weak circle of light.

At night, alone in his room, Mike would record conversations that had passed between them. No doubt there were times when El Khalidi's stories sounded far-fetched, but in the Middle East anything was possible, and Mike kept any scepticism well concealed.

The man he knew as El Khalidi was a tall, well built, dark-skinned man, about 1.8 metres tall and about 85 kilograms in weight. He was wearing thick-lensed glasses, a bushy black beard and moustache, and had long hair down to his neck.

It would begin after dinner, with El Khalidi telling them of his life, speaking good English with a slight Mediterranean accent. He was born, he explained, in Jerusalem around 1919 to a wealthy family, and was first educated at the German School. Members of his family had been mayors of Jerusalem. At the outbreak of World War II he was attending Beirut University.

The Middle Eastern theatre of war presented a confusing picture. French forces of the Vichy Government – allies of the Nazis – occupied Syria and were too much of a threat to Britain's oil interests in Iraq to be ignored. The British, in league with the Free French, took up arms against them. El Khalidi joined the British Army in Palestine and was granted a Viceroy's Commission.

El Khalidi paused. Night had fallen and the small room felt cold. Apart from the hiss of the single pressure lamp, the hush of the desert lay around them.

He continued. In late 1942, serving as Special Duty Officer in charge of Tribal Affairs, he was in Deir-ez-Zor in north-east Syria. During this time he was awarded the Distinguished Service Order for conduct in the field. But he was accused of being involved in the secret sales of arms to the tribes, a charge he vehemently denied. At court martial proceedings, he was acquitted on the evidence. However, a rumour went round that he had informed on his confederates – a fact that El Khalidi also refuted.

As a result of this incident, El Khalidi found his position untenable amongst officers of the 10th Division in Syria. He discussed the matter with General Jumbo Wilson, Commander-in-Chief Middle East, but, receiving no encouragement, was forced to resign from the British Army.

A resourceful man, El Khalidi was soon back in the thick of the action. One month later, he re-enlisted as a private in the Palestine Brigade. He quickly rose to the rank of Regimental Sergeant Major, but his good fortune was not to last. One day, on parade at Sarafand, General Jumbo Wilson noticed him. After the parade was over he was interviewed and upbraided by Wilson for rejoining the Army unknown as a private.

Eventually, El Khalidi was sent to the United Kingdom on a course at a staff college. While waiting for the course to begin, he was attached to the Welsh Guards and posted to France. He was, according to Mike, awarded an MBE for service there. He returned to Staff College in the UK, was given the King's Commission and attached to the administration staff of Lord Mountbatten.

In October 1945 El Khalidi was sent to Singapore and spent a year in the Far East. He toured widely, making a survey of the Arab population of the East Indies, many of whom, as noted already, were Hadhramis. He then returned to the UK and was married in Manchester to the Moslem daughter of a Syrian father and a Basque mother from merchant families. His wife was British by birth and had been educated at Cambridge where she had obtained a BA. El

Khalidi enjoyed three weeks in the company of his bride before leaving for Palestine to join the Army of Liberation under its Commander-in-Chief, Fawzi El Kaukji.

Events in Palestine were speeding towards the end of the British Mandate planned for 15 May 1948. The Jews proclaimed the independent state of Israel and the British withdrew. The Arab nations formed the Army of Liberation and invaded Palestine and Israel. During the conflict El Khalidi fought as second in command to El Kaukji, but did not agree with his leader. When El Kaukji was sacked, El Khalidi was appointed Commander-in-Chief and fought in the last battle of the Palestine Campaign on the Lebanese border in November 1948. He became very unpopular, however, with all the Arab governments during their quarrels over the Palestine War and lost all his property and income in Palestine.

For El Khalidi, life was never dull. In 1949 he was recommended for a Syrian decoration (Military 1st Class), and all the necessary documents were sent to General Husni Al-Zaim, Commander-in-Chief of the Syrian Army. Zaim refused to sanction his award. The request was referred to the premier of Syria (Kuwatly) and was immediately granted. But the matter did not rest there.

One day on parade, when El Khalidi and several others were to be decorated by the Syrian Government, Colonel Zaim inspected El Khalidi's Liberation Army. Coming up to El Khalidi and taking the decoration from the box, Zaim made to put it over El Khalidi's head.

Zaim said quietly: 'I am giving this because I am ordered to do so.'

El Khalidi stepped back, saluted and refused the decoration, and the parade murmured. Zaim was flabbergasted and ordered El Khalidi to take the medal. The latter replied that it would be better if Zaim disappeared, and he dismissed his men, so insulting the great Zaim. Later, Zaim wrote to El Khalidi asking for an apology for the disgrace, but El Khalidi declined.

Another pause in the darkness, a moment to reflect, before El Khalidi resumed his story.

He had got a job on the Middle East pipeline, and settled with his wife and baby in Damascus. But he was fed up with the Syrian Government and when Zaim's *coup d'état* brought him to power he supposed that this change of government would be a good thing for Syria. Zaim, however, became an absolute dictator and conditions worsened.

The stage was set for a final clash between the two men.

One night El Khalidi was invited to a party at the Officers' Club in Damascus, and although his wife was eight months pregnant with another child, he went along. Zaim arrived and everyone was presented.

On being introduced to the El Khalidis, Zaim turned to Mrs El Khalidi and said: 'I hope that your husband's civilian manners are better than his military ones.'

'My husband's manners have always been the same.'

Zaim persisted: 'I should have to separate you from your husband – I do not know of a ruder person in the whole of Syria.'

Mrs El Khalidi replied, 'I do – me,' and slapped Zaim's face.

The El Khalidis left the club and their second child was born that night, three weeks' early.

Three days later, at 1 a.m., a party of Syrian officers came to El Khalidi's house and searched it. Finding no incriminating matter they took El Khalidi to their headquarters, where Zaim was waiting for him in a room.

'You are accused of conspiring against the Syrian state.'

'A lie,' said El Khalidi.

'You are accused of conspiring against our person,' says Zaim.

'True if you like,' replied El Khalidi, 'as you are not the State.'

El Khalidi was then handcuffed and slightly beaten.

Zaim took out his revolver and laid it on the desk. 'Before you kill me El Khalidi, I shall first see you buried, and piss on your grave.'

El Khalidi paid insult for insult, and was told he would spend the rest of his life in jail. When the interview was over, however, he was sent back home and given three days to quit the country. He went to Lebanon and was ordered to leave there as well. But he threatened to reveal some of the secrets he had discovered while working for General Spears in Beirut during the war, so was granted leave to stay 14 days per year in Lebanon. Then, in 1949, he came to Hadhramaut as a Famine Relief Officer on a six-month contract.

And General Zaim? His dictatorship was very unpopular and he was overthrown in August 1949 by another military junta, and executed. El Khalidi could now return to Syria at will. He was, nonetheless, forbidden entry into Iraq, and had been sentenced in his absence to seven years prison in Jordan for conspiring against the Greater Syria Scheme.

'And by the way,' added Mike in his journal, 'he successfully petitioned George VI for his Moslem marriage to be recognized without registration.'

Mike and El Khalidi: it is not known if their paths crossed again, or whether Mike knew what became of him. One morning, as the first light gently illuminated the whitewashed battlements, El Khalidi went from view, a single figure passing unchallenged through the gate and disappearing into the brightening dawn.

But the tales of El Khalidi lived on.

ALL AFTERNOON A high wind blew, making surveying in the mountains difficult. The geologists returned to the Shabwa camp to find that Tony had moved their tents up to the higher ground, close to that of Rais Abdullah. After dinner, for about ten minutes, the rain poured down, beating on the canvas and deafening the geologists as they huddled in their tents for shelter. Outside, rainwater running off the silty ground of Shabwa was threatening to burst the ancient drainage channels: the party was warned to be ready to move out at a moment's notice. Before long, a stream of water was flowing into the main wadi next to their camp. It was a nerve-racking time as they sat and listened in darkness to the sound of rushing water outside and imagined what torrent might be on its way to engulf them.

They didn't have to wait long. The deluge soon encircled the camp; their tents now marooned on a shrinking island of sand. Rais Abdullah's tent was flooded and water came within a whisker of Mike's tent. They moved quickly to move Abdullah's soggy canvas to higher ground, and then packed their personal belongings and prepared to evacuate.

The floodwater stopped rising. When daybreak came, they were able to reflect on their good fortune: they had spent a wakeful night, but their island was still intact, their equipment unharmed. 'We spent the night in comfort – more or less,' wrote Mike.

The high wind and rain continued for the next few days. Measuring and sampling their way across the terrain around Shabwa in cold, damp weather, they found pools of rainwater on the cliff tops and in the wadis and no longer had to rely on supplies of drinking water sent on a truck from Bir Asakir.

The appearance of a rainbow, *Saif en Nebi* (Prophet's Sword), seemed to herald a change in the weather, although it was clear to the geologists by now that the main threat to their security was from human rather than natural forces. The Kurab tribe was friendly, but the presence of foreigners was still a novelty for them, and an earlier incident with one of their Kurab guides came back to haunt the party.

Out in the field an argument had sprung up between a guard and Tony over a cigarette. The tribesman wanted a smoke and tried to snatch Tony's cigarette from his hand. Rais Abdullah intervened and threatened to imprison the tribesman, but he was forced to back down and the tribesman was allowed to leave the camp.

News of the incident – no doubt spread by the perpetrator – reached the main body of the Kurab tribe, and two days later, guns blazing in the air, a group of Kurab men rode into the camp. They had come to arrest the perpetrator! As Rais Abdullah was explaining that the man had left the camp two days earlier, it dawned on the geologists that, far from being at large in the desert, the 'fugitive' was actually already in their midst, having ridden into the camp at the rear of the Kurab posse.

As with many awkward situations in the desert, peace was restored over several cups of coffee and a handshake. Perhaps this had been the Kurabs' intended outcome from the start, to secure a reconciliation with the exploration party, but the incident left the geologists with a sense of unease that subsequent events only served to exacerbate.

On 25 November 1949, the morning before the floodwater had inundated the camp, the geologists had been preparing themselves for another field trip when an RAF bomber roared over the hills and circled overhead. 'Rumours of Yemeni troop concentrations,' wrote Mike. 'Two thousand men at Jauf preparing rations for a raid.'

Yemen was an independent state, ruled by an Imam of the Zeidi aristocracy, which for centuries had harboured territorial ambitions over its neighbours. The British Government, wishing to secure the borders of its Western Protectorate, sought to reach an agreement with the Yemenis. In 1934 an Anglo-Yemen Treaty was signed, recognizing the territorial status quo. But British plans in the late 1940s to create a federation to replace the Protectorates caused much alarm among the Yemenis and their new ruler, Imam Ahmed.[5]

A familiar pattern began to emerge. In August 1949 an armed party from the Yemen crossed the border into the neighbouring state of Beihan, a member of the Western Aden Protectorate, and built a fort there. In September the RAF arrived, first dropping warning leaflets from the sky and then a few bombs around the fort. The Yemenis withdrew but – as soon as the aircraft had disappeared over the horizon – they were back again. The RAF returned, and this time their bombs did not shy from the fort, completely destroying it and forcing the garrison to retreat across the border.

The arrival of the geologists later in the year did not go unnoticed. A neighbour of the Yemen, the Sultan of the Upper Aulaqi tribe, was pressed by the Imam into action. He wrote a threatening letter to the surrounding tribes, ordering them to refuse passage to the Nasrani geological party.

For the geologists, the appearance of the RAF bomber on 25 November, albeit on a reconnaissance flight, brought home the reality of the Yemeni threat, but did nothing to reassure them of their safety. Dropping leaflets and bombs on restless natives was one thing: offering ground support was quite another. The Resident Adviser would have been most reluctant to disturb the Peace of Ingrams by attempting to raise a local militia: there was simply no question of sending in the troops.

So the Aden Government would make haste slowly. As Yemeni troops were massing on the border, the Government's riposte was to dispatch two armed Government Guards and two wireless operators with a wireless set to join the geological party from Beihan. On 28 November they received a message from the Political Officer in Beihan, Jimmy Watson, asking if the party was 'OK'– a well meaning enquiry, perhaps, but one that raised questions in their minds. 'Why?' asked Mike, wondering if there was more happening than Watson was letting on. The geologists' fears were soon confirmed by news that the Yemeni propaganda had reached fever pitch. 'According to the Yemenis,' Mike recorded, 'a large number of Nasrani (Christians) have arrived in Shabwa with nine cars. There is consternation in the camp.'

SEEING TWO HORSEMEN riding furiously towards you firing rifles in the air is not something that can easily be ignored, but in this situation – judging by the lack of response from the HBL guards – it was safe to do this. Reigning in their horses, the riders pulled up in front of the convoy and dismounted.

The riders were Shariff Saleh bin Nasr of As Seilan and his companion, a Bilari sheikh. Saleh was a short, fat man with a bushy, black beard, glittering eyes and a pleasant laugh, richly dressed in a green striped shirt with a white silk coat and coloured turban. He brought letters of greeting from the Emir Saleh bin Hussein, the ruler of Beihan.

On the face of it, the Emir's rule was well established. In 1904, the British Government had signed a treaty with the Shariff of Beihan, Ahmad am Muhsin, whose line claimed to be descended from the Prophet. The treaty was a safeguard, first against Turkish domination and second against Yemeni aggression. When Ahmad died, HMG favoured his two younger sons. Awadh was reputed to be a powerful, forceful and fearless leader, and Hussein was known as a shrewd, wise and fair counsellor. Mike commented:

> Somehow the Aden political service devised a scheme and successfully carried out what to Arabia must be a Gilbertian situation. The two elder sons were neglected, Awadh and Hussein were favoured, and HMG wanted Hussein to be the ruler.

To complicate matters, it was agreed that Hussein's son, Saleh, should be ruler. He was given the title of Emir of Beihan but, as Saleh was a mere boy, his father Hussein was deputed to be Regent and rule until Saleh came of age. Hussein received the title of Shariff of Beihan:

> So HMG got the man they wanted on the job and Hussein proved their choice to be worthwhile. Now, however, Emir Saleh is nearing his age (he is about 18) and Hussein is still a youngish man, and capable. When we arrived Hussein was in Aden and Saleh was ruling in his absence. Watson says that Saleh is developing as hoped like his father.

In reality, the Emir's rule was distinctly shaky. The tribes of the Balharith confederation held the real power in the land, and the Shariffs were only rulers by virtue of HMG's backing. Inevitably, there were tensions between the Balharith confederation and the Shariffs, with the result that, as Mike noted, 'both are a menace that need to be watched, and a source of trouble to be avoided'.

As if to remind them of the difficulties, the mountains of Yemen loomed in the north-west. The settlements of the Balharith tribe – clusters of small forts surrounded by cultivated land, groves of palm and *'ilb* trees, irrigation ditches and sweet-water wells – lay in the shadow of the mountains. It was hardly surprising that the Balharith had a close affiliation with the Yemen.

In the afternoon, the convoy made progress through the Beihan Wadi towards Aseilan. Here golden sand dunes ran against igneous mountains, and the wadi bed turned stony. Past the village the track ran on a gravelly terrace, with tiny sand dunes covered with *rakh* bushes. The going was generally firm, but there were patches of grey mucous sand.

Beyond Aseilan lay the ruined city of Qohlan, now a massive, sand-drifted, stone heap. The track ran along an airstrip, past the town of An Nuqub perched on a mound, down a long granite-walled wadi, through small villages of mud houses until at last the houses of Beihan Qasab were in sight and the convoy halted. All was peaceful and the town appeared quiet and still.

Then Rais Abdullah fired a single shot into the air and all hell broke loose.

'THE CLOSER THE bullets, the greater is the affection.'[6]

The arrival of outsiders – the first to arrive by car from the desert to the north – was an occasion for celebration. Every household seemed to have a rifle and every rifle was ablaze. What astonished Mike, once he had recovered from the initial shock of the fusillade, were the looks of genuine pleasure on the tribesmen's faces. Even Shariff Awadh bin Ahmad – reputedly the strong man of the country – wore a broad and genial smile.

Perhaps Rais Abdullah should have known better than to fire his first exploratory shot into the dark, overcast sky, but this seemed of little importance now. The townspeople were firing in joyous greeting, their rifles pointing upwards, their bullets disappearing overhead. The HBL guards responded in kind, firing 'about a hundred shots' as the convoy drove slowly and ceremoniously towards the centre of the town.

Mike had joked about being shot at in the past, making light of the tribesmen's aim; but now there was a real danger of being hit by a stray bullet. As the geologists noted nervously: 'the closer the bullets, the greater is the affection.' The bullets, and consequently the affection, were at times very close indeed.

A long line of people stretched before them. Only when the party halted did Mike notice Shariff Awadh, a tall, well-dressed, bearded figure carrying a rifle. Apart from his grin, he wore a white jacket with a red and green *futah* and white turban perched over a brown, intelligent face. A crimson fold of cloth hung across one shoulder and crossed at his waist. An ornamental dagger rested on his coloured leather belt, and a bandolier was slung over his other shoulder. The line advanced slowly towards them, men playing drums and flutes, girls dancing to the fore.

They were introduced to Shariff Awadh and other notables of the town. As the crowd looked on in glazed admiration, gathering around the expedition's stationary Dodges, the party was shown to the courtyard of the Government building where guards paraded before them, and Rais Abdullah took the salute. The Political Officer for the north-eastern area of the Western Aden Protectorate, Jimmy Watson, was waiting for them in an office. Sitting beside him was a young Arab wearing a red turban, 'well dressed and handsome except for a slight squint'. This was the Emir of Beihan, Saleh bin Hussein. A polite, if somewhat stilted, conversation ensued.

Pestered by swarms of flies the geologists found it difficult to relax, and were greatly relieved to be finally ushered from the room and conducted to their quarters.

The guest house was unlike anything Mike had seen in Arabia previously. A recently built mud construction, it was – they were told – reserved for visiting Sultans and VIPs. Their room was richly covered with matting, and cushions placed along the walls. A comfortable room, then, apart from the six tubular steel chairs placed oddly in a corner and a decor designed to challenge the eye: walls gaudily painted in crude designs of green and red and inscriptions scrawled in paint high on the ceiling. In the middle of the room stood a massive pillar of 'ilb wood, forked at the top and supporting the cross beams. Red, blue, yellow and green glass was set in the upper parts of the small windows.

Visitors came and went until about 5 p.m., when the geologists were left alone in peace. They washed off the residue of the long, dusty day in bowls of cool crystal-clear water, changed and enjoyed a 'secret whisky' before going to the Emir's house for dinner.

THE ENTERTAINMENT WAS about to begin, but for two of the guests in the room – René and Mike – apprehension was rising.

The geologists knew the form: dinner, tea and entertainment. Earlier in the evening they had enjoyed the Emir's banquet, a simple fare of a cooked sheep, eggs, rough bread, honey and sauce laid out before them. They had then repaired upstairs to the Emir's room. Here they found a Phillips radio and recent copies of *Life* magazine and the *Illustrated London News*, and sat around in various states of discomfort, drinking tea and orange squash. Tony Altounyan, Jimmy Watson and Rais Abdullah talked to the legionnaires, the Emir said very little, and the minutes ticked by.

Now they found themselves in the barrack room of the Government Guards. It was a long, narrow, dingy room with smoke-blackened walls, feebly illuminated by oil lamps. Emir Saleh squatted at a low table in the middle of the room, with members of the geological party on either side and a motley entourage of Government Guards, Tribal Guards, HBL men, tribesmen and bodyguards propped up against the walls at the far end.

A servant came and gave each of the guests a loop of woven wool (made by Beihan Jews), the so-called 'Bedu armchair' comprising a broad central band and a blue and green border. This was designed to be put over the head and drawn across the small of the back. The loop was then placed over the knees, giving the body complete support when sitting cross-legged. 'Trussed up' might have been a more accurate description; in the meantime, more cups of tea were passed around.

The geologists sensed that a different kind of entertainment was about to commence. Sure enough, a diminutive man with a crude goatskin tom-tom entered the room, followed by a tall man with a tiny double-barrelled flute, and three Yemeni gypsy dancing girls. These were dressed in long gowns, decorated with two green and black stripes and one bright orange. Each girl had a veil over her hair that was kept in place by silver ornaments, and each wore a silver necklace of squares that were held in place by thin silver chains. They carried heavy silver belts and wrist and ankle bands that tinkled as they shuffled barefoot across the dusty floor.

It was late evening and the room was already very hot. The dancers' faces were unveiled to reveal kohl-stained eyelids. The music began, but it was very discordant, and was almost drowned out by the beats of the tom-tom. The rhythm was fast. One of the girls started to dance, but this was not dancing as Mike had ever witnessed before: it was more like sprint meeting. The girl ran up and down the room over a length of about ten metres. A Government Guard then ran beside her. After five traverses, the dancing girl was replaced by another, and so on. 'There was nothing beautiful or exciting about the dancing, and it never varied,' reflected a downcast Mike. There was no escaping the monotony. Although the shrill piper may have varied his tune, the dance rhythm remained the same. The dancers' feet stirred up clouds of dust from the earthen floor and the atmosphere became thick with dust and smoke. Even one of their drivers put in a turn, 'then more dancing until we were fed up and went to bed'.

A few hours later – half-asleep, uncomfortable and stretched out on his bed – Mike was disturbed by a thumping noise outside. He got up, shuffled over to the window, and looked out to see dancers, drummers and pipers parading outside. Bleary-eyed and disbelieving, René joined him. It was the crack of dawn: did these people never sleep? In the dusty courtyard, the dancing girls began performing again, with drummers and pipers doing their level best to keep time. The geologists had little choice but to invite them indoors, a decision they immediately regretted. The troupe danced in, compelling the geologists to sit and listen to a reprise of the previous evening's entertainment.

As if there was a place to hide! At last, when it was judged diplomatic to do so, they offered silver, which the dancers accepted, thus bringing the proceedings and their torment mercifully to an end.

THE FIRST 24 hours set the pattern of their stay. More visitors came and went: there were more nerve-racking meals at night; the flies were always intolerable. It was a relief to get out and visit the environs of the town. The cultivations around Beihan were bright and verdant, fed with ample water supplies taken from wells around the town.

The Emir and his family took a close interest in the geologists' activities, accompanying them on all their excursions. But Beihan's granite surroundings did not offer an extensive work programme and, after brief visits to Neged el Morgat, an ancient customs-gate on the Yemen border, and to the Wadi Kahaur, the party travelled farther afield, heading for Aseilan.

The security situation was still tense: although their HBL guards were due to depart by Dakota, news of official Yemeni action caused two guards with a machine gun to be kept back to supplement the eight Government Guards with their single Bren gun.

On an overcast day, 14 December, the convoy set out for Leyadim with an additional escort of Balharith tribesmen who owned the salt mine there. They retraced their footsteps down the Wadi Beihan and established camp on its sandy bank at a distance of about 60 kilometres from the town. From there they followed a camel trail that snaked across a vast expanse of rolling sand dunes – this was still in use by camel trains carrying salt to the Yemen, as confirmed by a caravan of 15 'objecting' camels passing by.

The Leyadim salt mine was actively worked by 20 to 36 freed slaves of the Balharith at a rate of 2,000 to 5,000 camel-loads a month. Some of it went to Wadi Beihan and some of it to the Yemen, via Neged el Morgat, where the Emir of Beihan collected taxes. The geologists looked on while workers chipped away lumps of salt, leaving curved ripples on the rock face, and then they rejoined the party. The future economic possibilities did not go unnoticed: Mike would include an item on the salt mines in his geological report.[7]

After the Emir's party and the tribesmen had left for Aseilan, mapping was completed in cold, misty weather, and heavy rain fell on their return to camp. There followed a night of intense downpours, and the convoy had to pack up hurriedly and move quickly down the wadi to reach the higher ground before floodwaters arrived. Next day, they arrived at Bir Asakir in the afternoon and loaded all surplus stores hurriedly before setting off again. Owing to heavy rain the west road from the Hadhramaut to the coast was dangerous, so the party took the east road, reaching Mukalla on 19 December.

The geologists returned to Aden on Christmas Day, taking an Aden Airways flight via Mukeris, which gave them the opportunity to take in the geological sights from the air. They concluded that in view of the lack of exposures in the entire hinterland, further geological study was not recommended. Before completely condemning the area, however, they suggested that the subsurface conditions of the northern limits of the Aden Protectorate should be examined by geophysical or mechanical means.

In the meantime, back in Beihan, the insecure young Emir was left to ponder his future. When a visiting French archaeologist assured him that the oil prospects for his territory were very good, the Emir made enquiries about the results of the recent IPC survey. The geologists wrote back to say that there was only basement granite with no oil possibilities whatsoever.

The men without beards had departed, and the Emir's dream of rescuing his people from poverty was over.

The mud 'skyscrapers' of the Hadhramaut

1   Master of Belhaven, The Kingdom of Melchior, from p. 128. Reproduced by permission of John Murray, Publishers.

2   Ibid., p. 128.

3   Ibid., p. 128.

4   See Colonel Boustead's autobiography, *Wind of the Morning*. Boustead was indeed a colourful character who enjoyed a remarkable career, starting off as a deserter from the Navy in South Africa and fighting for the White Russians in 1917, before a long and distinguished service in East Africa and southern Arabia. Mike met Boustead many times, culminating in a rather embarrassing incident in Abu Dhabi many years later (see pp. 200-201).

5   The old Imam Yehia had been assassinated in 1948 and replaced by his son Ahmed, who tried to develop a frightening appearance by tying a string around his neck until his eyes were ready to pop out.

6   'Expedition to Southern Arabia' by R. Wetzel and D.M. Morton, IPC Magazine, November 1955.

7   IPC was interested in other ventures apart from oil, such as potash mining in Trans-Jordan, asphalt in Syria and salt mining in the Aden Protectorates. On this occasion, it was taken no further.

The 20th Century arrives in the Hadhramaut Valley

The convoy 'en route'

Hadhrami Bedouin Legionnaire

Scene from a Salt Mine,
Western Aden Protectorate

Scene from a Salt Mine, Western Aden Protectorate

Mike climbing a rock face

René with plane table and range finder

René with the Emir of Beihan on his right: 'He is developing as hoped like his father.'

Civic reception at Beihan with dancer in attendance

A Bedouin girl drawing water from a well

Hadhramaut Bedouin Legionnaire overlooking the desert

Chapter 11: Strangers Within the Gates

Lebanon, Jordan, Northern Iraq, 1950–1953

'Must westerners living there – those for instance in the service of the companies – live always as strangers and under feelings of constraint?'
IPC Handbook, 1948

Heather first joined Mike in the Middle East in the spring of 1950, when Mike was based in Tripoli, Lebanon. Her description of the flight from Blackbush is a reminder of how laborious air travel could be in those days:

The aeroplane was a Dakota and I was the only woman aboard, the other passengers being Company men either returning from leave or going out on their first job. I found the whole thing quite daunting. We stopped at Marseilles to re-fuel and then put down for the night in Malta, staying at the Phoenicia Hotel. We didn't get there until about eleven o'clock and by the time we had something to eat (there was no service on the plane) I was much too tired to do more than drop into bed. It only seemed a moment before we were being woken up, given breakfast and hustled out to the plane. It was just getting light and I saw little of the island before we were taking off and heading for El Adem on the north African coast. A quick stop to re-fuel and for the passengers to have some refreshment and then we were on the last leg of the journey to Tripoli.

Mike was waiting for her at the airport and, as they drove back into town, Heather had her first glimpse of life in the Middle East, the tall, whitewashed flats of the town contrasting with a Palestinian refugee camp on the outskirts. Their flat in the Ali Salti building, 96 steps to the top floor, looked over an orange grove to the sea – it was luxurious in comparison to what a newly married couple could have expected in England at the time. The few 'modern' conveniences – such as the oil stove they used for cooking – left much to be desired, however. Heather wrote:

There were three burners with wicks which you kept as clean as possible and woe betide you if they were not burning properly. If your back was turned they could start smoking in a second and cover the kitchen in smoky fumes and dirt. If you wanted to use an oven you had a kind of tin box which you put over two of the burners. The stove would take ages to boil water if you were in a hurry and yet would burn something which needed a gentle heat. My grandmother had a similar stove in Etchingham for all the years she lived there and it made me remember her with affection and wonder at the meals she turned out on it.

The flat was not quite so luxurious as had first appeared, especially when Heather found out that they were sharing their accommodation with others:

Mike was away and I decided I'd give the maid's room a good clean. Dusting around the skirting board I saw two feelers waving. Suspecting rightly that it was a cockroach I got the spray gun and gave it a burst. Out shot the most enormous insect I had ever seen, closely followed by another. The spray couldn't really cope with them so I had to resort to killing them with a shoe. I dispatched twenty-nine altogether from largest to the smallest. Then of course there were the bed bugs. We'd only been together for a couple of weeks when Mike woke up with two nasty red marks on his face in consequence of which he got a lot of ribbing in the office. The next morning he woke up and saw two small bugs crawling across the pillowcase. The decontamination squad was called in and they sealed the bedroom and fumigated it resulting in about fifty bedbugs lying dead on the floor.

After these revelations, Heather was content to leave the cleaning to the maid. They had a succession of maids, each with a story. To begin with there was Janet who brought them a gift, an adorable little bundle of white fur with a black patch over one eye. But, as Heather explained, looks could deceive:

Jackson grew and, being a pi-dog, was not really amenable to training. Added to that, we lived in a flat and giving him adequate exercise was a problem. Jackson had to stay at home and he made his disgust felt by doing his best to wreck the flat. He was particularly fond of eating books and we had to try all sorts of ruses to make the flat reasonably dog proof. He was also an absolute plague when we had guests in the evening and would try to chew their shoes. If we shut him in the spare bedroom he showed his annoyance by barking incessantly. When I became pregnant we decided we couldn't manage a baby[1] and Jackson so we gave him to a family who lived up in Mont Michel where he could have much more freedom.

The next maid was caught stealing money and the last one called Mary would regale Heather with lurid stories of the burglaries and murders that had happened in the town.

Heather recalled the incident when she lost her engagement ring. They were expecting a guest for lunch and she was in the kitchen making pastry. Taking off her ring, not wishing to get it covered in fat, she put it in her apron pocket. Mike and their guest came a bit earlier than expected and Heather whipped off her apron and hung it over the kitchen chair. Before they finished lunch, a couple of workmen came to do something in the bedroom and they had to wait in the kitchen until the room was free. As soon as her guest had gone, Heather went into the kitchen to retrieve the ring but the ring was missing. Thinking it must have dropped on the floor – which had just been swept – she searched the bin, and then every nook and cranny of the flat, but without success:

When Mike came home I told him what had happened and of course I was very upset but it was never found. The police were informed and they harangued the two workmen which also upset me because I think they were quite brutal but that was the end of the story.

Mike decided that Heather needed protection while he was away on field trips. In, perhaps,

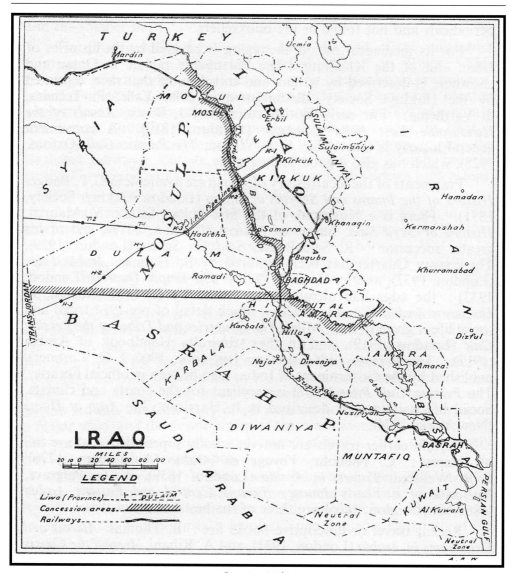

Iraq in 1948
© *Iraq Petroleum Company Limited*

an over-dramatic gesture, he bought her a small revolver and a supply of bullets. Heather had never fired a gun in her life and needed lessons. Finding a safe place to do this was a problem, but eventually they settled on the orange groves. Despite the practice Heather never felt confident about the revolver and was sure she could never have fired it in anger, or hit anything if she had. Nonetheless, she dutifully slept with the gun under her pillow while Mike was away.[2]

On the whole, life was good. Company personnel were spread around the town and the social life was active. Weekends would be spent on the beach or visiting the mountains, where they found a restaurant which served garlic chicken preceded by a lavish meze. There was an interesting fish restaurant down near the sea at El Mina. They went there on one occasion when a senior American geologist was in town. The staff of the geological department were all invited – about 12 in all – and the meal was a success, but Heather found it a most uncomfortable evening. One of the American wives started upbraiding the visitor for sending her husband away on field trips so frequently – she got very lonely. At that point, she started crying, putting a damper on the party. 'I think her husband was very embarrassed,' wrote Heather.

Heather went on a number of trips while they lived in Tripoli. One was to Aleppo with Mike where they stayed at the Company mess for a few days. Apart from the tales of Zuzu, Lucy and Big Rosie, her chief memory was going to the *souk* where there was heavy damask embroidered with gold and silver, and little shops selling gold jewellery.

ELSEWHERE, TIMES WERE changing. The full effects of nationalism were being felt in Iran, where nationalisation of the country's oil industry was proceeding apace under the leadership of Dr Musaddiq. Arab nationalism, an emerging theme of the 1950s, would take root across the Middle East to the detriment of the Iraq Petroleum Company's interests. However, in the summer of 1951, Company employees were largely untroubled by these concerns. Mike was posted to Jordan to look for suitable sites for water wells for the Jordanian Government. Mike and Heather stayed in Amman and, for the first three days while Mike was in the field, Heather was left to wander around the town or write letters and read in their hotel. One day, riding Mike's small horse, she accompanied him into the field. While Mike spent the day sampling a dry river-bed, Heather sat beneath an oleander bush to get a little shade from the heat. On the way back, they stopped at a police post where they were given sweet mint tea. When Mike eked out an extra day's leave they went sightseeing in and around Jerusalem before returning to Tripoli:

> We returned to spend the night at a Company mess at Mafraq before the flight to Tripoli. It was there that I played darts for the first time in my life and, as so often happens, had beginner's luck. We returned to Tripoli the next day flying in one of the little Rapides the Company owned. I remember the pilot particularly because he seemed to find his way by following the road below and then making for the Homs Gap. When there was nothing much happening he read his book.

After Peter was born, Heather's trips were curtailed. Nonetheless, she did manage a visit to one of the pipeline stations, H2, to spend a week there with a family while Mike was working in the area. The 12 pipeline stations – each 'a veritable township' – had been erected, 'three on the fringes of civilization and nine in pure desert'.[3] Although regularly serviced by the Company air transport fleet and possessing telegraph, telephone and wireless links, these pipeline stations were very remote. It was a restricted life for those unfortunate enough to be based there. With only about three British families at H2, together with a few bachelors, entertainment consisted of going to the club and holding dinner parties for each other.

The visit to H2 was memorable for another reason. One of the wives gave birth while Heather was there:

> Normally expectant mothers were sent up to Kirkuk two or three weeks before the baby was due but this one came a bit early and she had to have it at home. There was only an Iraqi doctor and though he was happy to deal with the birth he didn't know what

to do with the baby when it appeared. As I was the only woman on the station who'd had a baby they roped me in. It must have been a bit alarming for the girl but the birth was straightforward and I must admit I was fascinated seeing it from the other end as it were. All I had to do was to wash the little boy and hand him back to the happy mum. A doctor came down from Kirkuk the next day because the after-birth hadn't appeared and then mother and child went back with him to the hospital. The mother came down to Dukhan when we were there but she never had any more children. Perhaps that experience was enough.

LATER, MIKE'S WORK would take him to northern Iraq, to the mountains of Kurdistan. Kurdistan, in the high mountain ranges of the Near East, lies on the busy ancient trade routes between the Far East and Europe and was fought over by the Ottoman and Persian Empires. For the past 100 years the Kurds have campaigned for their own state but, apart from two brief periods in the twentieth century, there has never been an independent state of Kurdistan.

Nowadays the area known as Kurdistan straddles four states – Iran, Iraq, Syria and Turkey – with a sizeable population in a fifth, Russia. It gains its sense of coherence from an ethnic group known as Kurds rather than from any internationally recognized boundary. Kurdish society, even today, is essentially a feudal, tribal system, with an economy primarily based on agriculture. The Kurds speak their own language, unrelated to Turkish or Arabic, and have resisted the authorities that have tried to suppress the use of Kurdish. The majority of Kurds are Sunni Moslems, with a sizeable proportion of Alevite Moslems living in the northern and western parts of Turkey.

Kurdistan sits uneasily within its host nations, and much oil wealth lies within its unofficial domain. The mountains of Kurdistan attract a heavy precipitation and provide the sources of the main rivers of the region: the Tigris and Euphrates. In winter, heavy snowfalls block the mountain passes; in summer, the gentler slopes provide grazing for sheep, goats and cattle. To the south, a warmer climate and a rich soil render fertile pastures where grain, fruit and vegetables grow. Despite these natural resources, the Kurds are essentially a poor people earning a meagre living from a potentially rich land.

They are also a fierce yet intensely loyal people, as witnessed by an incident that occurred on one of Mike's expeditions:

> On the surveys the geologists were accompanied by Kurds as guides, chain men and sample collectors. On one expedition a Kurd popped up from behind a rock, demanding 'Your money or your life!' Omar, a Kurd in the team, an ex-British army paratrooper, explained vehemently to the highwayman that the geologists were his guests and eventually the highwayman let them pass safely. After they had passed by, Omar said: 'That man has insulted my nation, wait here, I am going back to kill him.' He was eventually persuaded not to.[4]

By the treaty of Sevres, signed on 10 August 1920, the victorious powers and Turkey had recognized the fundamental rights of the Kurds and Turks to constitute an independent Kurdish nation. These provisions were never carried out, however, and for many people Kurdistan remained a myth, a far-off land of high peaks and swirling rivers.

We can only imagine the cold, wet autumnal wind rattling the window-panes as Mike's mother, Lucy, sat at the fireside of her Huddersfield home, with old dog Chang curled up beside her, reading a letter from Mike, a vague picture of Kurdistan forming in her mind:

> It's cold here now. I went up to the Persian frontier last week. It rained here too – and snow fell on the mountain peaks around the camp. It's a lovely part of the East – high mountains, trees, streams, wild birds, squirrels, and in the higher parts, wild pig, bears, and ibex. There are even a few leopards.
>
> In the camp we have trouble. We are near a village, and all the cats come at night. I was stung by a scorpion about ten days ago, made a mess treating my foot with permanganate and couldn't walk for four days. Scorpions are nasty things – they have a terrible sting – the pain lasts for about twelve hours. The black variety can be fatal – I was stung by a yellow one.

Pre-war geological investigations in Iraq had been suspended as a result of civil disturbances, and were not resumed until 1946 when 'a planned campaign of stratigraphic research was set afoot'.[5] Under the overall charge of Colonel Henson, the project involved a vast amount of fieldwork and laboratory studies. René directed most of the work in Kurdistan, the Sinjar and the western desert, assisted by Mike and a number of other geologists such as Dr R.G.S. Hudson ('Doc'), Charles Andre, Harold Dunnington and Henry Hotchkiss over a period of six years. Deeper wells were drilled to locate older deposits: this resulted in oil being discovered in the Middle Cretaceous at Ain Zalah, Kirkuk and Bai Hasan.

IN THE SPRING of 1953 Mike and Heather were moved to Kirkuk, on the fringes of Kurdistan. In contrast to Tripoli, Kirkuk was an oil camp built exclusively for the staff who were employed by IPC and their families. There were offices, a hospital, a club and swimming pool, and a large number of houses of varied size. There was a shop, but the range of goods available was far inferior to that available in Tripoli.

Heather described her arrival at the camp:

> When I first went out we were assigned accommodation in a *barasti* house outside the main camp. There were three of them together. On one side was a bachelor mess and on the other lived Diana and Bob Mayes. The houses weren't very big but the chief disadvantage was that the kitchen was at the bottom of the garden. I suppose it had been designed for a family who employed a cook but my memory of it was running up to the house with the breakfast, bacon and eggs in one hand, and the other holding a mac over my head because it was raining. Mike always said they were the best breakfasts he'd ever tasted!

It was not too long before they were moved to a pleasant bungalow in the main camp, but they had some very happy memories of life in that *barasti* house. At first the weather was quite cold and they had a fire in the evening:

> We employed a 'boy' to do the cleaning and I remember one evening he had difficulty getting the fire to light. Before we realized what he was doing he came in with a can

of kerosene and nearly set the house on fire! They used to have Scottish dancing in the club once a week which I really enjoyed and I seem to remember going to a Burns Night Dinner which was a very boozy affair. Another memory was driving to see the 'eternal fires' – seepages of gas coming through the earth which were continually burning.

Summer was a different matter, of course – the heat was very dry, not the humid heat they had experienced in Tripoli. In the bungalow they had a cooling unit in one bedroom and one in the lounge. Ants were a continual problem. They had a food-storage cupboard with its feet standing in tins filled with kerosene to stop the ants climbing up. Food was not scarce, but they were limited in what they could buy:

I can't remember getting anything other than potatoes, onions, carrots and marrows in the way of fresh vegetables although you could buy lettuce and tomatoes. I can't recall ever getting fish, and the meat was frozen and not very good.

At the weekend in the summer they usually spent the mornings at the swimming pool, retiring to their beds in the afternoon because it was so hot:

I remember one afternoon we went to have a snooze when we were assailed by a horrible smell in the bedroom. We couldn't think where it was coming from until Mike decided that something must have died in the air conditioning unit and that's where the smell came from. He got the workmen to come out and have a look at it but having dismantled the whole thing they found nothing. It turned out that a cat we had been looking after for a Dutch couple who had gone on leave had cocked its leg against the counterpane! We called the cat Yiaouw because that was the only noise he ever made.

Kirkuk had a distinct social structure. In Tripoli, everyone had mixed in together and there was little awareness of one's place in the hierarchy; but in Kirkuk, a wife had different china according to her husband's job. Blue-band china (which Mike and Heather had) was for the lower orders, but management had gold lace. Later in Mike's career, when they moved to Dukhan, it came as something of a culture shock to find that everyone had gold lace!

In September Heather returned to England to await the birth of their second child, while Mike prepared for his next expedition.

MANY OF MIKE'S trips to Kurdistan were in the company of René Wetzel. They ran a number of photographic, stratigraphic and structural sections, and surveys, in various parts of Kurdistan, in order to define the attitude and composition of the strata within the concession areas. The information from these and measured sections led to a number of prospective oil-reservoir rocks being defined.

During this time Mike came upon a remarkable tribe, the Yazidis, renowned as devil-worshippers and shunned by their neighbours as a result. They lived in an area to the west of Mosul, around the Jebel Sinjar, and to the north-east, in the Kurdish foothills. Their religion and tribal ways did not encourage mixing with outsiders: Yazidis were forbidden to talk to other Kurds and to marry outside the tribe. They believed that they were the only descendants of

Adam, with the rest of humanity being descended from women and therefore inferior.

Their shrine at Sheikh Adi was named after their founder, and lent itself to the appearance of devil worship:

> The courtyard before the entrance contains various small buildings and mulberry trees through which the sun casts chequered patterns on the facade. The door is to the extreme left of the wall, which is interesting on account of its curious magical signs cut in low relief on the stones, the principal being the great vertical snake, carefully black-leaded, to the right of the doorway. Pilgrims kiss this emblem of Satan. Within the temple is dark, dirty and shabby ... the floor is greasy, with drippings from the oil lamps. On the north side of the temple a chapel, which they call Sheikh Hassan, contains an ark-shaped chest or tomb, entirely covered with draperies and from this, again, a low door communicates with a second chapel in which is the tomb of Sheikh Adi himself.[6]

In reality, their reputation as devil-worshippers was ill-deserved. True, Yazidis believed that an angel symbolized in the form of a scared peacock, Malik Taus, had fallen to earth and needed to be placated. But there was no hell in Yazidism, since Malik Taus had repented for his sins, having cried for 7,000 years and filled seven jars full of tears in the process, which, in turn, had been used to put out the fires of hell. They may have reserved a healthy respect for the devil, but the Yazidis never spoke his name 'Shaitan', and never worshipped him.

Their religion derived from an Islamic dervish brotherhood and combined elements of nature worship, Zoroastrianism and Christianity, resulting in a unique mixture and scenes not quite so demonic as first impressions might have suggested:

> Once a year, early in October, they assemble at Sheikh Adi and sacrifice a bull to the sun. On the doorway to the shrine is an embossed black serpent, symbol of Shaitan, which the pilgrims kiss. I attended this festival but did not see the sacrifice. Booths had been set up among the trees, near the shrine with its two fluted, pointed white cones, and the scene resembled a fair, crowded with happy, relaxed people. There was much dancing and singing, in which the women joined.[7]

WHEN MIKE CAME to look back at the places he had visited during his career, his thoughts would often return to Kurdistan, both to its people and its places. Even with the harsh conditions, days spent traversing a difficult terrain, working among a potentially hostile population, nights spent camped out with no modern conveniences, enduring a sometimes harsh climate, Mike and his colleagues retained a special affection for the untamed tribes and rugged wilds of Kurdistan.

---

1   Peter was born in February 1951.
2   As it turned out, there was never any reason to use the revolver, and Mike disposed of it in Kirkuk, leaving it with another geologist when he was posted to the Persian Gulf.
3   *IPC Handbook*, p. 9.
4   Adrian Humphreys' recollections.
5   F. E. Wellings, unpublished manuscript.
6   E. S. Stevens, *By Tigris and Euphrates*, Hurst and Blackett, 1923.
7   Wilfred Thesiger, *Desert, Marsh and Mountain*, p. 96 with permission of Curtis Brown on behalf of the Wilfred Thesiger Estate Copyright © Wilfred Thesiger Estate, 1979.

Khabour Valley, Kurdistan, 1952
Back row from 4th left to right: Mike Morton, R. G. S. 'Doc' Hudson, René Wetzel

Yazidi 'devil worshipper' tribesmen, Kurdistan

Chapter 12: The Bedouin Well at Thamud

Eastern Aden Protectorate, October 1953–February 1954

'No man can live this life and emerge unchanged'
Wilfred Thesiger, *Arabian Sands*[1]

If Mike had seen René's face, he could have been forgiven. It would not have been surprising if, looking through the porthole of the aircraft as it descended towards RAF Khormaksar, he had seen his own reflection and momentarily mistaken it for that of René. Mike had learned much from René Wetzel, and they had worked together many times, but now – in truth – their days of surveying together were over. 'No more ruddy fox-holes for me,' he could almost hear René say.

Almost four years before, they had left the Aden Protectorates far behind, occasionally teaming up again as Mike careered around the Middle East on the exploration carousel. Now Mike had come full circle, having surveyed in virtually every part of the Company's concession areas, from the Bekaa Valley to the Persian border, from the Kurd-Dagh mountains to the Gulf coast, and from Northern Oman down to Dhofar and the Eastern Aden Protectorate.

Now he was the leader of a geological party on behalf of the subsidiary company, Petroleum Concessions (Aden Protectorate) Ltd., for an expedition to the northern Hadhramaut. Earlier, in the spring of 1953, Mike together with Nick Fallon and F. S. Burgis, had carried out an aerial reconnaissance of the area, and this is where the Company's interest lay, centred on a desolate spot marked on the maps as the Bedouin well at Thamud.

IN OCTOBER 1953, Mike, Gilbert Todd and Adrian Humphreys flew from London by BOAC Argonaut via Rome and breakfasted in Cairo to arrive in Aden later in the day. Gilbert Todd was a young graduate and this trip was his first expedition since joining the Company; and Adrian Humphreys was an experienced geologist seconded from Iraq. They were met at the aerodrome by Peter Besse, the local Company agent and owner of Besse and Co., who was sporting a brand-new white Jaguar in which he drove them to the hotel where they were to spend the next six weeks preparing for the trip to Thamud.

It would take an overland journey of 1395 kilometres in a north-easterly direction from Aden to reach the well at Thamud, an ancient watering place used by Bedouins travelling across the southern rim of the Arabian Peninsula, and by those few venturing into the great desert known as the Rub al Khali.

Thamud marked the spot where the expedition planned to set up its camp. It was a wild, barren and virtually unexplored region, remote and inaccessible in the past, which remained the missing link in a geological chain stretching from the Yemen in the west to Dhofar in the east.

Mike's letters reveal how much there was to accomplish before the expedition was ready to set off. His first task was to see what the Aden Government was able to provide by way of a representative and armed escort. He had to meet the Resident Adviser, Sir Hugh Boustead who was residing in Sei'un. With this in mind, Mike and his party flew to Riyan and then on to

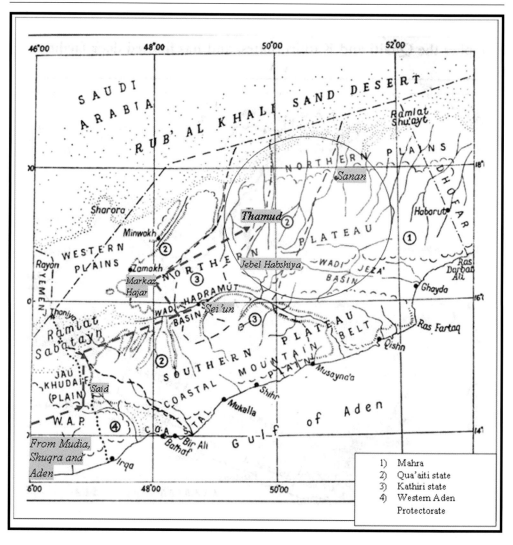

Thamud Expedition Itinerary showing the area of the 1953 survey

Ghuraf (the nearest airstrip to Sei'un) by Dakota on 20 October 1953.

The aircrew was unable to find the airstrip. After roaming around for 15 minutes they had to call on Mike to join them in the cockpit and bring them in. 'I think I should get a free trip for professional services rendered,' was Mike's sardonic comment.[2]

Tony Altounyan was unavailable for this expedition so it was necessary to find a new Liaison Officer. Discussions with Boustead about finding one were inconclusive. Mike set off on a wild-goose chase to find the Military Adviser, Captain Jim Ellis of the Hadhramaut Bedouin Legion, to discuss the security arrangements. Mike recorded:

Ellis did not arrive on the 22nd, and I spent an uncomfortable night on the floor of an

Arab house, rolled in only a single old blanket and being bitten from head to foot. My host did his best, but as his wife and servants were away, we did rather badly for food.[3]

He eventually caught up with Ellis in Riyan. Ellis confirmed that the Hadhramaut Bedouin Legion was going to occupy Thamud in the next few days, which would secure the expedition's northern flank. This was good news at last. 'The survey should have a very good chance of success, particularly as most of the Manahil (tribe) are south of the Wadi Hadhramaut following the grazing,' Mike concluded.

It was agreed that the party should return in early November. Adrian and Gilbert were to be installed at RAF Riyan, where they could be shown some stratigraphic sections around Mukalla and be taught plane-table mapping.

ALL THE WHILE, Mike's thoughts were preoccupied by another operation. In London, Company plans to land a survey party on the coast of Oman were taking shape. Communications to Mike around this time referred to this operation as DEF, and were marked SECRET.

From the very start of the Thamud expedition, it was intended that Mike should hand over the survey to Don Beydoun and, together with Adrian and Gilbert, join the DEF landings. But the autumn start-date was put back to December, then again into the New Year.

In the meantime, discussions with the Aden Government for the service of a Liaison Officer became protracted. Mike's preferred choice, Abdullah Hasan Jaffar, MBE, was employed by the Aden Government in Eastern Aden Protectorate, and was at first unavailable, being required for service in Mahra.

'Kennedy, McIntosh and Boustead of EAP ungrudgingly say that he is the best man for the job,' wrote Mike, 'but of course they would like to keep him.' At one stage, the Aden Government told the Company that the expedition could have Abdullah provided he didn't have anything to do with local politics. This was clearly absurd – the Liaison Officer's role was to establish contact with the local tribesmen and this restriction would make his task impossible. At length, the Government relented and Abdullah's appointment was approved. In fact Abdullah had no need for squabbles of this kind: he was from a wealthy family with a distinguished history of political service, a landowner of independent means who was keen to return to his estates for the harvest in March.

In Mike's view, the survey could not be prolonged much beyond March in any event because of the climatic conditions. May, like September, was the worst period in the area, when the 'Arbain' would bring 40 days of excessive heat prior to the monsoon.

For security, the expedition was given an escort of 14 HBL soldiers led by a lieutenant. In Arabic, m'lossin, meaning 'Lieutenant', sounds similar to mulazim meaning 'not necessary', so it was perhaps inevitable that the lieutenant in charge of this party should become light-heartedly known as 'Mr Not Necessary'. The banter was extended to his men – one of them named Tomatum possessed a vintage silver-plated rifle, its barrel so bent that it looked as if it could shoot around corners. Tomatum soon proved his worth by shooting a gazelle in the rump when it was galloping away from a moving Land Rover. As a result, that part of the anatomy became known as 'Tomatum's Bull's Eye'.

In addition to the soldiers there was one driver/fitter, two drivers, one assistant driver, two cooks, one cook's helper, and one wireless operator making up the camp staff. Transport consisted of six Land Rovers, an Austin Champ, a three-ton Bedford lorry and a couple of vans. As it happened the engine block of the Bedford sprang a leak (a matchstick was used to plug the hole), the brakes failed, the starter conked out and they had a puncture. The Champ proved too heavy for the journey, but salvation came with the Land Rovers. They had the latest aluminium light-weight bodies which proved more than adequate for the task. Geologists would report on their performance, making a number of suggestions ranging from the fitting of a sunshield to the position of the headlights, tools and spare tyre, which were subsequently taken up by the manufacturer.

Mike wanted all members of the expedition to be capable in all aspects of desert survey. To this end, he took Adrian Humphreys on to Aden Beach, a flat expanse of mud, sand and shingle, and told him: 'If you can drive on this, you can drive on anything.' Later, as the expedition was passing through the vicinity of Shabwa, the Land Rovers were driving in formation when Mike, who was leading the convoy, signalled a sudden stop, which the Land Rovers did some 20 metres short of a hundred-metres-deep hole in the ground. It was an old salt mine.

'I'm glad you stopped in time,' said Mike to the others, 'as I couldn't have got you out.'[4]

DURING THE SIX-WEEK period of preparation, Mike had to liaise with numerous bodies: the political officers, the RAF, the Royal Navy, the Army, commercial enterprises, and the port and airport authorities. The party kept in contact with London by using Bentley's Second Code, a form of cipher used for sensitive communications. Gilbert was put in charge of amassing stores and Adrian was in charge of the Commissariat and medicine chests. Stores included tentage, equipment, cooking utensils, cutlery, crockery, folding tables and chairs. Supplies were calculated on the basis of providing for five geologists, the camp boss and his staff and visitors for three months. Adrian Humphreys wrote:

> Amongst these figures was a request for 24 boxes of cornflakes. A query came back from the agent for procurement: did I mean 24 boxes, because each box contained 12 cartons?
>
> Mike came up to me with a big grin and said: 'You gannet! I shall have to hire another truck to carry your cornflakes to Thamud.'
>
> Apparently I should have quoted 'cartons' not 'boxes'. Subsequently, when any food was being talked about, Mike would say he had a registered gannet on board.[5]

A list of supplies was forwarded to London for approval, but this was not immediately forthcoming: 'no alcohol', was the message that came back. Only when Don Beydoun arrived and humourously suggested that he could not travel up country without alcohol – because he always had his food cooked in wine – did the Company relent. As Adrian noted:

> Some six geological man-months plus courtesy bottles amounted to a volume not far adrift from two or three boxes of cornflakes.[6]

From Aden, Mike organized three familiarization trips. Mike, Gilbert Todd and Adrian Humphreys stayed at Riyan as arranged between 3 and 14 November, and explored the country around Mukalla. Geological sections previously measured by Mike and René during their 1947 visit were revisited, and new sections were studied in the Shihr, Dis and Riyan areas.

In one sense, it was a reprise of Mike's 1947 expedition, but this time with a twist: life now mimicked art. The area now resembled a vast movie set and the geologists felt sidelined, as Mike explained:

> The people in Mukalla and the Wadi are up to their eyes in work regarding the visit of J. Arthur Rank Studios, and Harold Ingrams filming 'Arabia and the Isles', so unfortunately we are rather unwanted.

The second trip took them on a reconnaissance to Dhala, 96 kilometres north-north-west of Aden, between 22 and 25 November. On approaching the Yemen border, however, the convoy was stopped by the military on account of the Yemeni army shelling civilian vehicles, and the geologists were able to observe the geology of the Yemen only from a distance.

The third trip was to the north-east, where they saw rocks of the pre-Cambrian shield overlain by limestones of the Jurassic to Miocene age. Several of these limestones were sampled for their fossil content.

It was in November that Mike received a telegram announcing the birth of his second child, a boy, in Huddersfield: 'mother and baby doing well.' On 4 December, Don Beydoun arrived, followed a week later by Ted ('Peewee') Melville, a Scottish geologist with a keen sense of humour.

Mike fell ill with fever – a recurrence of the malaria he had first contracted in Mahra. He spent two days in bed before leading the party out of Aden on 17 December. In the meantime Gilbert Todd had contracted typhoid and was hospitalized, being left to join the expedition at a future date.

THE JOURNEY TO Thamud provided opportunities for surveying the terrain. Night stops were made at Shuqra, Mudia, Said, Eyad and Bir Asakir *en route* to the Wadi Hadhramaut.

On 23 December they met Captain Ellis who was to accompany them later in the trip. Ellis gave them an idea of what they could expect in the remote wilderness around Thamud. There was the Sei'ar, one of the most feared tribes of the region, who had a reputation for raiding. Then there were the Manahil and Mahra tribes who two years previously had set out from Thamud on a *ghazzu*, raiding both the settlements of the Dahm and those of the Yam and Abida tribes. They were pursued, attacked, and lost some of the camels they had stolen; but in the prevalent culture of 'an eye for an eye, a tooth for a tooth', reprisals were expected. HBL soldiers now patrolled the western boundaries of the Eastern Protectorate and peace, though restored, was fragile.

There was another presence in this dusty arena: the Kingdom of Saudi Arabia. The border between the Aden Protectorates and Saudi Arabia had always been vague, relying at one time on the so-called 'Violet Line'. It was called this because a line had been drawn in violet ink on a map in 1913 to mark the boundary between Turkish and British spheres of influence in southern Arabia. Ellis was constantly on the lookout for Saudi incursions across this line.

On arriving at the house of the local political officer, 'Jungly' Johnson, the geologists were greeted by a football match in full swing between boys from the village and those from a local school. Taken inside the bungalow, the geologists were ushered to the guest-room and invited to sit on rickety wooden chairs.

'Would you like a drink?' asked Johnson.

The geologists needed no encouragement, and Johnson produced two bottles of Gordon's gin. They were filled with water.

To the geologists this was a temporary setback, and Johnson's eyes brightened when they presented him with a box of unopened bottles of Gordon's gin.

'After the first one or two glasses of gin and water,' wrote Adrian Humphreys, 'it became more difficult to differentiate between the gin bottles which contained water and those which contained gin. We all sat round that night.'

Spending 25 and 26 December in Sei'un, they set about making the final arrangements for their expedition to Thamud, some 550 kilometres to the north-east. Mike struck a deal with a merchant called Bin Kathir to replensih supplies while the expedition was in the desert. At the post office, a building the size of a garden shed, he organized mail and other supplies to be delivered by camel to Thamud, a five-day camel journey. Finally, he wrote to the Company representative, Peter Besse, in Aden requesting various supplies, including a crate of Scotch which, preferably, should be accompanied 'and if possible covered with sacking'.

They stayed an extra day in Sei'un to await news of Gilbert Todd from Aden but, when there was none and Gilbert did not appear, the party continued its journey without him.

THE WADI HADHRAMAUT cuts a huge gash in the terrain of the Eastern Aden Protectorate, separating the southern and northern plateaux. The Northern Plateau, or *Jol*, runs along a geological axis known as the Hadhramaut Structural Arch. It slopes from the axis southwards towards the Wadi Hadhramaut, and very gently northwards to the Rub al Khali desert. Like its southern counterpart, the Northern *Jol* gently tilts eastwards, being highest in the west where it meets an escarpment of the Western Plains. To the east it merges with the Qara mountains of Dhofar.[7]

The wadis of the *Jol* tend to rise near the axis of the Northern Arch and flow in a northerly directly into the Rub al Khali, where the desert sands swallow them up. They are more gentle and wider than the gorge-cutting wadis of the south, and on the whole make for easy motor traverses.

Several degrees of frost were not uncommon in January at night, whereas day temperatures could rise to 32 degrees centigrade or more. At various times during the year, cold, dust-laden winds blew from the north, occasionally in winter coming from the heart of Arabia. Although the region was affected by monsoons, this effect was less regular in the extreme north and brought little rainfall there. The vegetation was very sparse. The *Jol*, apart from a scattering of bunch grass, camel thorn, acacia, tamarisk, and *'ilb*, was essentially a barren waste.

The journey to Thamud took the convoy four days, staying *en route* for two nights in a ruined fort built into the rocks. The early part of the route was difficult, up the escarpment and across the *Jol*, partly covered by sand dunes, but the last 100 kilometres was easy going. They reached Thamud towards the end of the fourth day and pitched their camp about 100 metres from the Bedouin water well, which had been restored with a concrete lining and a camel trough. Apart from the well there was nothing to mark Thamud as a place of significance, surrounded as it was by a featureless expanse of sand. When the surveyor Norman Stansfield joined the party, he fixed the well's position using BBC times and star positions: there was a discrepancy of 112 kilometres between its actual position and its position as shown on existing maps.

One of the first tasks of the survey was to map out a landing strip, which was quickly done. To give wind direction, a tyre was set alight just before the first RAF Dakota came in to land. The aircraft was directed to the airstrip by a mirror reflecting the sun's rays towards the aircraft, and by radio contact.

Life in the Thamud camp was fairly basic, relying on regular camel trains to keep them supplied with provisions. The RAF would also fly in supplies and fly out geological samples. Frank, the wireless operator, kept in touch with the RAF in Aden once or twice daily. On one occasion the geologists wrapped a delicate fossil in toilet paper, using up 40 rolls in the process. A message was sent to the RAF: 'please send forty toilet rolls.' Assuming the worst, the reply came back: 'Do you need a doctor as well?' The next Dakota duly arrived with 40 toilet rolls, but no doctor.

Before he left the region, Mike led the expedition on two side-trips. The first was a three-day trip to explore Jebel Habshiya, which lay to the south of Thamud, with the object of studying accessibility and making general observations. The second was to Sanan, a round trip made in the company of Captain Ellis. Sanan was an important, though foul, well on the Mahra-Manahil frontier. The place itself held little of geological significance, revealing water at a depth of about seven metres in gypsum. From Sanan, the traverse headed northwards to the edge of the Rub al Khali desert, then swung westwards, keeping to the flat, sandy belt, which averaged 65 kilometres width between the sands and the gypsum outcrops. Upon reaching Wadi Ardha, the party turned south and reached Thamud via the Wadi Jinab.

The geologists ventured into the desert with enough supplies of water to see them through their journey – wells could not always be relied upon, even if they appeared on their maps. In order to keep water cool during long journeys in the hot desert, the geologists devised a way of storing water in canvas-like bags, which could be hung from the front door hinge of a Land Rover. In this way, the slipstream of the vehicle would keep the water cool. The system was equally effective with cans of beer.

Water was precious in these desolate corners of the desert. The geologists, conscious of the need to preserve their supplies, used it sparingly, occasionally pouring only a mugful for a wash and a shave, sometimes not washing at all. The danger of running out could never be disregarded, and they were trained in various survival techniques. One method was to capture moisture from the atmosphere. Each geologist had a rubber ground-sheet that he put over his bedding. Invariably, small pools of water would collect in the hollows covering the sleeping person. Not surprisingly the water had a rubbery taste, but was nonetheless fresh. By special arrangement of the rubber sheet, one sleeping person could produce one cupful of water each night.

Another by-product of this process was not so welcome. The rubber sheets made a cool habitation for any self-respecting insect, snake or other small animal. One morning, when Peewee was folding up his bed, a family of two large and four or five small scorpions scuttled out and ran blinking into the daylight.

IN JANUARY 1954 Jim Ellis, when on patrol, came across an ARAMCO party in territory that he regarded as belonging to the Eastern Aden Protectorate. He instructed the party to return to Saudi Arabia, which they did. Boustead later told him that the Saudi party had not been across the Violet Line and therefore should not have been ejected. The British Government entered into fresh negotiations with the Saudi Government and arrived at a new demarcation known as the Riyadh Line. It was never made clear whether the Saudis accepted this line, and the threat of Saudi incursion remained high.

Mike left Thamud on 9 January 1954, handing leadership of the party to Don Beydoun. He travelled to Markaz Hajar, a driving time of 14 hours. Stopping overnight near an overhang, he was making ready his camp bed when a host of camel ticks rushed out, forcing him to retreat to the Land Rover. After removing the spare wheel and letting down the tailboard, the bed fitted and he spent a 'quite comfortable night'.

Mike flew out via the Ghuraf airstrip on 12 January. Before leaving, he wrote a letter to the surveyor, Norman Stansfield, who was passing through Ghuraf on his way to Thamud. After advising 'Stan' to settle new arrangements for purchasing supplies with the merchant Bin Kathir, and pick up the mail from Sei'un, Mike wrote:

> You stay tonight with Bert Fox of Desert Locusts who hopes to play canasta, so do humour him. I suggest you hand out a few of your tinned rations to help with the food. My bed is yours until you get to camp; if you have one with you, please air freight mine to Besse from here, 'to await arrival.'
>
> You have about 95 miles [150 kilometres] to Markaz Hajar in Raidat Sei'ar, then 227 miles [365 kilometres] to Thamud. Total driving time Hajar-Thamud on my last trip was 14 hours, with one night stop.
>
> Do most of the driving yourself for the car's sake, especially from the water pool (El Kareef) to Thamud, though the last 60 miles [90 kilometres] is not too bad. Advise you to let the Bedford go in front.
>
> Wish you all good luck – they're a bunch of mad bastards in Thamud.

YEARS LATER, MENTION of Thamud would conjure up very different memories, ones of an event that profoundly affected the morale of the geologists.

It will be recalled that the expedition had set off without Gilbert Todd, the young geologist who had fallen ill and was hospitalized in Aden. Expecting Gilbert to be joining them at Sei'un, the party arrived to find no sign of him and no news of his progress. In a letter to Peter Besse, Mike wrote:

> I was disappointed to find neither Todd nor mail on today's aircraft and, far worse, no explanation. However, not knowing the position, I'm writing this to you in case Gilbert is either west-bound or bed-bound … if Todd is fit he should now travel to Ghuraf on 5th January, which is the earliest we can collect him. It is not worth him waiting here in Wadi Hadhramaut.

Gilbert arrived at Ghuraf on 12 January, apparently recovered from his illness, in the company of Norman Stansfield, both bound for the Thamud camp. They met briefly with Mike at the airstrip before going their separate ways: Mike returning to London and Gilbert and Norman travelling on to Thamud.

When Gilbert rejoined the field party, nothing seemed to be amiss and the survey went ahead as planned. Peewee and Adrian left on 2 March, and Don and Gilbert set about mapping the Habashiya-Qarat Waggi area. But during a sandstorm in the night of the 5/6 March, Gilbert became ill and they returned to the camp at Thamud. Gilbert's condition deteriorated and, when he became seriously ill, an RAF air evacuation was arranged for the morning of 9 March. Six days later, Don received the distressing news of Gilbert's death in Aden.

It was a loss that the geologists would never forget.

Peewee, Don Beydoun and Adrian Humphreys on the Thamud expedition, 1953

A street scene in Mukalla, 1953: colour section p. iii
The Wadi Hadhramaut, Eastern Aden Protectorate (EAP): colour section p. iv
Bedouins taking water from the well at El Kareef, EAP: colour section p. iv
Peewee joining the dance: colour section p. v
The Bedouin well at Thamud: colour Section p. vi

---

1   With permission of Curtis Brown on behalf of the Wilfred Thesiger Estate, Copyright © Wilfred Thesiger Estate, 1959
2   Letter from D. M. Morton to F. E. Wellings, dated 25 October 1953, IPC 119 PC/44 Part 4 (258), BP Archive.
3   Ibid.
4   Adrian Humphreys' recollections.
5   Ibid.
6   Ibid.
7   See Z. R. Beydoun, *The Stratigraphy and Structure of the Eastern Aden Protectorate*, London, 1964.

Chapter 13: Duqm Expeditionary Force

Southern Oman, February–May 1954

'The leader who had 400 men would win.'

Ancient Omani belief

Throughout the early history of petroleum exploration in southern Arabia, with all its tortuous manoeuvrings and political dead-ends which seemed to make progress impossible at times, the resolve of IPC to explore the interior of Oman remained undimmed. In the midst of setbacks, moments of hope combined with an enduring faith in the presence of oil beneath the ground brought confidence that it was only a matter of time before the Company would find and eventually extract oil. 'The area in question is ideally located geologically for the occurrence of oil pools,' wrote the Chief Geologist of the Company.[1]

But the presence of Saudi forces in Hamasa ruled out an approach from the north, and a landing on the southern coast presented great difficulties. Any survey party would be at risk of attack from the hostile tribes of the interior, and estimates of the size of a military force necessary to protect it had quickly swelled from 25 to more than 250 men.

The Company had taken advice from Wilfred Thesiger, who cautioned against the Company attempting such an endeavour:

A landing on that coast with intent to examine the hinterland, protected by armed guards, would not be possible and, in fact, would be highly dangerous if attempted and would be resisted.[2]

It would be tantamount to the invasion of a hostile and foreign country. As if to settle the matter, the Sultan himself declared that 'the area in question is not safe for the Company's work.'[3] So the Company abandoned its hopes of launching an expedition and let matters rest for a while.

One gets a sense of activity taking place behind the scenes in the spring of 1953: Mike being told to prepare for a top-secret expedition, and references to a mysterious operation known as DEF starting to appear in official correspondence. The Company acquired a number of tank and infantry landing-craft, ex-World War II stock, in preparation for a landing on the southern coast of Oman, and outlined an area from Ras Duqm and Ras ru-Wais for investigation of a possible landing site. All that was lacking was detailed information about beach conditions.

At that time, knowledge of the Omani coast was sparse. In 1926 a geological survey party had landed opposite the islet of Hamr el Nafur, where oil seepages had been reported, only to be greeted by a hail of stones.

In the late summer of 1953, in secrecy, a team of Company personnel was assembled in Qatar with the aim of investigating the Omani coast. One of their number carried a valuable reference book:

Jacko was found to be studying an ancient book called *Slave Catchers in Oman* or some such title, by an early-Victorian RN captain who ran an anti-slaver patrol off Oman, was wrecked in a gale, and miraculously landed on the only shallow stretch for a long way in either direction. It seems he made his way along the coast to a settlement – that was a miracle in itself, since the Rub al Khali sweeps down almost to the sea in those parts – and after difficult parleys with somewhat hostile natives, made his way to safety and to authorship of his book, *with maps*.[4]

Thus equipped, a small advance party travelled to Dubai. One night, in the midst of a thick fog, the party set out from Dubai creek in a motor dhow and joined *MV Jamilla*, one of the Company's tank landing-craft that was anchored a short distance from the shore. The vessel travelled down the coast beyond Muscat to a wild and desolate shore, inhabited only by birds and fishermen: the perfect place for a landing of equipment and men.

And this, according to one correspondent, was how the Iraq Petroleum Company, with all the resources at its command, came to settle on the location of the landing point for the expedition, on the bay of Ras Duqm, on the south-eastern shore of the coast of Oman.

THE POLITICAL SITUATION in Oman remained volatile, with the Sultan's rule still uncertain in large tracts of his realm and destabilized by the growing Saudi influence on the Imam, and an increasingly strident Arab nationalism emanating from Cairo. Leaking news of a geological expedition to the interior would almost certainly have put the whole venture at risk. The Company had no wish to advertise its plans, but certain provisions had to be made.

First, there was a need to establish contact with the inland tribes. The Duru was perhaps the largest tribe in Oman, and Jebel Fahud lay within their lands. The brief of Edward Henderson, the Company's liaison officer, was subject to one important proviso:

Provided we could gain the support of the Duru and keep it, using a landing point in the south, we could work at Fahud and at other sites in the area and find out whether or not oil was there.[5]

Since without the Sultan's authority there was no channel of communication with the tribes, no contact was possible, and their possible reaction to an expedition remained an unknown factor. So the idea of a militia began to take root, and a new force of levies, the Muscat and Oman Field Force (MOFF), was created. But there were problems in raising a military force from scratch: by the time the force had reached 75 in number, 10 were imprisoned and 15 deserted. According to one report the entire force deserted, complete with uniforms and weapons, only to be rounded up a little later by a few officers. The commanding officer went off on leave, never to return, and was duly replaced by Percy Coriat,[6] aged 54, a former British Army soldier with a black patch over his right eye.

According to Percy Coriat's account,[7] when he arrived in Oman in December 1953, the existing force was in a parlous state, the troops spending 'their time either sitting in tents or loafing in Sohar town'. Force armament comprised British Army surplus stores, Vickers machine-guns, Bren guns, 4-inch mortars, .303 rifles and Mills grenades. Transport comprised three jeeps and three trucks. The levies' training proceeded apace and the Company began running convoys from Sharjah to Sohar to supply the force with more trucks and equipment.

The Sultan pushed on with his plans for a force under the leadership of Coriat. It *had* to be a force of 400 men, as the Sultan explained to Henderson: 'This, he said, was a mystic figure in Omani battles. The leader who had 400 men would win; he would almost be allowed to win and probably without the need for any fighting.'[8]

As Henderson pointed out, there would be major difficulties in gathering and maintaining such a large body of men in the primitive wilds of Oman. But the Sultan was adamant: 400 men it would have to be.

By January, the Company had confirmed Duqm as the landing place for the expedition. The Sultan gave permission for a landing – but no more than that – and the final preparations were under way. Coriat had a force of 120 men, not fully trained and well below the mystic figure of 400, but a force nevertheless.

LONDON WAS COLD, 'bloody cold', wrote Mike. It was January 1954 and he was now back in London, having just returned from the Thamud expedition. The freezing weather was something of a shock to his system: he had not experienced a UK winter for eight years. Now, instead of surveying rock formations and driving through palm-decked wadis, he was gazing up at the grey facades of office buildings and department stores, passing through streets crowded with unsmiling people and fume-spewing motor cars, the unwelcome end product of petroleum exploration. But it is likely that Mike was too preoccupied to take much notice of these things. Based in the IPC office in 214 Oxford Street, he was writing up his last field report and preparing for the operation to gain access to Jebel Fahud, code-named DEF.

No-one is certain today what the initials DEF stood for. An earlier IPC project, the Syrian pipeline, had been named ABC, so perhaps DEF signified the next major operation to be undertaken. Privately, among Company personnel, the operation became known as the Duqm Expeditionary Force.

Although Mike had been aware of the operation for over a year, he had been kept in the dark about its final details. On the surface, it was business as usual. He received instructions to travel back to Aden on 4 February with F. E. Wellings (now Chief Geologist of the Company) to stay with the Thamud expedition until 6 March. 'For some reason,' Mike noted, 'Wellings insisted that I go there via Tripoli and Qatar'. Mike was told that the DEF operation was not due to start until the middle of March, and that the very existence of the project was wrapped in secrecy. In correspondence, Mike simply refers to Duqm as 't'other place'. The plan changed quickly, however, and the landing date was brought forward to 15 February.

And so it happened that a small convoy of vessels gathered in the Muscat roads one pleasant evening, including the two landing-craft named *Jesoura* and *Jamila*. One vessel was loaded with stores and personnel, comprising about a hundred MOFF soldiers; the second vessel was loaded with Company personnel and vehicles. Wellings and Mike left Thamud on 9 February, flying to Aden where they were immediately whisked straight from the airport to a third landing-craft, the *Jawada*, which would approach the landing site from the south and rendezvous with the other vessels off Ras Duqm.

Five days later, with the fleet gathered off the coast and the landing party established on the beach, the plans that had been so long in the making seemed at last to be coming together. From the deck of his vessel, Mike – impatient to get on with the survey and seeing little activity on the nearest shore – waited for the signal to board the landing-craft that would ferry the geologists to dry land. The Duqm Expeditionary Force had arrived.

As darkness settled on the Duqm camp a southerly breeze sprang up, stirring up the dust and brushing the beach with flecks of surf. The Company ships lay at anchor some distance from the shore. Their escort *HMS Wild Goose* lay just over the horizon, far enough away to be unseen from the shore but close enough to come to the assistance of the landing party should trouble arise. In fact the landing had gone remarkably smoothly, the only hitch being the Company manager's ducking when he tried to disembark from the landing-craft earlier in the day.[9]

The landing party might not have been so apprehensive if they had had a better knowledge of the local tribe. The Janubah had no greater ambition than to fish the sea and graze their camels. As it was, the expedition had taken out insurance on its way down from Muscat. The convoy had called in at Sohar and picked up Salim bin Nasir, Sheikh of the Janubah tribe. The sheikh's presence with the landing party had undoubtedly helped to smooth the way.

Out in the bay the limestone islet of Hamr el Nafur stood like an emasculated lighthouse, gleaming dimly in the gathering darkness, taking on a fluorescent hue from the centuries of guano deposited on its rocky surface.

The tents had been pitched, bedding, food, cooking utensils unpacked, and the generators were up and running. Drums containing drinking water had been rolled in from the ships. The camp itself was set in a horseshoe-shaped enclave, with a flat *sabkha* in the centre. Several piles of assorted fish bones and seashells, whitened by the Arabian sun, were dotted around the camp, and a few derelict mud-huts, once used by the fishermen but now abandoned, lay close by.

Unloading the fuel supplies, heavy equipment and remaining vehicles – Nubian trucks, Dodge Power Wagons and Land Rovers – would take another four or five days to complete. At certain times it was tricky since the shallows were extensive and unloading could only be attempted with safety on a high tide. With the onset of low tide, the ships would retreat out to sea, where they would lie at anchor away from the shoals.

The evening breeze came as a welcome relief for all of those in the Company camp, for it lifted the smell of stinking fish that had pervaded Duqm Bay all day. On a large rock, a short distance from where the expedition had landed earlier in the day, the local fishermen would spread their gutted catch to dry under the hot sun. As it was, the breeze would provide only a temporary respite from the pungent smell – it would return the next morning and remain to haunt those left behind to establish a more permanent Company base at Duqm. The rock had quickly become known as 'Stinking Fish Rock',[10] but perhaps Mike, inured by years of working in the distinctly fishy environment of the Aden Protectorates, hardly noticed the smell.

In other circumstances the Duqm site might not have been a good choice for a landing. A natural harbour, perhaps, framed by Ras Duqm to the south and Stinking Fish Rock to the north, the bay gave adequate protection for the unloading operations to take place when the weather was good. But there was no fresh water in the immediate area, only a single, brackish well at Nafun where the 100 or so men of the Muscat and Oman Field Force had made their camp. The troops were still very inexperienced and help was not close at hand. Muscat lay approximately 400 kilometres to the north, and the British Colony of Aden some 1,600 kilometres to the south-west. The very isolation of Duqm, however, was also its best advantage:

there was no chance of the Company's presence being advertised from its far and desolate shore.

In the Company camp, Nick Fallon and Mike were busying themselves with the final preparations for their first trip into the interior.

Nick was a senior surveyor with the Company, about 1.8 metres tall with dark hair, who wore thick, black-rimmed glasses. He presented the appearance of a typical 'boffin', and had the intellect to match, being clever with a sharp wit. Rather belying his sedentary lifestyle, Nick was competent in the desert. Mike had first met him in Lebanon in 1948, then again in Oman the following year when they had both witnessed the 'shoot-up' in the Wadi Jizzi (p. 100). Astrofixing, observing the stars to determine terrestrial position, and the triangulation of potential oil structures such as Jebel Fahud, were Nick's specialities.

Nick had a dry sense of humour. On one occasion Mike arranged to meet him at a pinpoint rendezvous on the plains of the Jiddat al Harasis. As Mike described it:

> I said to Nick, 'We should meet again.'
>
> 'Why not?' he said. 'On the Jidda at point A, 12 noon on Tuesday. I'm off to the north west,' and off he went.
>
> On the Tuesday, I arose with a sad feeling: fill the tank, check the tyres, say goodbye and make bloody sure that the remaining geologists knew where I intended to go.
>
> I set off and all went well – car, watch, and eyes, thirty square miles [78 square kilometres] of the Jidda and I had to find Nick by midday. By half-eleven, I was pretty sure I was near – but in flat land, where is near? I took a right turn because – because why – I'll never know. I was wrong. I drove reciprocal, back on a course west and after five minutes found a patch of shade, from which Nick emerged.
>
> Time: 12:05.
>
> Nick said: 'You're late.'

The Duqm camp lay on the southern edge of the Hugf, an area of exposed ancient rocks lying on the eastern edge of the plateau known as the Jiddat al Harasis (see Geological Map of Oman *ante* p. 97). The rocks in the Hugf were exposed, described by another member of the expedition as 'a lunar-like landscape essentially devoid of human life, an area to be treated with respect and caution'.[11] In the Hugf they would find the routes were universally bad, and the going was a severe test for the motor vehicles.

The area of the survey could be divided into two roughly separate climatic zones: the Hugf and the Jiddat al Harasis. The Hugf was controlled by the influence of the sea. The temperature here rose from February through to June, when the breaking of the monsoon caused rapid cooling. During this period there would be heavy condensation at night, with consequent corrosion of metallic items. Rain, however, was recorded just once, rumoured to be the first in five years. On the Jidda, the temperature was usually much higher than on the coast (47 degrees Centigrade being recorded by Nick Fallon in early April). Nights were generally dry, but towards the end of the season and the approach of the monsoon, a southerly wind brought heavy condensation with mists which sometimes dispersed as late as nine o'clock in the morning. Shimmer, owing to high temperature in the middle of the day, would prove trying when surveying, especially towards the end of the season.

THE START OF an expedition was always an exciting time for Mike, and the sense of adventure he had felt on his very first expedition had not diminished over the years. A map spread across the top of a packing crate or table, its corners secured from the evening breeze by a geological hammer, a rock, a heavy compass and a hissing paraffin lamp; the camp still in some state of confusion; a generator chugging in the background as men still worked in a patchwork of light from flares and vehicle head-lamps; equipment spread about; people coming and going around an open tent, some looking for cutlery and blankets from a crate in the corner of the camp, others dropping off more boxes onto the ground. These were the universal images of the start of an expedition. The only sound that was missing on this expedition was the snorting and groaning of camels as they settled down for the night.

Mike and Nick would have examined the maps, such as they were, drawn from aerial photographs. 'Don't go that way, you fool,' Nick would say, pointing to some uncharted area such as Umm as Samim, 'the mother of poisons', reputed to be quicksands which could swallow men and camels whole.

Their maps had plenty of gaps, and the survey data were sparse in places. As Mike's previous exploits showed, 'getting in on the ground' could be a difficult exercise. Oman was a large, inhospitable country, with about 15 per cent of the surface being mountainous and the remainder wadi and desert. The interior was cut off by mountains on one side, and by desert on the other. But a wadi in full flood would subside and be traversed in time; mountain ranges would eventually fall under the geologist's hammer; and even the remorseless sands of the Rub al Khali could be overcome with detailed organization and planning.

Knowledge of the tribes of the interior was sketchy, to say the least. Bertram Thomas and Wilfred Thesiger had both travelled these parts, using tribesmen to negotiate their way across desert plains and through mountain passes. When the Janubah showed no antipathy towards the expedition, it was a good start. But the Janubah were hostile towards the Whahibi, who controlled territory along the coast to the north.

The Harasis were a nomadic tribe of small, wiry and desert-hardy tribesmen who, it was said, subsisted for three months a year on the milk of camels and goats. The Duru controlled the territory around the Jebel Fahud and Natih anticlines. With the expedition's activities initially restricted to the area around Duqm and to the south, it was still impossible to establish contact with the Duru – except through the Sultan's representatives who appeared to be making little progress in the matter.

News of a visit from the Sultan in March raised the geologists' expectations: it was hoped that he would allow the expedition to proceed northwards towards Jebel Fahud. In the meantime, the geologists were free to explore the southern Hugf, and the Jiddat al Harasis to the west and south.

'Don't go that way you fool!' These words would come back and haunt the expedition. Mike had two maps to consider: the map spread out across on the crate in front of him, marked in several places 'Relief Data Incomplete', and the map in his head, the one without trigonometric points and few reference points, a map of tribal allegiances that was constantly shifting, just like the sands of Umm as Samim were believed to be.

THE COMPANY'S PLANS had been well prepared, but there was one potential flaw. The Imam, a xenophobic religious leader, held sway over the hearts and minds of the majority of tribes in the interior, particularly those around Jebel Akhdar, and any move against him would be at the risk of civil war. The current Imam was Mohammed bin Abdullah.

The Imam was the leader of the Ibadhis, a religious sect that had split from mainstream Islam. Descended from two Khawarij who settled in Oman in 657 AD, the movement flourished, despite attempts by Caliphs to crush it. The Ibadhis believed in electing their leader from among their number, and had done so for hundreds of years, occasionally leaving gaps between the death of one and the election of another. They also believed that God was not a 'He' but an indescribable.

By the Treaty of Sib, signed in 1920, the Sultan and the Imam had arrived at an agreement. This involved dual and separate sovereignty: in the words of the British Political Agent at the time, this 'had done more to alienate the interior and to prevent the Sultans from re-establishing their authority than all the rest put together'.[12] By the early 1950s, the extent of the Sultan's authority over the Imam's followers comprised just the issue of passports, the receipt of customs dues and the submission of appeals to the Muscat Supreme Court. Otherwise, the inland tribes were subject to the Imam's rule.

Understandably, the Sultan was not prepared to give the green light for an advance on Jebel Fahud until his troops were fully trained, and they were a long way from being ready. Coriat had been forced to let a number of levies and Adeni officers go, leaving the force undermanned and without enough junior officers. In truth, the 'mystic 400' were now a depleted 100.

The Company was walking a tightrope. If it did nothing, the commercial initiative would be lost. If it pursued its plans, it ran the risk of being accused of furthering British imperialism in the region. In the worst scenario, the appearance of MOFF soldiers on the beach at Duqm would provoke a strong reaction from the Imam and inflame the Arab world. Although the landings raised a formal protest from the Imam, however, it soon became apparent that there would be no major resistance at this stage:

> The Imam sent a formal letter of protest to Major Chauncy, the Consul General at Muscat, who replied that the whole matter was a commercial arrangement between the PDO [Petroleum Development Oman Ltd] and the Sultan. There was some talk of wild action, but the only measure taken was by Suleiman bin Hamyar and the Janubah Sheikh Yasir, who ordered a messenger to hoist white Imamate flags in some of the coastal villages. Subsequent to-ing and fro-ing between the representatives of the Imam and the Sultan led to nothing conclusive.[13]

ONE MORNING, MIKE and Nick left the camp and drove up a camel track to the plateau, reaching it just as the heat of the morning sun was starting to be felt. Here was a vast, featureless gravel plain, stretched farther than the eye could see to the edge of the great desert, the Rub al Khali. This was the Jiddat al Harasis, a Tertiary-capped plateau crossed by a few dry wadis, occupied by nomads and precious little else.

Mike did not record the moment when he saw the Jiddat al Harasis for the first time, probably because he was too busy helping set up camp, ordering stores, exploring the hinterland and writing up geological reports. But we can imagine what it must have been like looking through Mike's eyes: gazing in the direction of Jebel Fahud, which lay over the horizon some 300 kilometres to the north. It was an alluring prospect for an ambitious geologist. Mike and Nick had doubtless discussed the fabled Fahud many times. Since the debacle at Wadi Jizzi they had waited five years to get another chance to reach the Leopard Mountain. The sun-compass, a wire rod fixed to the centre of the bonnet of their Land Rover, aligned in the direction of Leopard Mountain; shadows cast by a few rocks and scrub trees running away to their left; a wide, blue sky and a gravel plain: these few brushstrokes framed their first view of the Jiddat al Harasis.

If the survey had been a race, and a line drawn in the sand in front of them, this would have been the starting grid, their engines metaphorically revving as they waited for the starter's flag to fall. But it was no race, there were no revving engines and the Jidda lay in stark isolation all around them. This was no time for idle speculation but, for a moment at least, they might have reminisced about the last time they had attempted to 'get in on the ground', through the Dhahira plain to the north.

Nick swung the vehicle round towards the edge of the scarp, and driving northwards along it headed for a settlement called Nafud some 25 kilometres along the coast. Here, it was reported, the Janubah had a well. On the Jidda the going was good, generally on a surface of Miocene rock dusted by sand.

Supplies of fresh water were vital, of course, and the search for reliable supplies exercised the geologists in the early days of the survey. Although the water supply for the initial stage of the operation was mainly drawn from sea distillation units, the monsoon broke the sea-line later on in the summer. At Nafun (as opposed to Nafud) where the MOFF soldiers had established their first base, the wells proved adequate to keep the main camp supplied with water. Wells were sunk in Wadi Sai and to the north. At Ajayay two wells were drilled, the first being abandoned after striking water when the sand-line parted and the bailer became jammed in the hole. The second well struck water at a depth of 125 metres and went on to produce a water flow of 700 litres an hour.

Nor was Duqm the ideal place for a runway. A short landing strip had been established along a patch of hardened mud, or *sabkha*, a few hundred metres from the camp. The strip was adequate for small Dove aircraft, but not for hard-standing since the ground water level rose and fell with the tides. On one occasion, a Dove had sunk into the mud and needed full power to taxi out of the ruts to get airborne. As a result, landings were restricted to low tide. This situation could not be allowed to continue indefinitely.

Food supplies, with the exception of locally purchased fish (channard, *amour* and crayfish), were all imported by sea or air, under the control of the Commissariat Department of the Company. Heavy supplies all came by sea, but sea operations were cancelled from April onwards because of high seas caused by the advent of the monsoon. Petrol was brought from Aden by motor dhows chartered by Besse and Company, and a limited amount of foodstuffs was brought from Muscat in motor dhows by Messrs Khimji Rhamdas, contractors to the MOFF. Although deep water was available out in Duqm Bay, the necessity of having barges or landing-craft to ferry materials ashore was both time- and labour-consuming.

The Duqm camp was established. A routine of mundane domesticity was complemented each morning by the sight of a large man perched on a rock performing his ablutions, a picture 'reminiscent of a vulture eating his first meal of the day'.[14]

The first major geological reconnaissance of the Jiddat al Harasis began on 24 February 1954. The geologists piled up three Land Rovers with enough equipment and supplies for five days in the desert. There were camp beds, canvas wash basins, cooking utensils, kettles, tea and coffee pots, plates, cups, saucers, glasses, thermos jars, knives, forks, spoons, lamps and torches. Leader of the party was Dick Browne, Senior Geologist, Persian Gulf, accompanied by Mike as Area Geologist of DEF, Nick Fallon, Edward Henderson and Colonel Percy Coriat. The party had two drivers, six levies and six Bedouin guards. They left the camp in a convoy of Dodge Power Wagons and Land Rovers, together with a one-ton Austin truck, and followed the same camel track on to the Jidda as Mike and Nick Fallon had done a few days before.

While they were away, a new arrival landed on the Duqm shore. One of the first tasks undertaken by Don Sheridan,[15] was to accompany the transport engineer Frank Purvis and a local sheikh to find a suitable alternative to the existing airstrip. This they located on the firmer gravels, close to the camp and on the fringe of Wadi Sai. After clearing the airstrip, Duqm was tied into normal Company service flights (once a week) by Viking aircraft from Sharjah and the RAF Station on Masira Island.

By the time Don met Mike on his return from the Jidda expedition, the desert had already taken its toll of Mike's features. His red face almost matched his red hair, and his nose was burnt and cracked by the sun. Mike would take to wearing an Arab headdress during his forays into the desert, and found this and his fluent Arabic helped to build up a rapport with the local tribesmen. But, as Don described it, Mike's personality could swing between the ebullient and the dour, and he could give short shrift to anyone who wasted his time. This is perhaps why the tribesmen would refer to him 'Shaib al-Ahmar', or the 'Angry Red Man'.

Don's arrival at Duqm was followed by a longer excursion to the southern reaches of the Jidda, where interesting surface features known as the J and K Alphabeticals had been identified from the air. This area bordered the Dhofar province and, at that time, the boundary was uncertain. Cities Service Company had started drilling for oil at Marmul. Alphabeticals J and K were almost certainly Qaarharail and Marmul, well within the Dhofar concession which had been assigned to Cities Service in 1953. The IPC geologists shouldn't have been there – and perhaps they knew that.

Two more geologists, Peewee Melville and Adrian Humphreys, arrived from Thamud via Aden, bringing the field exploration team up to five. They were then joined by two senior Company officials, Dr F.R.S. Henson and Max Chatton, both palaeontologists, who worked with Adrian and Peewee on the Hugf, while Mike and Don returned to working on the Jidda.

There was an element of 'marking time'. The prospect of Fahud beckoning them over the horizon must have been difficult to resist; some members of the expedition, it was said, were tempted to make a flying visit to the structure in March, regardless of the Duru. But they held back, recognizing that any expedition towards the interior would have to await the approval of the Sultan who was due to arrive from Salalah by sea.

By all accounts, the 'frankincense Sultan', so described by James Morris in *Sultan in Oman* because of the soft scent of frankincense emanating from his person, was a small man, urbane, courteous, softly spoken and well informed. On this day, 18 March 1954, standing on the deck of *HMS Flamingo* to receive his visitors, he presented an impressive sight. He wore a full-length white robe covered by a brown, gold-edged *aba* draped across his shoulders. His dark face was set against a full beard of black with grey and white streaks, and a brightly coloured turban wrapped around his head. For ceremonial purposes, he wore a richly ornamented *khanja* that was strapped to his plump waist by a belt of yellow cloth, and in his right hand he held a thin camel stick.

The day was bright and breezy. On the shore, the Sultan's visit was an occasion for celebration. Fishermen watched along the beach and Whahibi and Janubah tribesmen, their differences settled for the day, lined up in a discordant group, hollering and randomly firing shots in the air. In a quieter group, the men of the MOFF, a specially picked selection of soldiers dressed in fatigue kit, stood on parade in lines outside their tents. From the Company camp, a small crowd of Company employees stood looking on.

A small supply boat, carrying senior Company, political and military officials, was dispatched through a moderate surf and drew up alongside the anchored ship. The dignitaries clambered aboard, anxious to set the right impression and get on with promoting the Company's case for extending field operations farther inland.

Among this group was Percy Coriat, the officer commanding the MOFF, no doubt praying that his scratch force would give a good account of itself. The small boat heaved under the strain of carrying seven large men and the Sultan as it chugged towards the shore. Upon arriving, the Sultan, retaining what little dignity he could in the circumstances, climbed out and alighted on the beach.

The tribesmen formed two lines facing each other and performed a slow, shuffling dance,[16] chanting as the lines approached each other and then disengaging, retreating in a rhythmic, swaying motion, while the younger men ran into the gap and danced a whirling, more frenzied, ballet. After several repeats, the dance ended in a round of enthusiastic cheers for the Sultan, who was then surrounded by his loyal subjects and led away from the fading crackle and smoke of musket shots in the air.

The ceremonials proceeded at a gentler pace after that. Coriat first led the Sultan towards the camp where the officers were drawn up in line outside the Mess tent and introduced them in turn. According to Coriat[17], the Sultan shook hands with all four of them without comment, but as they were marching away he asked: 'What is the name of the fat officer?' Coriat told him, and they continued their tour:

> We walked towards the men's tents where the men were drawn up in two extended lines facing outwards. Fifty yards from the front row the Sultan stopped – 'Are those the soldiers?'
> 'Yes, Your Highness. Would you care to walk down the lines?'
> 'I do not think it necessary for me to see any more of them on this occasion.'

The tour finished with an inspection of the oil camp and an entertainment in the evening, laid on by Sheikh Nasir in a marquee erected within the camp perimeter.

However, the Sultan was not impressed. He had expected to find the Company drilling for oil but there was no rig to be seen; he had hoped to find an efficient military force but found only boys in their place; and then Percy Coriat had suddenly announced his intention to leave the Sultan's service in six months' time.

Back on board *HMS Flamingo* the Sultan wrote a letter to Henderson, to be delivered after the frigate set sail:

> I regret I do not see my way to agree to your penetration at present to the whole limit which we discussed yesterday until we have a full force at the beach-head.

The effect on the expedition was crippling. 'He could hardly have made his point more clearly,' wrote a tight-lipped Henderson.[18]

The Sultan's decision came as a bombshell to the expedition: all travel north of latitude 20 degrees 30' was forbidden. Jebel Fahud was out-of-bounds, and there was no certainty about when, if ever, they would be given permission to travel north. To the south, a feature called the Black Ridge (at the end of the plain on the watershed), was used as a boundary point. The view from higher up the Company tree was that good fortune would prevail in the end – but the restrictions left the geological party demotivated, a condition that the increasingly enervating climate did not help to alleviate.

There was no time to dwell on the problem, however. F. E. Wellings arrived, the situation was reviewed, and new plans formulated; the J and K Alphabeticals still needed to be investigated. Feature J was an almost circular depression, elongated ENE–WSW and open on the west side, surrounded by a rim of Qara limestone; feature K showed a similar structure. After discussing the aerial reconnaissance photographs of the Alphabeticals with the geologists, Wellings decided that the party should concentrate its efforts on mapping the area. So they set off – Mike, Nick, Don, Peewee and Adrian – in a southerly direction, across the Jiddat al Harasis once more.

ONE DAY IN the field was much like another, but the harsh conditions were always challenging. How they managed to cope varied according to each individual. 'We were all slightly unbalanced,' wrote Don Sheridan[19], who described the routine of their desert life:

> A typical day began at about 5:30 a.m. Mike would normally be up first to give the cook and the rest of us a shake. If Mike hadn't called us at this time, we would surely have been awakened by the moisture seeping through our sleeping bags, for condensation was always heavy and on some days a thick white mist persisted for several hours.[20]

Water was carried in 40-gallon [182 litre] drums, or in the Commer tanks. Since no water supplies had been provided along the route, water was strictly rationed. A proper wash was considered something of a luxury, taken just once a week. Otherwise, washing was a cursory affair.

They would enjoy a cup of tea and a light breakfast, then set off in the Land Rovers to the area of the survey:

> Peewee and I worked the instruments while Mike and Adrian placed the stadia rods on features of geological interest. Observing became difficult after a few hours of work, the image of the rod becoming unreadable, dissolving and rejoining in the shimmer. Most mornings we had called a halt by nine-thirty for by then tears would be streaming from our eyes in our attempts to decipher the instrument readings.[21]

After a combined breakfast and lunch the rest of the day was spent trying to keep cool, as Don explained:

My favourite position was beneath a Nubian truck, simply because its ground clearance was such that you didn't bang your head in turning over. Mike made slow progress with a paperback edition of a book by Balzac, though personally I found that it was too hot or too bright to read. You would doze fitfully to awake drenched in sweat, with clinging clothes on chest, back and thighs, and a film of wet dust where your legs had touched the ground. Breathing was slow and laboured, for your lungs protested at the searing heat. Thirst always came at about three o'clock ...[22]

The camp would stir at four o'clock for a hot cup of tea, then Mike would make radio contact with Duqm.

The heat of the day having subsided the party would return to the survey, working until the late evening and returning to the camp in darkness. The nights were cold. They would gather around a fire dressed in thick clothing to enjoy a slug or two of whisky served in tin mugs before the evening meal – usually bully-beef, salmon, sardines, tinned stew or stew – was dished up. Owing to the lack of suitable tents, the party slept in the open.

THERE WAS A number of excursions to the north and south of Duqm, geological surveys combined with laying trails in the desert for others to follow. There were no problems with security, and relations with the local Janubah tribesmen were cordial. Mike still carried a box of Maria Theresa dollars around with him, kept safely in the toolbox of his Land Rover.

Adrian missed ten days of these excursions owing to a 'dysentarious condition in the nether regions', a condition that in his opinion had resulted from his drinking beer rather than the whisky the others had been drinking that had destroyed the offending bugs.

On their final return to Duqm on 17 May, the geologists celebrated Don's birthday by throwing a party:

Mike and Peewee provided music on a flute and mouth-organ, and Jack Lynan, the water-well driller, sang many songs in his fine bass voice: *Buddy can you spare a dime?*, *Red Sails in the Sunset, South of the Border,* or a host of similar songs can evoke instant recall and memories of that night and the company present.[23]

The geological season was drawing to a close: the party had surveyed the Hugf and the Jiddat al Harasis. In the Alphabeticals, no oil indication was found. Now the weather was unbearably hot, making fieldwork impossible, and the monsoon season was whipping up *shamals* across the Jidda, making travel arduous. It was time to break camp: Mike flew out on 31 May and returned to Qatar.

With the Sultan and the Imam at an impasse, and the expedition confined to the area south of the 20 degrees 30' line of latitude, the geologists knew that the real object of their expedition, the Jebel Fahud, was as far out of reach as ever. The mirage had disappeared – without any promise of returning.

Jesoura offloading on Duqm beach: colour section p. vi
Mike at Duqm Camp: colour section p. vii
18 March 1954, tribesmen line up to greet the Sultan at Duqm: colour section p. viii
The Sultan arriving on the Duqm shore: colour section p. viii
The Sultan strides along the shore with various advisers in tow: colour section p. ix
The tribesmen celebrate his arrival with dancing: colour section p. ix

1   N. E. Baker to S. H. Longrigg, letter dated 5 July 1949, PC27 Part 5 (189), BP Archive.
2   Stephen Longrigg to Dr W. L. F. Nuttall of the Ministry of Fuel and Power, letter dated 20 May 1949. Longrigg describes Thesiger as one 'who acts for us as an advance agent for exploring the wilder areas', PC/27 Part 5 (157) BP Archive.
3   Ibid.
4   Frank Wright 'Early Days in Oman and Dhofar', IPC newsletter No.5 January 1975, by permission of the IPC Society.
5   Edward Henderson, *This Strange Eventful History*, p. 90 (expanded and republished as *Arabian Destiny – The Complete Autobiography* – for publisher details, please refer to 'Acknowledgements' p. 258).
6   Coriat ran away from school to join up in 1914. After serving in Gallipoli and Palestine, he was awarded the DCM and Croix de Guerre. He joined the Sudan Political Service in 1922 and received the Order of the Nile and MBE in 1930. From 1946 he was employed in Libya, staying on after independence as adviser to the Governor of Tripolitania until resigning in 1953.
7   Percy Coriat, *A Soldier in Oman*. Excerpts reprinted with permission of the Bodleian Library of Commonwealth and African Studies at Rhodes House, ref: GB 0162 MSS.Afr.s.1684, Micr. Afr.572.
8   Edward Henderson, *This Strange Eventful History*, p. 89.
9   See the Prologue.
10 According to Percy Coriat in *A Soldier in Oman*, p. 51.
11 Don Sheridan, *Fahud – The Leopard Mountain*, 2000.
12 R. E. L. Wingate, Confidential No. 2052 in I.O L/P & S/10/427.
13 John Wilkinson, *The Imamate Tradition of Oman*, Cambridge University Press, p. 297.
14 Adrian Humphreys' recollections.
15 Don Sheridan had served in England and Germany with the Parachute Regiment and had then graduated from Trinity College before joining IPC as an exploration geologist in 1953. His book *Fahud – The Leopard Mountain*, provides a detailed account of the Fahud expedition.
16 A full description of the dance can be found in Sheridan, *Fahud – The Leopard Mountain*, pp. 30–1.
17 Percy Coriat, *A Soldier in Oman*, p. 64.
18 Edward Henderson, *This Strange Eventful History*, p. 106.
19 Don Sheridan, *Fahud – The Leopard Mountain*, p. 33.
20 Ibid., p. 32.
21 Ibid., p. 33.
22 Ibid., p. 34.
23 Ibid., p. 36.

Shaib al-Ahmar

Chapter 14: Greenaway Gardens

England, May–October 1954

'You want any 'elp with 'im mum?'

From the air, it all looked so insignificant, as the Viking aeroplane climbed into the sky, leaving behind the Duqm camp and following the coastline, the lunar landscape of the Hugf slipping harmlessly by. If Mike had wondered what the next season had in store the barren hinterland gave nothing away. He was no doubt relieved to get away, looking forward to enjoying the relative coolness of an English summer. They flew via Masira Island and Sharjah to Dukhan, where Mike spent a few days before flying on to London with Peewee Melville. Together, they were due to spend the next three months working in the London office writing up reports of the Oman trip.

IPC Headquarters Cartoon

Mike and Heather moved into Greenaway Gardens, NW3, soon after his return to London. They had been given a list of possible apartments from the IPC, and looked at a couple of places, but the ground-floor flat in Greenaway Gardens was obviously the best choice. It was in a large house in a pleasant, quiet and tree-lined road. Like many of the houses in the street this one gave the impression of having seen better days. It had been turned into flats, but they were all well maintained and, in Heather's words, 'there certainly wasn't a run-down look about the place when we arrived'.

The landlady was an elderly woman in a dressing gown who occupied a bed in a room upstairs accompanied by two Pekinese and a lot of gin bottles. Apart from the week or two before Mike and Heather ended their tenancy, she did not stir from her room. There were two permanent maids, one who lived in, and another who appeared to go home to her husband at night.

Mike and Heather had two rooms, a large one downstairs and a similar-sized bedroom upstairs. They also had a small kitchen across a hall, not far from the large kitchen that served the whole house. There were French windows, which opened out on to a large and pleasant garden. This was useful for their six-month-old baby since it was convenient to put his pram outside for his morning nap. There was also a small washing line outside. The lounge was well furnished with good quality items and there was a huge grand piano in the middle of the room. 'I think I upset the landlady by asking her if it couldn't be moved and she certainly refused with some vigour,' said Heather.

The other accommodation in the house comprised another large front room and between the two kitchens were another small bedroom and a laundry room. On the first floor were two large bedrooms, a slightly smaller one occupied by the landlady, and two others, one of them used as a bed-sit. On the top floor was a large flat occupied by four students whom they rarely saw except occasionally late at night – sometimes lying in an inebriated fashion at the bottom of the wide and rather magnificent staircase.

The other inhabitants of the house were an interesting bunch. Heather only really learned something about them when Mike's mother, Lucy, came to stay with her after Mike went back to Oman in October. Heather wrote about her:

She was great at winkling out the gossip and she found out that the man who occupied the little bedroom next to the stairs was in fact the landlady's first husband. He had fallen on bad times and she had agreed to take him in. The landlady had risen from a poor background and improved her status through three marriages – or perhaps 'liaisons' would be a better word. Her second husband was a financier who, according to gossip, was found in the Thames under rather suspicious circumstances. The third was her last, now deceased, who had made a fortune from small shops dotted all over London.

The other large downstairs room and bedroom upstairs had two sets of occupants while Mike and Heather were there. The first were a young married couple and their seven-year-old son. He was in his early 30s, rather portly with dark hair and glasses. She was blond and glamorous. They had a frequent visitor who their son referred to as 'Uncle'. They seemed to have many arguments and at one point she absconded with Uncle, leaving her husband to cope on his own. She did come back after a few weeks, however, and life seemed to go on as before. When they left an American soldier and his supposed wife took their place, though the maids of the household – according to Lucy – suspected that they had never been married.

The bed-sit upstairs was the home of a German girl and her English husband. His first wife had died and they had met just after the war. He was about ten years older than she was. Mike and Heather suspected she might have married him to get out of Germany, but they were a pleasant couple and seemed very fond of each other. They both worked in the city.

The furniture in the house was high class, as was the china. As Heather explained, this was not always a good idea with a young child in the apartment:

One day I broke the landlady's teapot. Later I went upstairs and confessed to her. Understandably she was not pleased and informed me that the tea set had been made by Spode and was the replica of one made for the late Queen Mary. I replied that in that case she should not have allowed her tenants to use such valuable china and perhaps realising the truth of that argument she said no more. However, next day she rose from her sick bed, ordered a taxi and went off to town to get a replacement. The whole episode seemed to put new life into her because for the few weeks before I left she made an appearance every day, even if it was only for a few hours.

While in London, Mike and Heather attended the 'Servants' Ball', as the annual IPC Ball was called – they only went to it twice in all the years Mike was in the Company. It was held at the Grosvenor House, Park Lane, and was a very grand affair: long dresses for the ladies and dinner jackets for the men. They shared a table with a colleague and his wife. There was dinner followed by a floorshow and dancing afterwards. The show consisted of a magician's act, with doves produced from all sorts of unlikely places, and the audience had visions of them being squashed up like concertinas in the magician's sleeves. It was a chance for the geologists to shake the sand from their boots:

By the time the whole evening ended Mike and his colleague were well away and didn't want to leave. The only way we could persuade them was for his wife to take Mike while I steered her husband. When we got outside there was a long queue for taxis but I saw two approaching and desperately flagged them down. We quickly commandeered them, much I'm sure to the annoyance of the people waiting farther down the road. By the time we got back to the house Mike was half asleep and the taxi driver asked solicitously whether 'you want any 'elp with 'im mum'. I replied that I'd be fine and we got into the house. Mike then sat at the bottom of the stairs and said he wasn't going any farther. However a little gentle persuasion got him upstairs where he proceeded to try to get into the wardrobe. I was feeling rather disgusted with him by this time and when he collapsed on the floor I decided to leave him to it, muttering darkly that it served him right if he got pneumonia. At this point Peter said, 'Mummy, what's Daddy doing lying on the floor?' It was quite cold and I ended up by taking pity on him and covering him with some blankets. I'm glad to say that he didn't feel too good next morning.

Chapter 15: Fahud

Central Oman, October 1954–May 1955

'We were looking at a creation of God that few human beings had ever seen.'
Don Sheridan[1]

Aplane-load of Bedouins landing on the Duqm runway in a Dakota must have been an incongruous sight. But these were the Duru sheikhs, dispossessed of their lands, their arrival the trigger for another attempt to advance on Jebel Fahud.

Mike had returned to Duqm at the start of the field season in the autumn. The field party – now consisting of Mike, Jim McGinty, Nick Fallon, Don Sheridan and Rodney Collomb[2] – established a camp at the top of Aqaba Bai, about 50 kilometres from Duqm on 11 October 1954. Conditions were not ideal and, owing to a shortage of tents, the camp was ill-equipped for the five geologists, who were forced to share a single tent. From this base, field mapping and stratigraphic investigation were carried out on the surrounding terrain.

At first there seemed little prospect of improvement over the previous season. The Sultan's prohibition on travel north remained. But elsewhere events were shaping a different destiny for the geological survey. The Imam had died in May, paving the way for the election of 35-year-old Ghalib bin Ali, supported by his ambitious brother, Talib. The mountains east of Ibri and the plains east of Wadi Halfain were inhabited by tribesmen owing allegiance to the Imam, and the Imam's actions had made their neighbours, the Duru tribe, very nervous indeed.

Jebel Fahud lay in the heart of Duru territory. The Duru were said to be able to muster 6,000 rifles. They were mainly centred on Tan'am in the Wadi al Ayn south of Ibri, where the Mahamid Sheikhs, under the paramount leader Ali bin Hilal, owned plantations and kept herds. Ibri was their market town, and the tribe extended north to at least the latitude of Dhank and the south-east of Halfain. Being mainly nomadic, the tribal families pastured their herds along the main wadis in the desert area, but also inhabited the wadis of the Hajar range foothills, particularly the Hamara Duru. In order to gain access to Fahud, the Company would need to work in close co-operation with the Duru sheikhs.

In August a contingent of Duru sheikhs had visited the Sultan's representative in Muscat to swear allegiance to the Sultan in return for a guarantee of assistance in the event of their being attacked by the Imam's forces. Of particular concern was the defence of Ibri and Tan'am, their capital.

It was to little avail: in September the Imam advanced on Ibri, and the Duru sheikhs fled to Sharjah on the Persian Gulf coast. By the time the geologists returned to Duqm for their next field season, a stalemate appeared to persist. Although discussions had taken place about regaining the Duru lands the Sultan appeared not to be fully committed to their cause, despite a guarantee of assistance.

What followed was a game of brinkmanship: the Duru anxious to regain their lands; Percy Coriat anxiously looking over his shoulder for authority to proceed; Henderson constantly negotiating with the sheikhs and Coriat; while the geologists got on with their work. Mike and

Jim McGinty set up a staging post at a site midway between Duqm and Fahud, to be known as Point X, for the storage of water and petrol supplies. Their efforts were not misplaced.

On 16 October 1954 a conference was convened in Duqm by the Company Field Manager, Angus Perks, at which an announcement was made:

> Owing to the occupation of Ibri by troops of the Imam of Nizwa, Ghalib bin Ali, the Mahamid Sheikhs of the Duru tribe have been forced to leave their lands, and now seek help to regain their authority in the area, through the auspices of H.H. the Sultan.
>
> The decision to use troops of the Muscat and Oman Field Force to re-occupy Ibri for the Sultan would, therefore, permit the Company to enter the Duru country, and permission to examine the Fahud anticline was given by the Sheikhs.[3]

On 17 October the Duru sheikhs boarded a plane and flew down to Duqm. Despite Perks' confident assertion that MOFF troops of the would assist the Duru in recapturing Ibri, it is doubtful that the Sultan (or at least the British Consul-General Chauncy and the Sultan's Foreign Minister, Neil Innes) saw it in exactly the same light.

Much was open to interpretation. On the eve of their departure, Percy Coriat announced that instructions received over the radio did not allow him to enter Ibri. But Coriat was open to persuasion and, as the discussions rambled on, he pointed towards Henderson and said: 'We will go to Fahud and argue there.'[4]

So it was that, some eight months after landing at Duqm, the expedition was ready to move on Fahud. The party was split into two groups. The advance guard, a contingent of 46 soldiers led by Major O'Kelly, would leave on 19 October. Included in this convoy were a number of Duru sheikhs, their followers, and members of the geological field party – Jim McGinty, Nick Fallon and Mike, accompanied by Edward Henderson.

They made an early start: the silence of the desert was broken at 4 a.m. by the sound of Land Rovers and trucks warming up. Then it was all go. Mike was busying himself with organizing his party's stores and equipment as men criss-crossed the camp, engaged in diverse activities and with varying degrees of *angst*. Drums of water, jerrycans of fuel, food, tents and equipment were loaded, and then it was time to load the more sensitive human cargo.

A kerfuffle broke out in the column: the seating arrangements for the Duru sheikhs and their followers were under discussion. It much resembled a school excursion with children arguing over the best seats on the bus. The sheikhs wanted a front-seat view and could be so accommodated on the front seats of the Land Rovers and trucks. But there was not enough room in the front for their followers, who considered it a great indignity to have to sit in the back of a truck with the soldiers. The geologists watched and waited, while Edward Henderson patiently negotiated a settlement. At last agreement was reached and the convoy was ready to roll.

Earlier in the year the party had located a better track through the Hugf on to the Jiddat al Harasis that was capable of taking the larger trucks. It was along this track, by way of the Wadi Sai towards the Aqaba Kharma, that the convoy now picked its way. Once on the Jidda it turned north-west, heading through Ajayiz towards the fuel and supply dump at Point X. The morning sun, rising over the desert, may well have raised expectations of a successful outcome.

Early progress was good as the gravel terrain was firm and flat, with little vegetation to impede their progress. The vehicles fanned out as drivers moved across to avoid the dust kicked up by the vehicle in front of them, and the convoy was soon travelling at a reasonable speed across the waterless plain.

Point X could have been anywhere. Noted in the geological report as being at a place called Hailat al Harashif, a desolate spot with a few scrub trees, there was nothing to distinguish it physically from a thousand other places in the desert apart from a collection of fuel drums and jerrycans lying around in the sand. However, relying on tracks of Mike and Jim's vehicle laid down a few days before, they had no difficulty in finding the site again.

They refuelled the vehicles before making camp for the night. Next day they drove across a flat stretch of sand, reaching some 80 kilometres per hour, and then crossed a series of wadis running from east to west where the going was more difficult. They had intended to reach the Wadi Amairi by the end of the second day, but by nightfall had to settle for the Wadi Mussallim, about 25 kilometres short, where they set up another camp.

Their route to Fahud ran along a wide corridor between mountains and desert. To the east, the Omani mountains arced round from the Strait of Hormuz to Ras al Hadd, and detritus from this belt of rugged country had been widely spread across the outlying plains. To the west of the range, the sands of the Rub al Khali formed a natural barrier. Rainfall from the mountains drained south-westerly along three main wadis, Amairi, Aswad and Al Ain, which, together with numerous smaller wadis, emptied into the *sabkha* of Umm as Samim.

Mike's letters reveal how electrified he felt at the thought of exploring new lands, and of meeting the Bedouin who roamed there – and this expedition was no exception. It was a journey into the unknown, the geologists coming to central Oman as if they were discovering the place for the very first time, which, in a geological sense, they were. They knew little about what lay ahead. At the start of their journey there was precious little information to rely on, only that gleaned from the travels of Thesiger, information provided by nomadic tribesmen, and from maps drawn as a result of over-flights.

The sparseness of the desert was to be expected but this gave way to a relatively dense tree belt extending along the courses of the major wadis. The Amairi, for example, was particularly well forested and, for several kilometres between Raqa and Umm as Samim it was difficult, and in parts impossible, for motor transport to pass between the closely spaced, tall acacias. It was, as the geologists reported, well furnished in parts:

> The most common tree in the area is the flat-topped *samr*, a thorny acacia with small leaves, popular grazing for the Bedouin goats. These trees rise 15-20 feet [4.5-6 metres] in the upper reaches of the wadis, the spread of the branches reaching a maximum at the highest point of growth. The Wadi Amairi is dotted with *ghaf* trees, also acacia, but without long spiky thorns. This tree has a long straight trunk that could grow to 25-30 feet [7.5-9 metres] in height. It is very common in the lower reaches of the Wadi Amairi, together with *tarfa* trees. A small, low bush-like dom-palm is common to several of the wadis, providing edible shoots at a certain time of year and the leaves are used by Bedouins for rope-making. Other low plants provide grazing for camels, such as *rak* (*Salvadora peraica*) being common, also *zehra* (*Tribulus*, sp.) and *quassis* (*Cyoerus*, sp.).[5]

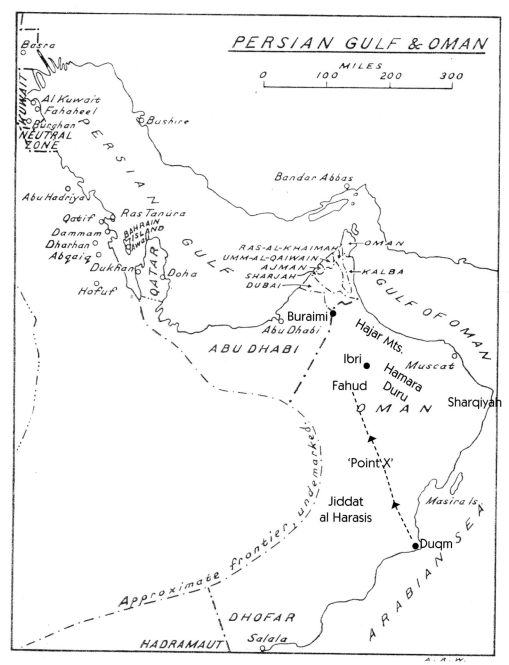

The route taken by the 1954 PDO Expedition
© *Iraq Petroleum Company Limited*

Along the way it looked as if an invisible hand had scooped up the local population and taken it elsewhere – deserted wadis, deserted dwellings – with only a few lizards scuttling for cover under nearby rocks as the convoy trundled by. Since the expedition was unsure of what reception lay ahead, a small group of soldiers went ahead on a recce of the Wadi Amairi. They found a scrawny tribesman cowering by some bushes and asked him what he was doing there. The tribe had left him behind, he explained, to keep watch on the intruders. The Duru had fled the area the day before, the sound of the convoy's engines having been heard long before the first vehicle appeared over the horizon.

At the end of the third day the convoy reached the Wadi Amairi and set up camp at the Muqbira well. Meanwhile, the second party was on its way from Duqm. This comprised a heavier contingent of trucks packed with supplies, another 50 MOFF soldiers under the command of Percy Coriat, the remainder of the Duru sheikhs and their kinsmen, and Company personnel, Angus Perks, Peewee Melville, Don Sheridan, and Rodney Collomb. This second party similarly took the direct route from Duqm to Fahud, much to the surprise of the Duru guides who had expected them to navigate in the traditional Bedu manner, going from one water well to the next.

THE CAMP AT Muqbira well was just over 30 kilometres from the jebel as the crow flies, and the shape of Fahud was visible from the top of a nearby hill. Mike and his boss, Jim McGinty, were determined to make an early sortie to the jebel. Jim was a tall, thin, bespectacled man who had been working in Palestine when Mike arrived there in 1945 and was now Senior Geologist based at Dukhan. In the company of Henderson, Nick Fallon and one 'sleepy' tribesman, they set off early in the morning, heading north-west across the desert.

The low rise of the jebel grew out of the distance; and the whale-like shape they had seen on over-flights now gave way to a more rugged, incised look, erosion having worn away a once-smooth exterior.

The journalist James Morris, on a visit with the Sultan the following year, portrayed the mountain in rather bleak terms:

It gave an impression of great heat and heartlessness, with its tawny rocks and bare, dry hillsides. The effect of it all was portentous, if not ominous; and I did not have to remind myself that this remote and unattractive place might one day be the source of lavish power and wealth almost unimaginable.[6]

As might be expected, the geologists' notes were factual and restrained:

Fahud arches abruptly from the gravels which cover thousands of square kilometres of this desert belt, and reaches maximum elevation of 120 metres above the surrounding plain, 340 metres above sea level.

The structure has a classic anticlinal form and its slight asymmetry is difficult to discern. The western half of the fold is covered by a Palaeocene limestone which, by virtue of its little-eroded surface, preserves the true anticlinal shape. At the eastern end, however, erosion has removed this limestone from the crestal area, and a cirque with opposing scarp and dip slopes reveals older beds of rock.[7]

Of course, having seen the 40-kilometre-long jebel from the air, bumping about the hot sky at low level in a de Havilland Dove, it would have held few surprises when they first saw it at close quarters. But this is not to say that the scientific mind could not fail to be moved by the sight of Fahud rising above the terrain. The mystique remained – a jebel seen but untouched – and this must have been a special moment for the geologists as their Land Rover drew closer. There was no mist, cloud, or dust storm to hinder their view: only a faint morning heat haze. A geological jewel was spread out before them. Don Sheridan made his first visit to the jebel a few days afterwards. Later he wrote: 'We were looking at a creation of God that few human beings had ever seen.'[8]

The party busied themselves with their tasks: Mike and Jim collecting rock samples, Nick surveying the surrounding terrain, returning to camp in the late afternoon.

THE VIABILITY OF the expedition now depended on a speedy resolution of the military situation. This meant retaking the Duru village of Tan'am and the town of Ibri from the Imam's followers. But, when the second group led by Coriat arrived at the Muqbira camp on 23 October, Coriat made it clear that MOFF troops were not going to advance towards either Tan'am or Ibri. His instructions from Muscat were clear on this point, he said.

Henderson and others set about trying to change Coriat's mind. Mike was always interested in tribal affairs and, although he was not a professional diplomat, he would have become involved in the negotiations with the Duru sheikhs through his knowledge of the Arabic language and good working relations with the tribes. One evening, watching from the sidelines, Don Sheridan witnessed the comings and goings of the senior members of the expedition:

> Edward Henderson, a figure still in immaculate whites, left our circle of light and walked off into the darkness, down the wadi to join the Duru sheikhs. Later he came back, called the Colonel (Coriat), and the pair went off together. A long time later after Peewee, Rodney and myself had eaten our supper they came back. Now joined by the senior Company people, the group walked off to join Major O'Kelly. Shortly Mike came back, opened his bedroll, produced a bottle of gin and stomped off into the night, head down walking rapidly, stiff-legged as was his wont. After a suitable interval Nick came back, found a bottle of gin in his bedding and he too made off into the darkness with his prize.
>
> 'Quite a party those buggers are having,' remarked someone.[9]

The pressure was on the Colonel. Intelligence reports now indicated that the Imam's men had not taken Tan'am after all. If the Duru sheikhs did not re-occupy the village, it would send a very poor message to the Duru at large, as well as strengthening the Imam's hand: losing face was a heinous crime in the eyes of a Bedouin tribesman. There could be no turning back.

Again it seemed to boil down to interpretation, with Henderson trying to persuade Coriat to act in a way that did not breach his instructions. 'Come on, Percy, if the Duru move towards Tan'am and your troops tag along behind, what harm is there in that?' was the gist of it. Coriat would be close at hand if trouble befell the advance party, but at a distance safe enough to say that his troops had not in fact 'advanced' on the Imam's troops. His men would simply be protecting Company personnel. In this way, it was argued, Coriat would not be breaching the letter of his instructions.

At last the Colonel was persuaded. It was agreed that Edward Henderson, with Nick Fallon as his guide, and Angus Perks, should accompany the Duru sheikhs on their journey to 'liberate' Tan'am, with Coriat and his men keeping in the background. In the meantime, the radio link with the Sultan's representative in Muscat was broken – something to do with the 'poor' reception, it was claimed – and from now on Coriat would be forced to react to events as they unfolded on the ground.

The force set off, leaving the geologists behind. As it happened, the initial intelligence reports had been reliable: the Imam's troops had not occupied Tan'am, and the Duru sheikhs were able to enter the town with ease. Ibri was the next step – further intelligence suggested that, although the Imam's men occupied the fort, their morale was low, they were running short of ammunition and supplies, and the townspeople were being obstructive.

These factors militated in favour of a peaceful settlement. Taking Ibri by non-violent means suited Coriat and the Company perfectly well, but it was a risky strategy. In the event of failure, the force would lose the initiative and the expedition its momentum; the Sultan's standing among the tribes of the interior would be weakened; the Saudi influence in the Dhahira enhanced; the Company's hopes of developing oil resources in the region dashed; and those of their rival, the American oil company ARAMCO, strengthened.

Although the immediate objective was to survey Fahud and its surrounds, and the security of the survey party was vital, it was also important in the longer term that free passage be established and maintained throughout the interior. This was because, in the future, in the event of a successful oil strike, the Company planned to run a pipeline eastwards to the sea. Ibri was the key.

THE DURU TRIBESMEN lay in the shelter of the rocks that littered the mountainside, a few pickets keeping watch over the town of Ibri which lay in the plain below. It was a cold, clear night. The town was dimly lit. Snatches of the settlement, a dwelling here and a defensive wall there, were tantalizingly silhouetted by flickering firelight and the occasional lamp. Noises could be heard from the surrounding plain: the sound of chattering voices, a man wailing some old battle song, a dog barking. The main Duru force, camped in a wadi to the south of the town, were out of harm's way, with strict instructions not to move forward. The men of the Muscat and Oman Field Force were suitably placed, ready to move on Ibri in the morning.

Thesiger had avoided this place in his travels. Its lush vegetation, date palms and fruit groves appeared pleasant enough, but this was a town with a murky history of tribal intrigue and fickleness, with its inhabitants showing no strong preference for either the Sultan or the Imam in the past.

The Imam's men appeared very much in control at this time. The Imam's white flag was raised over the fort, although barely discernible as it hung limply in the moonlight. His men were standing guard on the battlements, with their inevitable collection of antique musketry. Occasionally a shot would be fired and a bullet would come winging its way into the hills, travelling more in hope than endeavour since there was not much chance of it finding a human mark, concealed as the Duru men were, out of sight and out of range.

In the confused rituals of tribal custom, it was sometimes difficult to tell whether a shot fired was meant to be hostile or welcoming. This scene, however, presented the prelude to a major battle. At dawn the MOFF levies would begin their advance towards the whitewashed battlements of Ibri, both sides armed, ready and dangerous.

Despite his misgivings, Coriat had formed a reasonable force of fighting men from the rabble he had first encountered in Muscat the previous December. And there was something in the make-up of the old soldier that was looking forward to a fight. At one stage, when they were leaving Tan'am, the Colonel had jumped into a Land Rover and, waving his stick enthusiastically in the air, declared: 'We are off to Ibri!' as his vehicle disappeared into a cloud of swirling desert dust.[10] It had taken Edward Henderson's best diplomatic skills to calm the excited Duru tribesmen left behind in the Colonel's wake. There was a significant difference between attack and reconnaissance, he explained, and it was in this latter context that Coriat's wild declaration was meant.

The fort of Ibri was surrounded by dwellings: mud huts sprawled around its base, with the Imam's garrison inside, not daring to venture out. From the south a string of date palm groves led towards the town, screening the approaches. In the morning 300 Duru men moved quietly forward through these groves. From Coriat's lookout on a hillside to the east, it was impossible to see how far the Duru had advanced, but the fact that only an occasional shot had so far been fired augured well. Henderson arrived and took his place next to Coriat, both men anxiously watching as the situation unfolded below.

Nothing much happened for a while. The MOFF did their best to give a show of strength to suggest a significantly larger force than the 96 men they had concealed on the hillside. The Company General Manager, Angus Perks, began directing the big Nubian trucks around the crest of a nearby hill, in full view of the fort, the drivers returning the trucks out of sight to repeat the manoeuvre once more, giving the impression that an overwhelming military force was being transported in. It was surely an intimidating sight for those defending the town, many of whom had never seen a motor vehicle before.

Then the diplomacy began. At noon, the commander of the Ibri garrison, a short, squat man aged about sixty named Saifyan, came out of the fort and began negotiations with Henderson and the leader of the Duru sheikhs. Well aware of the danger of losing face among the Duru sheikhs and their followers, Henderson negotiated persistently, making sure that their terms were clearly understood by the Imam's men: they should surrender before any blood was spilled.

Saifyan was presented with a stark choice. Already worried about the reaction of the Imam's brother, Talib, to the news that the Ibri garrison was negotiating with the Duru, Saifyan now had to decide whether to make a stand and fight or to surrender and face Tariq's wrath. Which was the lesser evil?

According to Coriat, Saifyan had 'shifty eyes'. Although he appeared small and insignificant in stature and suffered from the heat as the day wore on, now – when it mattered most – he did not lose his wits. He caused confusion among the besiegers by sending conflicting messages to the garrison of the fort. At 3 p.m., after talking for hours in the hot sun with the Duru sheikhs and Company representatives, agreement was reached that Saifyan should send a message to the fort instructing his men to surrender. Yet Henderson sensed that something was wrong and had the message intercepted. It turned out that, rather than instructing his men to surrender, the message urged them to fight on. Harsh words were spoken, and Saifyan was forced to write a letter clearly spelling out the terms of surrender. The messenger returned to the fort and it was with some trepidation that Henderson and the sheikhs waited for an answer.

The men inside the fort were only nominally under the command of Saifyan. In the Omani tradition, each man was an individual and would not hesitate to express his point of view. After a lengthy delay, a shout went up and a sad line of 50 men, some young, some old, came shuffling out of the fort towards them. Henderson described what happened next:

> It was a scene I shall never forget. The fifty men had walked slowly out of the gap between the houses which gave on to the wadi bed where we now were. They made a line in the shade with their backs to a wall which enclosed a date grove … the Omani is a proud man, he walks in short quick steps holding his body stiffly upright, head back, with natural grace. Their very way of walking distinguishes them. These men were all Omanis. Their jaunty sprightliness had gone, but yet they held their customary pose with dignity. Not surprisingly they seemed astonished. They had never seen foreigners, certainly not Europeans, before.[11]

It was a bloodless victory, yet a victory all the same. The Imam's claim to a large part of the interior was rebuffed and the Duru were free to return to their lands. The Sultan had reasserted his sovereignty and, although this was not the last they would hear from Imam Ghalib and his brother Talib, it was an important step towards preventing the break-up of the sultanate of Oman. It cleared the way for the exploration for oil; and the men of the MOFF had come of age. In tribute to their one-eyed Commander, some of his men took to wearing a black patch over their right eye.

All that remained was for the victors to occupy the town and celebrate by firing the 'Big Gun' of Ibri, a muzzle loading cannon, perhaps a Portuguese relic from the sixteenth century. The subsequent *feu de joie* did not go exactly as planned:

> There was a tremendous muffled explosion followed by a crash. Piles of dried mud and stones came hurtling about our heads. For a moment there was consternation, and men sprang for their rifles – some of the inhabitants began scuttling out into the palms … the Ibri gun would never be fired again.[12]

ON 8 NOVEMBER 1954 the geological party broke camp at Muqbira well and moved to a site just south of Fahud, to begin their work in earnest. The immediate aim was to survey Jebel Fahud in more detail, now confirmed as the most favoured prospect in the area, so that the structure could be approved and a site for a first well located. A series of reconnaissances was made with Dr Henson, and an airstrip marked out on the hard gravel south of the new camp.

The next stage was heralded by the arrival of F. E. Wellings and Stephen Gibson, Managing Director of the Company, whose party arrived on 14 November and was welcomed with a guard of honour. Wellings often wore a straw trilby and, as befitted his position in the Company, puffed a Churchillian cigar. A tent was erected for a meeting and men were packed inside, geologists and visitors, as presentations were made. Wellings could not fail to be impressed by what the geological party had achieved in such a short time, and he quickly reached a decision: subject to structure mapping and a magnometer survey, drilling would commence.

The structure mapping of Fahud started on 17 November, and the geologists, spending most of their daylight hours in the field, were able to complete it by 12 December. The cross-section maps were drawn and the structure contour map was completed before Christmas.

Work ceased for Christmas, when Don Sheridan and Rodney Collomb took local leave in Cyprus. Peewee Melville was evacuated from Fahud to Dukhan hospital at Christmas with a serious stomach illness, and did not return to fieldwork until 1 February 1955. Jim McGinty was recalled to London to discuss the Fahud structure contour map, and to decide on a drilling location early in the New Year. Mike returned to London to spend Christmas with Heather and the children, going back to Fahud in early January.

It was hard work, but the geological indications were good. For the location of the well to be sited the geologists had to be sure that the structure was favourable, and that no igneous rock lay beneath the surface where the drilling was to take place. When the evidence was collected and presented to F. E. Wellings, he made the decision to locate the well within the cirque of Fahud. After all the hardships they had endured, and the efforts made to access Fahud over the years, this was a truly momentous step. Wellings marked the occasion with light-hearted ceremony by marching over to the proposed well site and peeing on the ground.[13]

LATER COMMENTATORS WOULD remark that the expedition suffered from logistical problems. It was true that lines of communication were stretched: twice-monthly supplies of petrol, oil, lubricants and spares from Duqm, were difficult at times, particularly when the Monsoon season arrived. There were occasions when the normal hard-lying rations (for example, corned beef) were not available in Duqm and reconnaissance work had to be curtailed. It grew increasingly difficult to keep the MOFF contingent at Ibri supplied with fuel.

Otherwise, the Commissariat managed to keep the men supplied with all their food – except for a few purchases of local goats – during the season. There was no other source of food within 140 kilometres of Jebel Fahud, so everything had to be brought to the camp. A generator was obtained supplying electricity for lighting and communications. An electric deep-freeze was supplied later in the season. A regular supply of fresh meat and vegetables was carried by a Dakota service flying into the Fahud airstrip.

In an assessment that could have been written by the Personnel Department, the geologists reported:

> On the whole, an excellent variety of food was available and the innovation of a supply of fresh food in geological camps in South Arabia was a most successful element in keeping morale high amongst the geologists and local staff.[14]

But water remained a problem. From the setting up of the Fahud camp to their departure in May the geologists searched for sources of fresh drinking water. In the meantime they relied on supplies shipped in from Ibri. One Thorneycroft three-ton Nubian truck was used continuously to bring water from the *falaj* at Ibri to Fahud, a distance of 138 kilometres. According to needs, either a one-ton Austin or Commer load-carrier was also made available.

A water-well programme was started in January 1955, and with a Ruston cable-tool rig, Fahud wells 1 and 2 were drilled in the south flank. Both wells found water at between 45 and 50 metres, but it was extremely saline and unpotable. These wells, however, were to be useful for the Fahud drilling-water and for camp services such as showers. The Wadi Hania was drilled in two places, and saline water was tapped at about 25 metres.

As a result of the decision to drill, the Fahud camp had begun to expand at a rapid rate and its demands were increasing. A second airstrip was needed, capable of taking larger aeroplanes such as Bristol Freighters which could bring in the heavy equipment required to construct and maintain an oil rig and camp for the personnel running it.

Mike was detailed by managers in Qatar to find a suitable site for a Dakota to land on, with a length of 1,000 metres, and dutifully explored the options. After much groundwork, he was pleased to find a suitable site: 1,000 metres as instructed. On the eve of the airlift another message came through: 'Ensure the airstrip is 1,200 metres long.' Mike could scarcely believe his ears and his comments were 'unrepeatable and were not communicated to Qatar'.[15]

The airlift of heavy equipment for the proposed drilling camp at Fahud, comprising three Bristol freighters per day, operated during February and March, the frequency of the flights greatly increasing the number of visitors to the camp.

LIKE AN OLDER, decrepit relative, Jebel Natih lay some 16 kilometres to the north of Jebel Fahud, a structure once higher than Fahud but now eroded down to 305 metres above sea level. From the crest of Jebel Fahud, Natih was plainly visible. Only seldom, when three-day sand- and dust storms caused by *shamals* swept through from the north-west, did instrument work become too difficult to perform.

Central Oman was in many ways a primitive world. There was no satellite weather chart, in fact no existing weather records at all, and the expedition presented the geologists with the opportunity to compile the first climate data for these parts. They found that the months of November and December were cool, with consistently fine weather. The temperature then began a steady rise before peaking in the summer. Maximum temperature for January to March was in the 20-30 degree Centigrade range, with a known minimum of 9.4C; by April, the temperature topped the 38 mark. There was a gradual rise through May and June until the peak was reached in July when, on one occasion, 54 degrees was measured at Fahud.

Natih was mapped during January and February, and other reconnaissance geology was done during this period. On 8 March 1955 the party moved to Awaifa on the Wadi Amairi, where a fly-camp was established. From this base Maradi was mapped. More long-range reconnaissance was done during this period, and the fly-camp was struck at the end of the month.

Although cloudy days were encountered from January to April, rainfall was sporadic, tending to originate from localized thunderstorms which pursued a curved track inland from the coast, and affected only a small area. These thunderstorms, when occurring over the mountains, usually caused the wadis to spate far out into the desert, and at these times travel was impossible.

At the Wadi Awaifi, the geologists experienced these conditions at first hand. Don Sheridan described the scene following a night of heavy rainfall:

> I awoke the next morning with bright sunlight in my eyes, to hear Peewee shouting for us to look at the wadi. The sight was fantastic. What had been a dry river-bed at dusk the previous evening now contained a torrent of muddy water in which entire trees and bushes swirled. It was about a kilometre to the far bank and the water must have been 15-20 feet [4.5-6 metres] in depth in the middle of the wadi.[16]

These heavy rains and floods isolated the geological party at Awaifa and caused a breakdown in the Ibri water-run. Construction staff living in the Fahud camp were eventually supplied by some 20 drums of fresh water flown in by Bristol Freighter from Umm Said in Qatar. Mike was scathing about these deliveries, remarking that 'here was the camp cut off on both sides by flowing fresh water and we aren't allowed to draw water from the wadis!' The jerrycans had been used in Umm Said for diesel or kerosene and had not been properly cleaned, with the result that water in them was undrinkable.

THE DURU CAUSED no problems. Fahud was off the beaten track, and held little interest for the Bedu. Their movement was mainly along the Amairi and Aswad wadis. The intermediate desert belt was bare, possessing little grazing. A small detachment of troops was attached to the camp at Fahud and also to the Awaifa fly-camp. On some occasions one or two soldiers were taken on reconnaissance, but the geologists mainly relied upon Duru *rafiqs*.

Sheikh Mayuf of the Duru, whose lands included Fahud, was a frequent visitor, often with a large entourage. Rations were always given to visiting Bedu, and local relations were extremely cordial. Mike and his team worked hard to build up a good rapport with the local tribesmen and labourers. Labour was recruited from the Duru families in the Wadis bu Haraimi and Amairi, though the survey party itself used mainly imported Muscati coolies. Sheikh Mayuf tended to influence the influx of Bedouin labour, but the local labour was found to be co-operative and on the whole independent of the Sheikh's control.

At first the geologists attended to the minor medical needs of the local population and to other needs beside. When the second airstrip was being built, an old Bedu, whose son worked as a labourer on the Fahud site, died. Burials in the desert are by tradition, and of necessity, performed quickly, with the deceased according to Islamic ritual being wrapped in a white sheet or shroud. There was no white sheet to hand, so the Bedu's son, already well known on the site, approached the geologists for help. Mike took the inner sheet from his sleeping bag and gave it to the son. His father was duly wrapped in the sheet and buried close to the Fahud camp.

Ibri and most of the mountain villages were infested and malarial, and although the geologists took Paludrine during visits to those areas, others not so fortunate, particularly drivers, were occasionally infected. During this period, all serious medical cases were referred to a Pakistani doctor, Khoraishi of the MOFF, based at Ibri. The nearest Company doctor was at Duqm. The arrival of an Indian male nurse in March, well equipped with supplies, freed up the geologists from their medical duties.

It was just as well; these were busy times for Mike and his team. In addition to the geological work, they were engaged at various times in path-finding for convoy routes from Duqm, discovering and marking out airfields, finding the location of water-well sites, controlling the water-well drilling party, administering the Fahud camp during building, and accompanying non-geological Company visitors on inspections. They extended their structure mapping to the Gala's Nose, a small feature adjacent to the eastern end of Natih, and regional mapping on 1:200,000 scale north-west of Maradi.

Security was maintained by the MOFF, whose headquarters were now located at Ibri. Soon after the fall of Ibri Edward Henderson contracted malaria and was shipped out, being replaced by Stuart Watt who acted as Company representative at Ibri thus staying in touch with local politics. Stuart was particularly active in the field, helping to open up new areas for exploration.

At the end of the first season in central Oman, the geologists could afford to feel pleased with what they had achieved. The survey party had successfully penetrated the interior, the first body of Europeans to enter this part of Arabia in force. They had been allowed to carry out their work unhindered. They had completed the structure mapping of Fahud, Natih and Maradi, and the first well-site had been chosen. A camp had been established and an airstrip set up to enable the heavy drilling equipment for the well to be brought in. All in all, the geological balance sheet was definitely in credit.

The field season closed on 13 April 1955, to allow the Company to concentrate all efforts on developing the drilling camp. In time, the camp would develop from a collection of tents to air-conditioned huts with a range of facilities, including a mess raised above the ground on a criss-cross of struts and a bar known as 'The Swinging Tit'. There were geological Nissan huts, office huts, four-man accommodation units and several smaller huts. Instead of being a simple home to a few geologists and their helpers, the Fahud scene was ever-changing, with a seemingly endless stream of personnel flying in and out.

Here, in the heart of the desert, they had indeed 'built a village of men'.[17]

MEANWHILE, DEEPER IN the desert to the north of Fahud, mysterious manoeuvrings were happening. While the Saudis had settled themselves in and around Hamasa, the small village on the Omani side of Buraimi, and tribes loyal to the Imam were all around in the mountains, the Company was running fuel convoys under their noses. To relieve the stretched supply line through Duqm, the MOFF contingent at Ibri relied on fuel convoys from Sharjah on the Persian Gulf. Aided by the Trucial Oman Levies, the business was conducted in the strictest secrecy, as P. S. Allfree described while waiting for the arrival of a fuel convoy at a remote desert location:

> All went as planned. A low grumbling, as of distant thunder, rolled sullenly over the other side of the sand barrier; it was the sound of many vehicles churning and grinding their way up and over the dunes. Some hours later, the first truck arrived. By midday the last of them had come waddling down the slippery red slopes of sand, on pillow-flat tyres.[18]

After an overnight stop, during which Allfree established contact with an MOFF contingent which was due to conduct the trucks toward Ibri the next day, the trucks started up again. Allfree wrote: 'I fell asleep then; when I awoke in the morning, they had all gone, leaving only a deep trail of ruts which led into the depths of Central Arabia.'[19]

F. E. Wellings at the Fahud 'spudding in' - January 1956: colour section p. x

Three-ton Thorneycroft Nubian on the Duqm-Fahud track
'As a result of the rough track the wheels have been temporarily used to
ensure the safe return of the rest of the convoy owing to extreme tyre wear.'

(Reproduced from IPC 292, Geological Report 217, BP Archive, copyright of Iraq Petroleum Company Limited)

1   Don Sheridan, *Fahud – The Leopard Mountain*, p. 54.
2   Rodney Collomb had recently joined the party, having graduated from Oxford University in the summer.
3   Geological Report No. 217, 'Structural Surveys in the Fahud area of Central Oman', p. 9, IPC 292, GR 217, BP Archive.
4   Edward Henderson, *This Strange Eventful History*, p. 114. (expanded and republished in 1999 as *Arabian Destiny – The Complete Autobiography* – for publisher details, please refer to 'Acknowledgements' p. 258).
5   D. M. Morton, E. M. Melville, D. J. Sheridan, G. R. Collomb and, T. B. H. Jameson, 'Structural Surveys in the Fahud Area of Central Oman', PDO Geological report, No. 217, 1954/1955 Season, IPC 292 GR 217, BP Archive.
6   James Morris, *Sultan in Oman*, 1957, p. 73, with permission of A. P. Watt on behalf of Jan Morris.
7   D. M. Morton, E. M. Melville, D. J. Sheridan, G. R. Collomb and T. B. H. Jameson, 'Structural Surveys in the Fahud Area of Central Oman', PDO Geological report, No. 217, 1954/1955 Season, IPC 292 GR 217, BP Archive.
8   Don Sheridan, *Fahud – The Leopard Mountain*, p. 54.
9   Ibid., p. 52.
10   Edward Henderson, *This Strange Eventful History*, p.126 (expanded and republished in 1999 as *Arabian Destiny – The Complete Autobiography* – for publisher details, please refer to 'Acknowledgements' p. 258).
11   Ibid., p. 135.
12   Percy Coriat, *A Soldier in Oman*, p. 122.
13   Don Sheridan, *Fahud – The Leopard Mountain*, p. 60.
14   PDO Geological report No. 217, IPC 292 GR217, BP Archive.
15   Don Sheridan, *Fahud – The Leopard Mountain*, p. 75.
16   Ibid., p. 77.
17   Antoine de Saint-Exupéry, *Wind, Sand and Stars*.
18   P. S. Allfree, *Warlords of Oman*, 1967, p. 49, reproduced by permission of Robert Hale Ltd.
19   Ibid., p. 49.

Part of the first expedition to Fahud, October 1954

(Reproduced from IPC 292, Geological Report 217, BP Archive, copyright of Iraq Petroleum Company Limited)

The first Dakota lands at Fahud

(Reproduced from IPC 292, Geological Report 217, BP Archive, copyright of Iraq Petroleum Company Limited)

Dove G-AJHX had an ill-fated history. Mike recorded that the aircraft crashed at Fahud on 30ᵗʰ January 1955 - 'premature retraction of one wheel caused postponement of a geological reconnaissance flight'. The same aircraft was involved in a second accident almost twelve years later.

Mike, Peewee, Rodney Collomb, a Muscati labourer (saluting), Nick Fallon, Don Sheridan

Peter Walmsley
(Resident Geologist)
looking down over the first
drilling rig, Fahud No. 1
(Reproduced with permission
from the PDO Archive)

Fahud No. 1
(Reproduced with permission
from the PDO Archive)

Chapter 16: Return to Buraimi

Oman, October 1955–May 1956

'The search (for oil) goes on, and with it the conflict with neighbouring states, to whom boundaries, formerly of little account, have now acquired immense significance in view of the oil-bearing potentialities of the region.'
Illustrated London News[1]

Many years later the moment when a truck came lurching out of the desert along the track from Ibri seemed to hold a special significance. Some would argue that the breakdown of arbitration talks in Geneva over the Buraimi affair was the turning point, others that the subsequent military action was far more important. But for the geologists, looking forward to their first evening meal in a camp they had spent the best part of the day constructing near the village of Sunaina on the Dhahira Plain, 70 kilometres to the south of Buraimi, the excitement began when a single truck came along the track from Ibri.

In truth, 'The Buraimi Dispute' had never really gone away. In August 1952, the Saudi Amir of Ras Tanura, Turki bin 'Utayshan, had occupied Hamasa village in the Sultanate part of the Buraimi oasis with 40 bodyguards, vehicles, and a radio transmitter and receiver. He brought with him letters of introduction to all the leading sheikhs of the northern Omani tribes. He announced that he had been appointed by the Governor of the Eastern Province of Saudi Arabia to rule over them, and proceeded to distribute gifts to the tribesmen with alarming generosity.

The story that unfolds is one of lost opportunities. At first the Sultan and Imam combined in defence of Oman. The Sultan bolstered his remaining supporters in the area with men and arms, and advanced up the Batinah coast with his own force. The Imam, proceeding along the other side of the Hajar range, planned to join up with the Sultan's forces. Together, so the script read, they would throw the Saudis out of Buraimi. It sounded like the perfect ending to all the difficulties that had existed between the two rulers since the Treaty of Sib.

But there were other, more subtle, forces at work. The US Government strongly backed the interest of the Saudis and ARAMCO in the region, and applied diplomatic pressure on the British Government to stop the Sultan's advance. In a forerunner to the Suez crisis HMG buckled, and advised their Consul-General in Muscat, Major Chauncy, to stop the Sultan's progress at Sohar. The Sultan had no option but to disband his army and cease his alliance with the Imam. Instead of reuniting their country in an alliance between the Sultan and Imam, a Saudi wedge had been driven between the two.

Back in Buraimi, matters stalled. On 26 October 1952, a standstill agreement was reached whereby neither side was allowed to reinforce its existing troop levels around Hamasa, but should allow routine supplies to pass through. Turki settled into a square house recently built in the village. In 1954 he moved out, but the Saudis were allowed to keep 15 policemen in the oasis, provided they lived in a tented 'Neutral Zone' camp outside the village that was supplied by air. The dispute went to arbitration proceedings at Geneva but, while the talks dragged on, the Saudis set about extending their influence among the northern Omani tribes, lavishing money and arms on them in an attempt to suborn the sheikhs into declaring for the Imam. In this way, the Saudis hoped to realize their ambition to dominate the whole of the Arabian Peninsula.

Britain could not allow this state of affairs to continue indefinitely. In October 1955, after the Saudis had been in occupation of Hamasa for almost four years, the British – weary of political manoeuvrings and questioning the impartiality of the adjudicators – withdrew from the Geneva arbitration proceedings.

Meanwhile PDO was pursuing its own exploration plans, edging forward into the Dhahira plain. It was a tricky process – many of the villages remained loyal to the Imam – but the area was still an attractive prospect for oil.

At the start of the geological season, Mike and his team had set off from Fahud with the intention of exploring the Dhahira Plain. They took two Thorneycroft lorries loaded with equipment. After stopping for a night at Ibri and skirting the areas believed to favour the Imam, they reached a place called Sanaina, within sight of Jebel Hafit, about 70 kilometres from the Buraimi oasis, at 11 a.m. on 21 October 1955.

They set about establishing a camp – an ill-humoured affair as the out-of-practice geologists laboured in the heat to put together the tents. By 6 p.m. they had finished, and were about to settle down for their evening meal when from the distance came the sound of a motor growing louder.

Presently a MOFF truck appeared along the track from Ibri. The driver carried orders from Colonel Cheeseman, commander of the Ibri garrison, which were conveyed to Mike succinctly: 'Sorry Mike, you have to strike camp. There's a possibility the Saudis may come this way.'[2]

If the Saudis were expelled from Buraimi, it was feared they would counter-attack through Sanaina. There was nothing more to discuss and, without further ado, the geologists struck camp and returned to Ibri, where they waited for news from the north.

EVENTS IN BURAIMI were now moving rapidly to a close. On the evening of 23 October, Edward Henderson (on secondment as a Political Officer for the British Government) was summoned to the Political Residency in Manama, Bahrain, and invited into the Resident's study. Sir Bernard Burroughs explained that the Geneva arbitration talks had broken down and the British Government, together with the Omanis, was about to take action to expel the Saudis from Hamasa and its environs. A British-backed military force, 220 men of the Trucial Oman Levies,[3] would travel to Buraimi and ask the fifteen Saudi policemen to leave Hamasa peacefully. Air transport would be provided. There were obvious concerns; Sir Bernard listened politely to Henderson's arguments, and then said with a smile:

'Do what you can, those are the orders.'

And so Henderson was duly dispatched to Buraimi to oversee the peaceful conclusion of the Buraimi affair. However, arriving on 25 October, he discovered a battle in progress. The Levies had entered the outskirts of Hamasa earlier in the day and encountered some 200 tribesmen, as well as the fifteen policemen; one squadron had been cut off by heavy cross-fire coming from the village and was now pinned down.

The sun climbed ever-higher in the sky, the crackle of small-arms fire filled the air and a Lincoln bomber droned lazily overhead. Henderson travelled from one sand dune to another, eventually meeting up with a man who had a special interest in the proceedings: Sheikh Zayed bin Sultan of Abu Dhabi. Although this was not Zayed's battle, its outcome had grave implications for Abu Dhabi, since Saudi Arabia had long cherished territorial ambitions towards part of that sheikhdom.

For the renegade sheikhs, losing to Oman was unthinkable: surrender would mean delivery into the hands of the Sultan and being condemned to the dreadful Jalili dungeon in Muscat. Yet Zayed was one figure in whom they might put their trust.

The negotiations, such as they were, were conducted through a Bedouin messenger who criss-crossed the battlefield for the best part of the day; and it was late in the evening before there was any sign of movement from the sheikhs. Henderson would later describe how he saw the dim lights of an old Ford car coming out of the darkness and, with the aid of hurricane lamps, guided the car towards the tree where he was standing; how the car came straight towards him, lurching to a halt a short distance away. As a group of Bedouin climbed out, one figure was unmistakable: a small, sturdy man, his face illuminated by the hurricane lamps, it was none other than Saqr al Naim, Sheikh of Buraimi, the wily 'Old Fox' in person.

Nothing much had changed since Henderson's first encounter with the Old Fox back in 1949. Sheikh Saqr still occupied his decrepit old fort at Buraimi where, it was rumoured, he had a fortune in silver stashed away. But Saqr's influence among the tribes had waned, and his appearance would have been an anti-climax had it not been for the others in his group, men of influence such as Sheikh Rashid of the Al bu Shams, who now stepped forward into the weak circle of light. It was time for a deal to be struck.

After discussion, the shooting stopped, and a Dakota transporter was arranged for the following day. Henderson wrote:

> The buzz of early-morning flies woke me at six o'clock and I drove over to the Levy Headquarters. The Levies had spent the night in the open, since their tents had not yet arrived from Sharjah. By the time I reached them, the sheikhs and their main group of followers had already been taken to the airstrip to await the Dakota that was to carry them to Bahrain.[4]

Meanwhile, back in Buraimi, there remained the unfinished business of Saqr's 'treasure'. While the Levies occupied Hamasa, Henderson went with a detachment of men to Saqr's crumbling fortress to look for the fabled fortune.

In one part of the fort, the search party uncovered a dark hole, 12 metres deep and measuring 3 by 1.2 metres. At the bottom of the hole, they found a prisoner, a man who had been imprisoned for the past eight months. The soldiers pulled him out and, perhaps blinking gratefully, the man was led away to safety.

In another part, they found a long room which was lined with ten large Kuwaiti chests. When at last they opened the chests, the full extent of the Old Fox's hoard was revealed:

> ... we found them filled almost to overflowing with silver rupee coins dating way back into the last century; the coins and notes amounted to over one hundred and seventy-five thousand rupees.[5] It was the thousand and one nights over again.[6]

ONE HUNDRED AND thirty kilometres away in Ibri the geologists had set up camp on the edge of the MOFF parade ground, a place where 'strident bugle calls drifted and faded in the evening air'.[7] They set about surveying the surrounding area, necessary work but overshadowed by developments elsewhere. The military were on a state of high alert, with a Saudi counter-attack expected through Sunaina; and with their camp pitched where it was, the geologists had a prime view of the soldiers' comings and goings. News from Buraimi was anxiously awaited.

Ever since his trip to the Buraimi Oasis in 1949, Mike had been keen to get back to take a closer look at the Jebel Hafit range and its surroundings: with the Dhahira Plain largely unexplored, the geology looked promising. In the Tertiary age the area was under the sea, a place where fish and plankton had lived and died, eventually leaving fossils and limestones which were then uplifted by movements of the Earth's crust. These became the anticlines known as Jebel Hafit and Jebel Huwayyah, which in time would become well known as the home of 'Fossil Valley'.

And so, when news of the recapture of Hamasa came through and it was thought safe to proceed, Mike was quick to seize the opportunity to return. All that was needed was a pretext and, as fortune would have it, this came promptly in the form of an invitation from Stuart Watt, the Company's liaison officer, to join him on a visit to an MOFF officer based at Qabil, at the southern end of Jebel Hafit.

On 3 November Watt and the geologists set off for Qabil to the north-west. They had little inkling of the reception they would receive. At Qabil they found their MOFF contact no longer in residence; he had left for Buraimi to take charge of Sheikh Saqr's fort, following the Old Fox's flight to Saudi Arabia. To the party it seemed the most natural thing in the world to make their way to the fort to find him, taking in some interesting geology on the way.

Buraimi was not what it seemed. There, in the dusty surroundings of the jebel and its nine small villages, a diplomatic charade was being played out for the benefit of the outside world. Its theme, scripted by the Foreign Office in London, was that the expulsion of the Saudis had nothing to do with oil. It did not include a guest appearance by the geologists, who were the last to be told.

Mike recognized the importance of observing the diplomatic niceties to achieve his geological aims. It had been apparent since his Aden days that the political stance of professional diplomats could make or break an expedition. But although operational objectives might be clear to the geologists in the field, strategic objectives could be obscured in a fog of diplomatic indecision and delay. For the geologist, it was a simple case of seeing interesting geology on the horizon and getting on with surveying it. Diplomats, Mike suspected, saw geologists as an inconvenience, men 'swanning about' without thought for the political consequences of their actions – and in this he might not have been far from the truth.

Watt led the geologists to the Old Fox's fort, where Major Anderson briefed them on the current situation: the Saudis had been expelled, the threat of counter-attack had subsided, and the position was secure. After setting up a makeshift camp in the courtyard and cooking supper, they decided to visit Hamasa, going to the new square house that had been built for Turki during the Saudi occupation, which was now the headquarters of the Trucial Oman Levies.

The geologists had not appreciated how unwelcome their arrival would be. They entered a heavily protected courtyard to be halted by a guard. First one officer, then another more senior one, was fetched, each showing displeasure at the presence of these sand-rimed visitors. The geologists were led up to the first floor where they engaged in an awkward conversation with the officers until Edward Henderson arrived 'dressed as ever in immaculate whites'. But even

Henderson, their old friend and ally, appeared ill at ease. Mike engaged him in small talk and 'the conversation rallied somewhat, although Edward, too, was put out by our presence.'[8]

Henderson and the officers had made their feelings known: in their eyes the geologists' presence was at least an embarrassment, at worst a public relations *faux pas*. Henderson's status was subtly different from the last time the geologists had worked with him: during the push to Fahud he had been employed by the Company, now he was taking his instructions from the British Government. The Buraimi Dispute had nothing to do with oil – this was the message the Foreign Office wanted the watching world to hear.

The geologists needed no second bidding. Next day Mike took his party through the Wadi Jizzi and back again to Buraimi, where they stayed in the fort for just one more night before returning once again to Ibri.

The geologists' work kept them in and around Ibri until December, while tribal tensions unravelled around them. The prospect of a Saudi counter-attack on Buraimi never materialized, although the Saudis would continue to wrangle diplomatically over its claim to the oasis for many years. At a meeting in Dhank the sheikhs of the Dhahira plain were persuaded to swear allegiance to the Sultan and forsake the Imam, and the Muscat and Oman Field Force conducted a brief campaign to put an end to the Imam's resistance once and for all.

The Force moved against Nizwa, the Imam's stronghold, a straggling oasis in a mountain valley guarded by a colossal fort. As reported in the *Illustrated London News*, it was a bloodless campaign with only one shot being fired:

A BRITISH OIL VENTURE IN A TROUBLED REGION

The quest for oil has brought dreams of untold riches to the desert nations of the Middle East, and in many cases – notably those of Saudi Arabia, Iraq and Kuwait – the dreams have been translated into dollars and sterling enough to set their rulers among the richest men in the world. The search goes on, and with it the conflict with neighbouring states, to whom boundaries, formerly of little account, have now acquired immense significance in view of the oil-bearing potentialities of the region. At Jebel Fahud, in the Omani desert, the British engineers of the Iraq Petroleum Company have set up an oil rig and drilling is scheduled to begin this month. Fahud, however, is sufficiently near the Saudi Arabian border to cause some unease to the Sultan of Muscat and Oman, whose territory it is. This factor, indeed, is the key to the recent campaign, described elsewhere in this issue, to overthrow the Imam of Oman, who was known to be a puppet of Saudi Arabia and to have received arms and money from abroad for the purpose of disputing the Sultan's sovereignty.

One of the briefest and strangest of campaigns ended on December 15th when Nizwa, an oasis in a remote mountain valley of Oman, surrendered without resistance to the Muscat and Oman Field Force. The short campaign was conducted by the Sultan of Muscat and Oman, Said bin Taimur, against the Imam of Oman, a rival potentate who virtually ruled the mountainous interior of the country and had recently established a dubious contact with both Egypt and Saudi Arabia, and had attempted to set up a totally independent State of Oman. ... The only resistance met during this strange campaign was at Firq, where a single shot was fired from the fort. When the leading squadron reached Nizwa, a straggling mile-long oasis in a mountain valley, they reported that the Sultan's red flag was already flying over the battlements of the Imam's massive circular fort. The Imam had apparently decided to make a midnight exodus from the Nizwa fort by climbing down a rope after he had failed to rally last-ditch resistance. The Muscat and Oman Field Force has British officers, who are employed and paid directly by the Sultan of Muscat, who was personally responsible for the conception and timing of the operations. The Field Force, under Lieut.-Col. W. A. Cheeseman, numbered 350 men, with forty-three vehicles, four old pack guns and four 3-inch mortars. The story behind this campaign, like many more in the Middle East, has oil in it.

The key to the operation is really Fahud, a point in the Omani desert where British oil men are hoping to find deposits of exceptional value. Drilling is to begin there this month and to enable these operations to proceed satisfactorily, local political stability and security are essential. [9]

The theme of feigned British disinterest, so apparent to the geologists at Buraimi, now reasserted itself in the context of alleged British non-involvement in Omani affairs:

A new treaty of friendship, commerce and navigation between Britain and the Sultan was signed in 1951, which reaffirmed close ties which have existed between the British Government and the Sultanate of Oman and Muscat for over a century and a half. It was stated that the Foreign Office was not in any way directly concerned with the recent campaign, which it considered to be, in essence, a policing operation within the territory of the Sultan of Muscat. The British Government has, however, accepted the Sultan's request that they should represent his interests in the Buraimi oasis dispute. [10]

The Sultan, deciding that the time was right to visit his newly recovered domains, broke out of his self-imposed exile in Salalah and journeyed north. He travelled in a convoy of seven lorries, in the company of the Wali of Dhofar, two sheikhs of the Ya Wahiba tribe and some of their tribesmen, a Hawasina sheikh, a Bedouin navigator, 60 retainers and the journalist James Morris.

Stopping only briefly during the day for prayers they crossed the Jiddat al Harasis, arriving at a fuel dump that resembled Point X. Here they came upon a dejected sheikh, who had been patiently waiting for many hours. Despite his demeanour, the sheikh bought good news: retiring with the Sultan to the shade of a half-formed tree he said that the northern territory was peaceful, with the Sultan's forces firmly in charge. The convoy continued on its way.

They visited Fahud following the tracks laid down by the Company vehicles in the months before. By now the original approach along the Harashif–Muqbira track had been discarded in favour of a track that was partially graded, running from Harashif to Awaifa via the salt-dome area, then west to Fahud. Then the Sultan's convoy was able to travel along a network of newly established tracks, completing its journey to Muscat via the Wadi Jizzi.

When he arrived at the Fahud well, Morris found that 'the tall steel derrick stood haughtily near the eastern edge of the cirque, surrounded by crates, iron things and bits of machinery'. None too impressed with what he saw, he dwelt on some of the 'dreadful possibilities that oil wealth would bring' before concluding 'that there might not be any oil beneath the sands of Jebel Fahud. There were such places.'

With hindsight, this proved to be an uncannily prescient prediction of the outcome of Fahud No. 1.

THE CINE FILM flickers: a number of London dignitaries, we are told, are visiting the rig after a boozy lunch in the Mess. The first drill bit swings on a chain towards the drill floor to be screwed on to the drill pipe 'making up the bit'. And then the drill pipe slowly rotates, signifying the start of drilling operations. It is 18 January 1956, Fahud No. 1 is being 'spudded-in' and Resident Geologist Peter Walmsley is filming the proceedings.

In a moment, some familiar figures spring into life: the Chief Geologist F. E. Wellings wearing a hat and smoking a cigar, General Manager Angus Perks and Jim McGinty look on. Wellings steps down from the drilling platform to meet Mike Morton, wearing a baseball cap, and shakes him by the hand.

The drilling has begun.

Mike's visit to Fahud for the spudding-in was a flying visit; his party had now moved south to camp at a place called Haushi in the northern Hugf. This was what Don Sheridan called 'his little world': six Arab labourers, an Indian wireless operator and medical dresser, a Goanese cook, a Lebanese camp-boss, a Jordanian mechanic, a head boy from Muscat and the geologists Mike, Tom Jameson, Rodney Collomb and Don himself. There was also a Duru driver by the name of Aziz who Mike had found squatting under a tree in the Wadi Amairi and to whom he offered a job. He learnt to drive and became Mike's devoted assistant.

It was while they were packing up the Haushi camp that Don and Tom discovered the first real evidence of oil in Oman – the Saiwan seep – radioing the news to Fahud using Bentley's Second Code, an essential precaution to avoid the 'ever listening ARAMCO knowing'[11] about the find.

Towards the end of January, Mike and Max Chatton made an initial reconnaissance of Jebel Kaur. Access was gained to a deep exposure on the north-west face of the mountain in Beni Ghafir territory. A recce to a deep section on the south-west side of the mountain was cancelled because of the 'marked annoyance' of the villagers of the Beni Hinna tribe.

A full survey of the area depended on Stuart Watt's negotiating skills. In the meantime, the interior remained volatile and geological traverses were a risky business; trigger-happy tribesmen were still active behind the bushes and boulders around Jebel Kaur. For the month of February, Jim McGinty reported:

> Political considerations prevented the Kaur camp from being set up during the month. This was caused by nervousness among the villagers at Dan who had to be persuaded of our good intentions. Nevertheless, the party was fired upon on the 28th. [12]

Mike was fortunate to be elsewhere on business when this incident occurred. A bullet passed through the windscreen of the Land Rover being driven by Don Sheridan, who commented on his return that 'if Mike had been in his customary seat beside me, he would in all probability have now been dead'. Officially Mike was phlegmatic about the incident, noting that it was caused by the tribesmen's surprise at seeing the party rather than by any hostility towards the Company.

Shoot-ups became an occupational hazard. Generally, the marksmanship of the Omanis was no better than that of their counterparts in the Aden Protectorates, but it is unlikely that this thought provided much consolation to those who might be killed by a stray bullet than by one aimed in their direction. Despite this danger, the geologists managed to penetrate Jebel Kaur before moving on to complete the field season in Sharqiya province in eastern Oman.

The Sharqiya was an unsettled place and the shoot-ups continued in their haphazard way; by April, Mike had reported nine incidents in which the exploration party had come under rifle fire. Again, these were not caused by any particular animosity towards Company personnel: there were underlying tribal tensions in Sharqiya. The Sultan had preferred one man as the paramount sheikh, or *tamima*, of the Sharqiya Hinawis, much to the disgust of another. The tension between these two men, Ahmad bin Muhammad al-Harithi, and his uncle Ibrahim, erupted to the surface in May 1957, when the province was plunged into civil war.

THE CINE FILM flickers again: the camp in the shadow of Jebel Kaur appears, white tents in a sparsely vegetated desert. There are Land Rovers parked up and fuel drums lying around; an Omani, too large for the donkey he is riding, his feet almost trailing the ground as his donkey trots by; a Bedu woman with a young camel approaches the convoy and Mike engages her in conversation as she accepts a gift of tinned food from their supplies. There is an expedition to the Jebel, the geologists picking their way through the foothills, guided by a toothless sheikh, and the inner face of Jebel Kaur rising sheer in front them; later, in the Hamara Duru, with its contorted rock formations, a tribesman on a camel goes past, his rifle slung upside down under his shoulder, driving a flock of goats before him.

And all the while, the sun beating down, the drilling bit turning, and these last manifestations of an ancient way of life flickering away into oblivion.

---

1   *Illustrated London News*, 7 January, 1956.

2   Don Sheridan, *Fahud – The Leopard Mountain*, p. 93.

3   The Trucial Oman Levies was a British-trained military force originally set up in 1952 as a direct result of Turki's incursion at Hamasa.

4   Edward Henderson, *This Strange Eventful History*, Two Abu Dhabi sheikhs were allowed to return to their tribes. The remainder went into exile in Dammam, Saudi Arabia. Some would join the Free Omani Army supported by Nasser and the Saudis in the forlorn hope that one day they would return to liberate their lands from the Sultan's rule.

5   A few days later the hoard was duly handed over to an astonished representative of the Sultan of Oman. In today's money, the hoard would be worth approximately £350,000.

6   Edward Henderson, *This Strange Eventful History*, p. 168.

7   Don Sheridan, *Fahud – The Leopard Mountain*, p. 93.

8   Ibid., p. 98.

9   *Illustrated London News*, January, 1956, with permission from the Illustrated London News Picture Library.

10 Ibid.

11 Don Sheridan in an email to Alan Heward, February 2003.

12 Senior Geologist's report dated 26 March 1956, IPC 295 Exploration Monthly Reports, PD(O) 0.6731, 1954–57, BP Archive.

1955 camp scene with Rodney Collomb, Tom Jameson and Don Sheridan: colour section p. x
The approach to Nizwa, 1956: colour section p. xi
The fort at Nizwa: colour section p. xi
Jebel Akhdar, the Green Mountain: colour section p. xiii

Chapter 17: The Lord of the Green Mountain

Oman, October 1956–February 1957

'Mountains soared to the clouds and beyond, carpeted with misty meadows, where grapes and pomegranates, walnuts and nectarines dropped ripe into the outstretched hand.'

Warlords of Oman, P. S. Allfree[1]

There remained one more player in the Omani Game. His name was Suleiman bin Hamyar and he styled himself Lord of the Green Mountain, otherwise known as Jebel Akhdar. The mountain was of keen interest to the geologists, and of strategic interest to the Company, in that it controlled the approach to the Semail Gap.

The Semail Gap was important for two reasons. First, it provided the route for a pipeline in the event of oil being struck at the Fahud well. Even before drilling had commenced, a survey of possible pipeline routes had been carried out. The geographical difficulty of finding a suitable route was complicated by tribal interventions, as the survey party soon discovered:

> There was another wadi which offered a good smooth route. We travelled down for a few miles and every so often we came across a barrier built of dry stone walling, rather like the North-West Frontier in the north of India. We were soon to find the reason. Rifle shots caused us to stop and get our heads down quickly. The source was obvious then. Two tribes were having a feud and we were caught in the middle. The stone walls marked the tribal boundaries and the tribes used them just as in the North-West Frontier as good firing positions. We left hurriedly, luckily unharmed.[2]

The modern world had once more met the medieval: while technicians were plotting routes for a pipeline camel trains were still passing up and down the Gap, carrying goods for the villages and returning to Muscat with dates, grain and goatskins.

Second, the Gap presented an answer to the problem of supplying the Fahud camp. Since the landing in February 1954, the Fahud operation had been supplied by sea through Duqm, resulting in a land journey of over 300 kilometres. The route itself was difficult, and the effect of the monsoon season on the sea around Duqm Bay caused major disruptions to supplies. The opening of an airstrip at Fahud helped to ease the problem, with much heavy equipment for the drilling rig being flown in, but there was still a need for an all-weather port. After reconnaissance along the coast, the Company settled on Saih al Maleh as the site of its new port. By late 1956, work was under way to build a road through the Semail Gap.

Then there was the Green Mountain itself. There was a certain romantic mystery about the mountain that fascinated visitors to Oman:

> In those days Oman Proper, the Green Mountains, the domain of the Imam, was a legendary land redolent of romance. There, it was said, the dry and forsaken wastes of

sand gave way to green-clad hills, sparkling streams, castellated cities with bannered turrets and spice-rich markets; mountains soared to the clouds and beyond, carpeted with misty meadows, where grapes and pomegranates, walnuts and nectarines dropped ripe into the outstretched hand … there reigned the Imam, cloaked in mystic splendour, and there stalked Suleiman bin Hamyar, Lord of the Green Mountains, King of Nebhania, unchallenged tyrant of the verdant plateau.[3]

And finally, there was the geology of Jebel Akhdar or the Green Mountain, which as part of the Hajar range had attracted the keen interest of the geologists since Dr Lees had carried out his survey in the 1920s. The Green Mountain was believed by some to have taken its name from the colour of the rocks that formed it and by others from the lush vegetation on its slopes. In fact, Semail Ophiolite, the green rocks of the Green Mountain, does not occur on Jebel Akhdar but to the north, south, east and west of it. The name must therefore reflect its cultivated and natural vegetation.

Three hundred million years ago the continents of the Earth came together to form a single super-continent, Pangaea, that spanned the globe from north to south. It wasn't long – in geological time – before it broke in two, and the rift was flooded by an equatorial ocean that eventually stretched from the Americas to the Far East. Today, little remains of this Tethys Ocean, though much of the oiliness of the Middle East is derived from the abundant life that thrived there.

In Oman a slab of ocean floor from Tethys was pushed up over the land as the continents moved together again, leaving a large deposit of green ophioloite rocks. In looking at these rocks, it is no wonder that geologists get excited about them for they are – in a sense – gazing at the inside of the Earth.

WHEN THE SULTAN conducted his tour of Oman in December 1955, he set up camp at Nizwa and awaited the arrival of Suleiman bin Hamyar. James Morris waited with him, as they 'eyed the mountain with interest, half hoping to see battalions of wild camel-men emerging from its recesses, flaunting the flag of the Imamate'.[4] What eventually came down was not exactly what he had expected although, if it was a spectacle he had wanted, he was not to be disappointed:

> We saw approaching us from the mountains a moving pillar of dust, quite unlike those surging clouds that had, in the past few days, heralded the arrival of so many camel trains. It was either a tribal band of unprecedented character, we thought, or something totally different, peculiar to the Green Mountain, like a camel-drawn dray or a sledge, pulled by mules, such as you sometimes see in the southern states of America. But as the pillar grew nearer, and we were able to see into the middle of it, as you might into the interior of a small tornado, we saw that it was something infinitely more astonishing: a perfectly good, well-kept, fairly modern American convertible.[5]

A Negro slave rode shotgun on the boot. The car stopped outside the camp and the slave jumped down, opening the door with a flourish:

> Three sheikhly figures were sitting inside, rather cramped, and they stepped out slowly,

shaking out their grand clothes like ball dresses, and carrying their weapons rather as a lady might clasp her jewelled evening bag.[6]

Two of the figures were callow-looking youths, but the third 'who swaggered behind them like some great Sicilian bandit, was Suleiman bin Hamyar himself'.[7]

Suleiman was the third (and perhaps most unpredictable) part of the Sultan–Imamate equation. He was the paramount leader of the Beni Riyam, which belonged to the Ghafiri confederation of tribes and numbered some 11,000 members. Thesiger described him as 'a powerful if not very congenial personality', and the reality of his kingdom was much harsher than romantic notions of a green mountain would have us believe. His tribesmen controlled a high plateau some 30 kilometres by 20, rising to 3,000 metres in places with sheer drops, and the wadis on either side, making Jebel Akhdar largely inaccessible to outsiders, and hence unexplored.

Suleiman has been described as a large man with a powerful face and greying beard, often appearing in a blue and white turban and blue *aba* with gold edging. According to custom, he carried a dagger and camel stick, which came in handy for certain conjugal activities:

Suleiman stayed on his mountain, where nobody could reach him anyway, biding his time and striding from village to village selecting his companion for the night. The tyrant had a stick, which he would place over the lintel of his choice's door. When the good man of the house returned from the day's labour and saw that symbol, he would discreetly keep out of the way until the horrible old reprobate had finished with his wife.[8]

Since 1945 Suleiman had been playing his own game. He entered into an agreement with the other main Ghafiri leader to support the Sultan in the event of the Imam dying and the Sultan occupying the interior of Oman. In 1946, with the death of his main rival, Suleiman became the most powerful leader in the interior. By 1949 he was approaching the British Political Resident in Sharjah with a request to be recognized as an independent ruler, describing himself as 'Lord of the Green Mountain and the Beni Riyam State'.

When Thesiger set off for northern Oman, he was told that only Suleiman could grant him access to the Green Mountain. On meeting him, Thesiger was soon apprised of Suleiman's ambitions: taking the explorer to one side for a whispered conversation, Suleiman told him that he wanted recognition from the British as sovereign ruler of an independent state of Jebel Akhdar, promising Thesiger access to the mountain if he could help him in this matter. It was an impossible condition to fulfil, and Thesiger was forced to turn back.

In 1952 Suleiman was in Riyadh with the sheikh of the Janubah tribe, raising suspicion that he had entered into negotiation with ARAMCO for the grant of oil concessions in the interior of Oman. And when the DEF expedition landed at Duqm in 1954, it was Suleiman and his Janubah ally who ordered the white Imamate flags to be flown in some of the coastal villages.

It was impossible to predict what Suleiman might do next.

The 1956/57 season started with growing tension over the Suez Crisis. The effect of Arab nationalism was being felt elsewhere: in November 1956, saboteurs blew up three pumping stations along the Mediterranean pipeline; and in December an attack took place on an oil well in the Dukhan field, resulting in a fire that burned throughout the Christmas period.

Although the Persian Gulf was not directly affected by the Anglo-French confrontation with the Egyptian President Gamel Nasser, the surge of Arab nationalism, fuelled by broadcasts on Cairo radio, had an unsettling effect on the workforce in Oman. Mike's Lebanese camp boss at Fahud had declared his intention to join the Egyptian Army to support the fight against the British, and was found lecturing the workforce and tribesmen to this effect. By this time Heather and the children were living in Dukhan, and Mike returned to Qatar on 1 November 1956 to prepare for the expected evacuation of women and children to the UK, only to return to Oman on 10 November when evacuation fears had subsided.

The focus of this season was on Suleiman's back yard: the geologists were very interested in gaining access to the Green Mountain. The best way to survey the mountain's structure was to penetrate one of the deep ravines that led into its heart where, it was believed, they would find rock formations exposed in the steep wadi walls. And since these rock formations were thought to be like those lying under the Fahud cirque, they might also reveal what lay in wait for the Fahud No. 1 drill-bit thousands of metres beneath the ground.

Only two wadis had been identified as being suitable: Wadi Mu'aydin, which formed a gorge behind Suleiman's fort at Birket al' Mawz, and a wadi that ran from the other side of the mountain through Awaibi. The gorge was also of interest because of rocks identified by Wellsted[9] in 1835 – these might link to rocks in the Hugf and so provide a vital clue to the geology of the region.

Thus Birket Fort controlled access to important geological features and to the Saiq Plateau and Jebel Akhdar. 'It is hoped to get a representative section below the fault in Birket al' Mauz,' wrote Mike. From October 1956 a long and frustrating series of negotiations took place between Stuart Watt, the new Company Liaison Officer, and Suleiman's representatives, in an attempt to gain access through these wadis, but without agreement being reached. 'It is hoped that these will be concluded before long.' Mike continued:

> The Political Department is doing its utmost to secure us access … but it would appear that the Muscat Government considers geologists to be rather a nuisance.'

Suleiman, as ever, waited to see which way the political wind was blowing, hoping that independence and oil would bring him the wealth he craved.

THEIR FIRST CAMP – nicknamed 'Mayerling' – was along the half-made road between Fahud and Azaiba, in the Wadi Semail. The party made a series of surveys along the edge of Jebel Akhdar, taking in some insignificant gorges on the way, marking time while the negotiations with Suleiman continued. Mike decided to concentrate his effort on securing access through the western wadi at Birket Gorge, staying with Tom Jameson[10] in the Semail camp where they could be close to the gorge, while the two other members of the party travelled south.

As Tom Jameson observed, it was a thankless task:

> After the Suez debacle, Mike and I were stationed for most of the autumn in the Wadi Semail with a brief to sample the Birket al' Mauz gorge. This was never allowed to take place as political events in Muscat dictated otherwise. Instead we two were confined in

camp to do some sampling along the sides of the Wadi Semail. We were not allowed to venture more than 100 metres on either side nor along in the direction of Muscat. It was a most frustrating period for both of us.

In true geological style, they found other distractions to counteract the boredom:

We played cards, probably drank too much whisky – 'Red Eye' – and endeavoured to do some work … I had an old Remington '22' bore which was used for much target practice but quickly hidden when our 'guards' appeared to check on us. Firearms of any description were completely forbidden.

The Semail camp lay some 130 kilometres away from the Fahud camp, which was now a small community with all the conveniences. Mike and Tom Jameson visited Fahud for a darts competition on 10 December, and invited Peter Walmsley to accompany them back to Semail the following day.

The trip took us three and a half hours, and the scenery gradually changed from vast areas of flatness to less flatness and increasing hills. Eventually we arrived at the camp. This is in the bottom of the Gap with Jebel Akhdar rising to 10,000 feet [3,000 metres] almost straight out of the desert some two miles [three kilometres] away, and more mountains rising to about 6,000 feet [1,800 metres] behind the camp.[11]

Upon their arrival at the camp, a collection of tents and small caravans situated on the gravel plain in the lee of the mountains, the geologists had lunch and then went to bathe in a *falaj* about a kilometre away. These watercourses ran down from the mountains keeping the villages supplied with fresh water. Small half-inch fish were to be found in the water, and the bathers ran the risk of being tickled by the fish that nibbled harmlessly at their skin.

Peter and Tom continued their journey to Muscat. Mike was left behind to ponder how to gain access to the Wadi Mu'aydin. Tom returned to the camp and the waiting game went on. Promises were made and broken, and frustration grew:

December

Due to political restrictions, very little fieldwork was done during the month. Furthermore the promise (always unfulfilled) of entry into the Birket al' Mauz gorge kept Morton and Jameson tied to the Wadi Semail …

Accordingly, the date was provisionally fixed as January 2nd, but over the Xmas period, the date was again changed to 9th January.[12]

For ten days over the Christmas period Mike and Tom stayed in Dukhan, Mike being reunited with his family before returning to the Semail camp in the New Year. The entire geological party gathered at Izki to enter the gorge on 9 January 1957, but again the arrangements fell through. Then, following discussions between the Sultan and Suleiman, a final date for a survey party to enter the wadi was given as 11 January 1957.

The omens were not good, however; when they arrived at the fort Suleiman was not there. Later, in the afternoon, they were granted a brief audience with Suleiman, and the way seemed clear for a visit to the wadi. Together with Stuart Watt they waited for the arrival of their guides, sitting in the shade of a large tree. 'Time dragged and we started walking to and fro in front of the fort in an attempt to lessen our impatience,' wrote Don Sheridan. Eventually, when the guides arrived, the party set off, and driving their vehicles towards the wadi travelled a distance of about 1,000 metres before the terrain forced them to continue on foot.

They reached a 'bat-infested' sheer cliff in the Hawasina formation of rocks. The guides told Mike that they had been instructed to take the party to see this cave and no farther. The guides stopped and started pointing to some natural caves high in the wadi walls. Mike nodded and kept on walking up the dry river-bed.

'Stop!' cried the guides. 'You cannot go further. Suleiman told us to bring you to the caves and no further.'

'But we want to go there,' said Mike, pointing up the wadi.

'The Sultan said you wanted to see the caves, nothing else. You can go no further for Suleiman has no control of the mountain people. It will take a long time to negotiate a safe passage.'

Mike turned on his heel, so furious that he was speechless. He stormed back to the cars and drove off furiously, barely stopping to eject the guides at the Birket fort. It was a thoroughly dejected party that returned to camp that night.

Suleiman's refusal to allow him full access to the wadi weighed heavily on Mike's mind; protests were made to the Sultan, and negotiations carried on through Stuart Watt.

The routine of camp life went on. Then, one day towards the end of January, as Mike described, the unexpected happened:

Alone in the camp we called Mayerling, I was doing the accounts, and the monthly report at the end of January. The camp steward came to my tent and announced: 'Sheikh Suleiman bin Hamyar to see you.' I went out to find this impressive Omani Sheikh, in splendid dress and sporting an impressive beard.

'I believe you want to see the Wadi,' he said, 'Come now, and we shall visit.'

I was escorted into the Wadi Mu'aydin by the Lord of the Green Mountain and his son, who kept me covered with a Colt, and although I was not permitted to sample, I could recognize the rock formations I saw.[13]

It was left to Don Sheridan, George Littledale and Rodney Collomb to penetrate the Jebel from the other side, from Al Awaiba. They accomplished this on camels in April, Don and George swimming the last part:

'No dragon; no treasure; no castle; no princess; only sunlight and the same jagged, grey-green rocks through which we had passed the previous day. George waded ashore. We had swum through the centre of Jebel Akhdar.'[14]

The time was rapidly approaching when Mike would have to pack up his things and leave. Promoted to Senior Geologist, Persian Gulf, he was due to take up his new post in

Dukhan. Heather had given birth to their daughter, Ann, and the family was settled there. At the beginning of February, he took F. E. Wellings and a party for a tour to Haushi in the south, and then made plans to return to Dukhan.

It was time to catch a plane.

WHEN THE NEXT opportunity for disloyalty to the Sultan presented itself, Suleiman did not tarry. In April there was the revolt in the Sharqiya, and in May the Imam's brother landed on the Batinah coast to raise a rebellion. Perhaps swayed by a report on Cairo Radio that suggested British support for the Sultan was waning, and that oil had been struck at Fahud, Suleiman declared in the Imam's favour. In the villages of the Beni Riyam they raised the Imam's white flag and vowed to fight to the death. The Saudis, as ever, provided equipment and moral support. In the torchlight of a village gathering, rifles being waved in the air, it was easy to believe that the Lord of the Green Mountain would arise from the conflict to become the king of all he surveyed.

The campaign that followed was difficult and hard-fought, involving the Sultan's forces backed by British troops and the SAS. It culminated in a battle for control of Jebel Akhdar, from which the Sultan emerged victorious in January 1959.

After the battle, Suleiman, the Imam, and his brother Talib fled to a safe house in the Sharqiya. Suspecting their presence, a senior officer of the Sultan's Forces went to the house with a view to capturing the rebels himself. He arrived at the front door with a small detachment of men, knocked, and the householder answered the door.

'Is the Imam with you?' asked the officer.

'No,' replied the householder.

Talib, hiding inside the house, turned to Suleiman and asked, 'Shall I shoot this stupid Nasrani?'

'No, he's not worth it. Let him be,' was the reply.

The officer departed and the three renegades escaped into the night, travelling by sea to the safe confines of Saudi Arabia.

AGAINST EXPECTATION, FAHUD No. 1 well did not strike oil in significant quantity. At one point a small discharge of oil and gas raised hopes of a larger strike, but the well was dry. Drilling was completed at a depth of 3,760 metres in the Paleozoic evaporites, probably Cambrian, on 28 May 1957. 'A salt cored anticline,' noted Peter Walmsley in the drilling report. Subsequently he wrote:

> Much is made about Fahud No. 1 being a dry hole and a failure. In fact, it did have some minor oil-shows in the Wasia Limestone and a consequent drill-stem test produced some gas. Mind you, it was a pretty puny affair for the Middle East; the petroleum engineer actually lit the flare with a match![15]

The geologists had drawn up plans for addressing the problem, but these were never implemented:

> We realized at the time that the Wasia was abnormally thin and that the bulk of it

was most likely faulted out. Indeed, Mike Morton had mapped a fault cutting across the structure not far from the well site. As a result we put forward a proposal to skid the rig and restart the well on the other side of the fault. Unfortunately, this proposal foundered somewhere up the management tree.[16]

As F. E. Wellings concluded:

Unfortunately, it was a dry hole except for some minor shows. Because the stratigraphy was unpromising, we did not drill the neighbouring anticline, Natih, and decided to drill something geophysical elsewhere, which proved to be no better.[17]

The story was much the same in the rest of Oman. Between 1956 and 1960 three further exploration wells were drilled, at Ghaba, Heima and Afar, with two seismic parties and a gravity party at work, and still no major indication of oil.

Today we know that the Wadi Mu'aydin has one of the best exposed and most complete sections through the Cretaceous-Permian carbonates overlying the Pre-Cambrian, with cap rocks and reservoir rocks similar to those encountered at Fahud. A proper examination of these sections, had it been allowed by Suleiman in 1957, could have confirmed that the oil prospects for Fahud were good after all. How different the outcome would have been – the Company striking oil, Suleiman declaring for the Sultan, and Jebel Akhdar left in peace.

But it was not to be. By 1960 approximately £12 million had been spent in Oman with little to show for it. The supply of crude oil exceeded demand, prices were low and political instability was continuing – all these factors led to a major re-think of the Omani concession. Three of the IPC partners decided to withdraw, leaving Shell (85 per cent) and Partex (15 per cent) to take it on.

A subsequent drilling programme revealed new oil sources and indicated that oil might be present at Fahud after all, in the Wasia Limestone. Only a few hundred metres from the original test well site a second test well was sunk at Fahud, and in 1964 found oil in commercial quantities:

In the course of development, it was found that a fault which is not apparent at the surface had cut out the productive part of the Wasia reservoir in the original Fahud dry hole.[18]

As the original geologists had suspected, there was an underground fault in which the reservoir rocks had dropped a thousand metres. They had missed striking oil by less than a hundred metres.

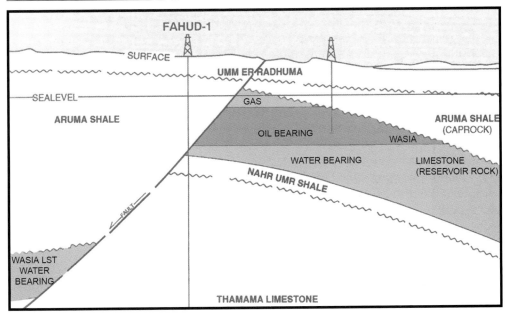

A cross-section showing how close the Fahud No.1 well came to striking oil
(Reproduced with permission from the PDO Archive)

Satellite image of Fahud showing the presently defined field and the location of wells
1 and 2 (Reproduced with permission from the PDO Archive): **colour section p. xii**

1   P. S. Allfree, *Warlords of Oman*, 1967, p. 47, reproduced by permission of Robert Hale Ltd.

2   George Laurence, 'The Oman – Before Oil', article in *IPC Newsletter*, Issue No. 104, October 1999.

3   P. S. Allfree, *Warlords of Oman*, 1967, p. 47, reproduced by permission of Robert Hale Ltd.

4   James Morris, *Sultan in Oman*, p. 105, with permission of A. P. Watt, on behalf of Jan Morris.

5   Ibid., p. 106.

6   Ibid.

7   Ibid.

8   P. S. Allfree, *Warlords of Oman*, 1967, p. 54, reproduced by permission of Robert Hale Ltd.

9   Lieutenant James Wellsted was an early explorer of Oman who published a book entitled *Travels in Arabia* in 1838.

10 Tom Jameson joined the party early in 1955.

11 'The Oman in 1956', article in *IPC Newsletter*, Issue 115, July 2002.

12 Mike Morton, IPC 295 Exploration Monthly Reports PD(O) 0.6731, 1954–57, dated 5 January 1957, BP Archive.

13 This intriguing account, written by Mike later in life, only came to light after he passed away.

14 Don Sheridan, *Fahud – The Leopard Mountain*, p. 184.

15 Peter Walmsley to Cliff Porteous, letter dated 18 February 2004.

16 Ibid.

17 D. M. Morton, 'The Geology of Oman', Proc. *5th World Petroleum Congress*, 1959, p. 293.

18 F. E. Wellings to E. W. Owen, letter dated 25 March 1968, in *AAPG Trek of the Oil Finders* by E. W. Owen. AAPG ©1975. Reprinted by permission of the AAPG, whose permission is required for further use.

Chapter 18: Covered Wagons

Persian Gulf, February 1957–June 1971

'Here come the Mormons to Salt Lake City!'

'Stretch' Nygaard

A storm was approaching Dukhan, looming over the oil camp and bringing the day to a premature end. Suddenly without a flicker, the lights went out, plunging the camp into darkness while gas flares illuminated the perimeter in orange, dancing lights. A fly-screen slammed, a cat yowled, and the cook Fernandez wailed something indecipherable from the gloom of his quarters. The air-conditioning units were dead and the last of the ceiling fans creaked towards stillness: the artifice of coolness was fading fast. For the petroleum children, the power cut was entertaining: the Company camp was the children's playground, and the impending storm another reason for staying up.

The Bedu would have found little of interest in the Dukhan oil camp. It presented a strange sight, a neat orderly settlement set on the side of a barren mountain. Jebel Dukhan, or 'smoky mountain', was so called because of the clouds which could be seen gathering around its summit; and unofficially because of the smoke from the gas flares that fringed the camp perimeter. This was a functional rather than beautiful camp, although patches of green could be seen here and there – a few oleanders and Parkinsonias spread about the meagre gardens of the camp bungalows.

For those engaged in the oil business there were worse places to live than the camp at Dukhan. For a subscription of 30 rupees they could enjoy all the facilities that the Club could offer – a library, restaurant and games such as tennis and billiards. Cricket, hockey and football were also played. There was a bus service at 4 p.m. every afternoon to the beach where there was a changing room with a shower; and tables and chairs and a shaded area. A raft was anchored a short distance from the shore. About ten metres from the beach club there was the sailing club with a clubhouse, and about seven small Firefly dinghies.

The club was the focal point of the camp social life, and the bar was open every evening. The entertainments were sometimes bizarre. One man's party trick was to tap drawing pins into his bald head with a hammer. On another occasion, newly-arrived palaeontologist Tom Harris visited the bar to find someone demonstrating 'Cumberland wrestling'. The man, wishing to demonstrate his prowess, invited members of the audience to jump at him. Keen to make an impression, Tom stepped forward, engaged in combat and emerged with a broken elbow. And then there were the madcap antics of the geologists: one Friday morning, the General Manager of the Company was dismayed to find that all the road signs in the camp had changed overnight, Sheikh Abdullah Road having been over-painted to become 'Shake A Leg Road', and so on. Only when the culprits had been rounded up and made to restore the signs did a sense of normality return, and the proper routine of camp life was restored.

Striking a more conventional note, there was a camp theatre and a thriving amateur dramatics group. The highlight of the year was Christmas, with a formal ball on Christmas Eve and, for the children, the arrival of Father Christmas at the air strip in the Company Dove. A Fancy Dress

Dance followed on New Year's Eve. On New Year's Day, when all the players had hangovers, a football match was held with Black Velvet – Guinness and Champagne – being served at half-time. Once a year, the Company staff played the Indian monthly rate employees at cricket and usually lost. As regular as clockwork, curry lunch was served every Friday in the Club restaurant.

Qatar was a Moslem country and the consumption of alcohol and gambling were strictly against both religious and civil law. Consumption of alcohol was allowed but strictly regulated on camp as employees were constantly reminded that they were living in a foreign land, and that they were representatives of their own countries. The Company was allowed to import alcohol for staff consumption, provided that the liquor was always kept under lock and key. Liquor was 'rationed' for families to 12 cases of 24 cans of beer, eight bottles of spirits and three bottles of liqueurs per month.

This was in many ways a microcosmal colonial society. There were servants who addressed the master of the house as *sahib* and his wife as *memsahib*. Families were permitted to engage local 'boys' for housework, but it was more usual to engage an Indian servant through the Company. The minimum wage of an Indian cook was £4 per week plus food, and an untrained boy could be obtained privately for £1 15s (£1.75) per week, plus food.

There were four different types of house: A to D. Mike and Heather lived in a C type, a stone house with either two or three bedrooms. Facing them were the A type houses, built in the camp of varied size and styles – one where the camp lighting engineer lived. The D types were on the hill behind the main camp. These were among the first houses to be constructed and were semi-detached. At the opposite end of the camp from the club were the supalites, pre-fabricated houses that were among the last to have been erected.

Not far from the C type was a guest house, used when a Company executive or visiting dignitary came over from Umm Said. There was also the Ruler's guest house, which members of the ruling family used when they visited Dukhan. It was rare for them to stay, for they preferred to visit Dukhan on the occasional day trip in their gleaming fleet of expensive motor cars.

A short left turn off the Sheikh Abdullah Road brought into view the barasti-style houses for the monthly rate Indians, with their own club, and the Police quarters nearby. In the opposite direction, along the Sheikh Ahmed Road, lay other houses for the daily rate workers, comprising labourers, artisans, Indian and Pakistani quarters.

The Commissariat was the camp shop, selling groceries, fish, meat and fresh fruit and vegetables shipped over from Bahrain on dhows, Gray Mackenzie barges, or by aeroplane. There was an open-air cinema, a Roman Catholic church, and Anglican services were held in the Club.

The winter climate in Qatar was pleasant with hot days and cold nights. October to April was bearable but then came the '100 Days of Hell' when the heat became excessively humid and debilitating. There were other reminders of the hostile environment that surrounded them. Storms could last for two or three days, the *shamal* from the north and the *suhaili* (bringing in sand from the desert) from the south. People would close curtains to try to keep the sand out of their houses, but it would still get in and walking outside became almost impossible: the swirling sand stung their faces and got in their eyes. One year a plague of locusts arrived to devour the sparse greenery of the gardens. Children ran outside with any implement they could seize – tennis racquet, golf club, cricket bat – to swat the locusts out of the sky.

Once the storm had arrived, the wind would moan across the sand and rattle the corrugated roofs, causing fly-screen doors first to tap and then slam incessantly. The petroleum children would watch in fascination as vivid flashes of lightning forked over the sea and the thunder rolled in, bringing torrential rain. When it had passed – the wind had dropped, the last flashes of lightning had disappeared over the horizon, the thunder had rolled out and the clouds had taken the rain away – the rattling corrugated roofs and slamming fly-screen doors would be silent again.

In the morning, a Dakota carrying Mike from Fahud touched down at the Dukhan airstrip. As he stepped down from the plane, Mike took a deep breath: the desert air smelled fresh after the storm. He saw his wife and children waving, and waved back: the geologist-explorer was home.

A NEW SCENARIO began to emerge. In 1959 a decision was taken to develop the newly found oil fields of Abu Dhabi, using Bahrain as the base for the company that would eventually become the Abu Dhabi Petroleum Company (ADPC). Many members of staff were transferred from Dukhan to Manama, the capital of Bahrain. Mike and his family duly moved to Manama to await the move to Abu Dhabi. In contrast to the dusty surroundings of the oil camp at Dukhan, they found Manama to be green and vibrant. Bahrain means 'two seas' in Arabic. This is because the rains in Western Arabia 800 miles away enter gently dipping aquifers and spring out of cracks in the sea floor close to Bahrain.

Hitherto a backwater in Company affairs, Manama now became the hub of the embryonic company. Its parent, Petroleum Development (Trucial Coast) Ltd, had maintained a quiet guest house in the town for several years, during which time its interests had been overseen by Peter Brown-Greaves. The influx of a large number of Company people taking up residence must have been quite a shock to him, the status he had enjoyed in the past becoming much diminished. It was a rag-bag invasion: there was no camp as such, and no camp mind-set to adjust to as families were allocated rented houses scattered all over the town. They enjoyed a more diverse lifestyle than Dukhan had been able to afford.

There were times when the oil business seemed far away. If it had not been for occasional trips to the American oil camp at Awali, or on barbecue trips to the south, travelling in convoy, imagining what the real desert must be like, it would have been easy to forget the drill rigs and desolate tracts that typified Middle Eastern oil. Manama gathered itself in a canopy of palms. A bustling down-town perpetuated the illusion of a cosmopolitan life. There were many Europeans living in the town who were unconnected with the oil industry. Company families, no longer confined to the club for their entertainment, mixed with others from different walks of life. Bahrain provided a base for banking, construction, transport, import/export – in those days it was a springboard for those wanting to do almost any kind of business in the Gulf.

So it came as something of a shock to the families when the move to Abu Dhabi became a reality in 1966. Heather wrote:

> The Company gave the wives a day of sight-seeing so that we had some idea what to expect. We were continually told what beautiful houses we would be living in and indeed they were very pleasant. However, I think some of the wives who had only lived in Qatar and Bahrain were a bit dismayed by the lack of facilities and barrenness of the place.

They made the best of it: from those early days, Abu Dhabi would remain bright in the memory, as bright as any glossy photograph of blue sky and sandy beaches could be. It was a time when Abu Dhabi town was starting to grow, emerging from its *barasti*-hut, fishing-village origins, to become the modern city of today. At first the ADPC compound seemed out of place against the backdrop of a *barasti* fishing village. The houses were a modern design of bungalow with a double roof, each flat roof overlain with a barrelled exterior designed to protect the inner roof from the direct heat of the sun. As one wag[1] commented: 'Here come the Mormons to Salt Lake City!' referring to the similarity between the barrel-vaulted roofs and the covered wagons of the early Mormon settlers.

There was a pioneering spirit among the first Company personnel to settle on those shores, not simply borne of the barrenness of the place, but from a sense that anything was possible. The traditional image of an oil camp was there. The Company compound was proclaimed by a water tank on a hill and set apart from an old town, dominated by a whitewashed fort. All the basic necessities could be obtained from the town: a *suq* in which fish, still twitching, could be haggled over and shops where Asian shopkeepers sold everything from sewing machines to cheap watches from Hong Kong. But enormous change was on the way.

With oil wealth pouring in Abu Dhabi boomed, and a new metropolis emerged from the desert. New buildings sprang up at an ever-increasing rate as the infrastructure of a modern city was drawn in the sand. At times development seemed to run away with itself: there were taxi drivers in gleaming American limousines who swept along the dual carriageways that ended in bumpy, sandy tracks, leaving them to bounce along on their springs. At dusk *chapatti* ovens glowed in the shadow of shell-like apartment blocks. The shoreline became edged with a brand new corniche where local men still came to say their evening prayers on the sand.

Buildings fell as quickly as they rose. As engineers would tell anyone willing to listen, the local sand had grains that were too soft and too uniform for concrete. Buildings built one year crumbled the next. The town grew into an eclectic mix of old and new, east and west: there were office blocks, apartments, hotels, shopping malls, mosques, cinemas and a church with an Anglican vicar who played the guitar. Signs of garish opulence brought on by new-found wealth were soon beginning to emerge, as Mike and Heather discovered when they visited a palace under construction:

> On a Friday the only person there was an old watchman and we spent a quiet afternoon looking over the building. It was nearing completion and I remember thinking how inappropriate was the dark red, gold patterned wallpaper which adorned the walls of what was to become the *majlis*. The palace was huge, with a private cinema, many bedrooms, bathrooms and reception rooms.

Beyond the town limits modern life was barely making an impact. Infrastructure was virtually non-existent and desert customs endured:

> In the early days we made a car journey down to Dubai with Tom and Ray Jameson. It meant travelling across *sabkha* most of the way with occasional forays through the sand, always hazardous as neither family had four-wheel drive vehicles. I remember we did get stuck at one point but were rescued by some Arabs who were passing by. No one would ever fail to help out in the desert.

For Mike and Heather, life settled into a routine. Heather worked as a teacher in the newly established community primary school, Mike worked in an air-conditioned office of ADPC, poring over the reports of the geological teams in the field, aerial reconnaissance photographs and maps of southern Arabia.

AFTER HIS TIME in Oman, from the knowledge and experience he had accumulated in the field, Mike wrote a paper entitled 'The Geology of Oman'. In 1959 he travelled to New York to deliver it to the Fifth World Petroleum Congress, and the paper became a standard reference for those studying the geology of Arabia.

By the 1960s the Iraq Petroleum Company had entered a period of retrenchment. Its *raison d'être,* to act as a vehicle for a number of large oil companies acting in concert, was slowly ebbing away. The process had begun with the abandonment of the Red Line Agreement in 1948, followed by the influence of Arab nationalism, a series of unproductive explorations in southern Arabia, and a decline in the opportunities for new oil exploration in the Middle East. Plans were drawn up to reduce the number of exploration staff, with Mike being assigned to a post in Iraq. Owing to political difficulties, however, this post never materialised. In 1962 Mike was appointed Head of Geological for the Qatar and Abu Dhabi Petroleum Companies, the concession areas of which included part of the lower Persian Gulf region known as the Trucial Coast.

There was better news from the Trucial Coast. Since the first discoveries of oil in the Middle East, expectations of finding major oilfields there had been high. The region was well placed within the Persian Gulf geosyncline, and close enough to other oil-rich lands such as Qatar and eastern Saudi Arabia to hold out an alluring prospect of oil.

Nevertheless, the early history of oil exploration in Abu Dhabi was filled with disappointments. An oil concession agreement between Petroleum Development (Trucial Coast) Ltd and the ruler, Sheikh Shakhbut, was signed in 1939, but World War II suspended operations. In the autumn of 1946 a young Nick Fallon arrived with a small party to survey the territory. From 1949 onwards, several seismic teams were active, avoiding those western parts of the territory where the frontier with Saudi Arabia was disputed.

In an area of 68,000 square kilometres, much of it covered by sand dunes and salt flats, field exploration relied heavily on seismological and gravimetric surveys. Conditions were harsh, and problems of access, recruiting and retaining labour difficult.

The first test well was drilled at Ras Sadr in 1949, but was abandoned two years later at a depth of 3,962 metres. This was followed by another well at Jebel Ali, which was abandoned at 3,764 metres. Over the next few seasons a number of test wells were drilled, but without success. In the winter of 1953/54, a first well at Murban drilled to 3,836 metres produced gas but no oil.

By now, the 'oily boys' were a rather eclectic bunch. In 1954 a British volunteer with the Trucial Oman Levies came upon the Company oil camp at Tarif, on the Trucial Coast:

They were an odd crew, these Oily Boys, as we called them to their disgust: tough-talking Texans; even tougher talking Glaswegians pretending to be Texans; young bespectacled scientists from Birmingham who drank only lime juice; and jolly bearded men who subsisted on nothing but brandy.[2]

At last, in 1959, after a number of test-wells had been drilled across the territory, Murban No.3 below 2,560 metres showed a promising oil flow of 5,000 barrels per day. Off-shore oil production started in 1962, when the tanker *British Signal* left Das Island with 50,000 tons of oil, soon to be followed by production from the Murban field (the Bab dome) lying some 110 kilometres to the west of Abu Dhabi town.

And so, after the initial setbacks, Abu Dhabi became the most brilliant star in the Company's dwindling constellation. Mike and his colleagues had much success in field exploration, for this was the time when major discoveries of oil were made in the sheikhdom. The biggest find was Bu Hasa, a truly giant oil field. It came about when a well was drilled on a separate structure about 50 kilometres to the south-west of Bab. As Tom Harris explains:

We were looking for the same 180-foot [55-metre] reservoir rock of Bab when we plunged into the 450++ ft [140++ metres] of the Bu Hasa reservoir of the same Cretaceous age but a different facies [rock type] of Shuaiba reef limestone. It was extremely exciting.

These and subsequent oil discoveries assured a rich future for the penniless sheikhdom. Abu Dhabi had long since abandoned its claim to be part of the Pirate Coast and had moved away from its dependence on the declining pearl industry. Now it was beginning to wake up to the wealth that oil revenues would bring. In 1955 Sheikh Zayed had played a pivotal role in the Buraimi crisis. Then, in 1966, he replaced his brother Shakhbut in a bloodless coup, thus opening the way for rapid economic expansion. Petroleum Development (Trucial Coast) Limited became Abu Dhabi Petroleum Company, and the era of oil production in Abu Dhabi dawned.

In July 1967 Mike became Review Geologist, Persian Gulf. This appointment drew on his wide knowledge of the southern Gulf region to study problems that until then had been given a low priority, such as the geologically complex Hafit and Al Ain areas and Jebel Dhanna.

Jebel Hafit became known as 'Mike's Mountain'. Mike had first visited the 22-kilometre-long hogback of hard Eocene limestone with Dick Browne in 1949. Twenty years on his geological work drew him back there.

Mike once described a meeting on the jebel:

It was a warm day – I climbed a gully up the east side of Jebel Hafit. My German shepherd dog tagged along. It was a pleasant spring day, and the sampling of the rocks was easy, also the note-taking. Satisfied with the day's work, we crossed the ridge to the next gully. Suddenly, the clink of limestone, a hush – Blocky uttered a low growl. All was still.

Another clink. I gripped my hammer and stepped forward, down the dry gulch. Around the corner – there – a khaki clad figure, bent over. He was climbing up and he saw me.

'Hello,' I said, as he was obviously a Brit.

He extended a hand and said: 'Roddy Jones, Abu Dhabi Defence Force.'

Likewise, I pushed forward my free hand, and replied: 'Morton, ADPC.'

We passed by, like ships in the night, not knowing and not caring.

DURING MIKE AND Heather's time in Abu Dhabi, an old acquaintance from the Aden days appeared. It happened when Tom Jameson was leaving the Company and returning to the UK with his wife. They invited their friends to a farewell party at a hotel and, as Mike and Heather entered the foyer, Mike spotted someone he knew and said 'You go in; I'll join you in a minute'.

It was Sir Hugh Boustead. Heather knew a little about Sir Hugh, having heard Mike's stories about him, but thought no more about it at the time. It was a riotous party and they were quite late home.

In those days, the office hours were from 7 a.m. to 2 p.m., when work finished for the day. After seeing the Jamesons off at the airport next day, Mike and Heather went home for a light lunch of cold meat and salad: it was their house-boy's day off. They were sitting in the lounge having a pre-lunch beer when the doorbell rang.

'Who on earth can that be?' asked Heather, knowing that most people simply wanted to go home and relax after a long morning in the office.

Mike went to the door and greeted the visitor. It was Sir Hugh Boustead again. Heather's immediate thought was that he had come to the wrong house.

As Heather recounted:

However, Sir Hugh walked in as if he was expected, was introduced to me and Mike asked him what he'd like to drink. He chose sherry, which was a most unexpected choice because in that hot climate it wasn't something that people normally drank. What's more, unless you kept it in the fridge it was inclined to become rather thick and undrinkable. Fortunately we had some which wasn't too bad but, as Mike went to fetch it, he stood behind Sir Hugh's chair facing me and gestured with his finger towards his mouth. With horror I realized what he was trying to tell me. He'd invited Sir Hugh to lunch the previous night and forgotten to tell me!

There was nothing Heather could do but make excuses and disappear into the kitchen to see what could be done to spice up the very meagre lunch they'd intended to have. A couple of tins of soup were opened, together with a tin of ham and a few more tomatoes and lettuce leaves added to the salad. The best she could offer for dessert was tinned fruit and ice cream. Meanwhile, Mike put a bottle of wine in the fridge hoping that it would cool rapidly enough to make it palatable.

Time passed. Heather searched out some fancy place-mats and re-laid the table with their best china and wine glasses. At last they sat down to lunch:

It must have been fairly obvious that this was not the fare normally offered to a guest, nor were we dressed in our best clothes to receive one, so it was not too much of a surprise when, in the middle of the cold meat and salad Sir Hugh turned to me and said 'Tell me my dear, did this wretch tell you I was coming to lunch today?' There was no point in trying to disguise the fact and so of course I said that he hadn't. From that moment on he was wonderful and kept saying to me things like, 'My dear, shall I kick him under the table for you?' or 'Shall I challenge him to pistols at dawn?'

IN THE SUMMER of 1971 it was time for Mike and Heather to leave Abu Dhabi and return to live in their cottage in Wales. Mike was to look for another job in the petroleum industry at the age of 47.

Meanwhile, in Oman, the old order had changed. In 1970 a bloodless coup had resulted in the Said bin Taimur, Sultan of Oman, being ousted in favour of his son, Qaboos. The way was open for the Musandam Peninsula, to which access had been denied for 50 years, to be explored again.

The mountains were calling Mike to return: the lure of exploring the remotest part of Oman impossible to resist.

ADPC Houses, the 'covered wagons'

[1] 'Stretch' Nygaard, of the General Geophysical Company.

[2] P. S. Allfree: *Warlords of Oman*, 1967, p. 32, reproduced by permission of Robert Hale Ltd.

Blocky the Desert Dog

This photograph shows Blocky on the crest of a dune, with driver, on survey with Mike. Blocky was probably 90% Alsatian and 10% pi-dog [stray], the give-away being his curly tail. Blocky's left ear had been damaged in a fight with local pi-dogs; hence the lop-sided look. It was said that he had been born in the stables of the Shah of Iran; and rumour had it that he had been ill-treated by a man with a rifle. As a result he had a life-long hatred of anyone carrying a weapon. He was immensely loyal, and accompanied Mike on many of his expeditions to Jebel Hafit.

Chapter 19: Musandam Welcomes You

The RGS Expedition to Northern Oman, 23 August–12 November 1971

'...fresh smell the shores of Araby,
While breezes from the Indian Sea,
Blow round Selema's Sainted Cape'

Lalla Rookh, **Thomas Moore**

From the rocky crags of the Musandam Peninsula, on a fine day, it was possible to look across the Strait of Hormuz and watch ships sailing to and from the Persian Gulf, against the backdrop of the Iranian coast. Towards the end of summer vessels loaded with dates would sail from Basrah, heading south for the markets of India, Oman and East Africa. On their way around the Musandam Peninsula, their crews would throw fruit into the sea as a means of securing good fortune for their voyage. It became known as the 'Sainted Cape'.

Today, a sign on a metalled road greets visitors with the words 'Musandam Welcomes You', with no suggestion of its formidable past. Tribes with a ferocious reputation, a rugged coastline of 600 kilometres, a place of jagged peaks, sheer cliffs and valleys drowned by a rising Pleistocene sea, these had conspired to deter all except the most determined traveller. Recognizing the sensitivity of the tribes, Said bin Taimur, Sultan of Oman, had closed the area to outsiders, a ban that lasted until his overthrow in 1970. IPC field parties had been allowed to explore the Ruus al Jibbal in 1951-2, but not the Peninsula itself.

The upland Shihuh tribe was unknown and wrapped in mystery. They were migratory, coming down from their low stone huts in the Ruus al Jibbal – the heads of the mountains – to their *barasti* huts to harvest their date plantations on the coast in June through to September. In winter, on small terraces, they cultivated enough wheat and barley to sustain their own needs, and kept goats.

The Shihuh remained, to the outside world, a wild people living in most primitive conditions, shy and suspicious of strangers. Although practising Islam, they retained an empathy with a primitive past through various superstitions: *jinns*, *janns* and *umm-subiyas*, the she-devil, all played an important part in their beliefs.

In 1623, a Portuguese force arrived at Khasab, causing the local inhabitants to flee into the hills. The Portuguese stayed to rebuild the Persian fort. In 1624, the Portuguese Admiral Ruy Freyre sailed along the coast from Muscat, arriving at Limah on the eastern side of the Peninsula to find a Persian garrison in residence:

This fortress was built on the summit of a hill out of range of our artillery, and they did not wish to submit since there was a garrison of 400 Persian soldiers within; on the contrary, they fired some volleys of musketry into our Armada which caused us to lose eight men killed, and many others wounded.

It seemed to the General that this war was becoming unduly prolonged, so he ordered three hundred well-armed Portuguese under their ordinary captains, together with a force of four hundred Lascarians under the command of Manuel Cabaco, to be disembarked in three separate places, with orders to put to the sword all whom they should find within the fortress.

These men speedily effected their landings, and stepped ashore amidst a storm of shot that was fired from the fortress with the intention of hindering the landing. Having landed, they climbed up the hillside to the fortress, which they carried by assault in the first rush, cleaving a way. They put to the sword all those they found therein, without mercy to age or sex, and then they burnt the city and razed the fortress, not leaving anything alive in that place nor one stone upon another. All this was done with the loss of only six Portuguese and twelve Lascarians slain, and a few more wounded. [1]

The fleet then sailed north to Kumzar, a fruitful recruiting ground for the Portuguese fleet, and received a rather more friendly reception:

After this bellicose fury was finished, the General sailed along the coast, and rounding Cape Musandam he arrived at Kumzar where he was well received by the inhabitants of the settlement, since all its townsmen had formerly served as sailors in our Armadas of rowing vessels at Hormuz, and they were people who had never been unfaithful to us.[2]

In time, the Portuguese were expelled and Persian influence declined. Then the British arrived to suppress the pirates who were harassing the trade routes to India. In 1864 the Persian Gulf submarine telegraph was completed around the Peninsula but was abandoned only four years later.

Rumours about a strange tribe persisted. 'There is coffee-house babble of a mysterious race of light-skinned people who live somewhere in the mountains, shun strangers and speak a language of their own,' wrote an American Missionary, the Reverend Zemmer.

Like the Mahra tribes, a fierce reputation was cultivated to keep outsiders away. In March 1930, a sheikh of the Shihuh wrote to the British representative warning of the consequences that would follow if their independence were threatened:

'We will declare Jihad and kill whosoever arrives in our quarter and will allow none of them to return. ... This is what we have told you, we drink the blood and we do not care.'[3]

Quite where the Shihuh had come from was another mystery. Some speculated that they were of Persian stock; others that they were the descendants of the people of Azd, who fled from the Yemen when the Marib dam burst in the third century AD. The language of the Shihuh, once described as a language of grunts, was eventually identified as a dialect of Arabic.

Water held the key to the Shihuh's way of life. Flash floods would occur, leading to great surges of water down the wadis to the sea, but the water did not settle in the mountains: the limestone rocks were generally impervious and any water retained in cracks and fissures would sink to sea level. On the coast, the Persian *falaj* system was used to carry water from wells to the villages through tunnels and channels carved into the rock. In the mountains, stone cisterns measuring thirty metres by six known as *birkahs* were built to retain the water during the rainy season, and the Shihuh jealously guarded them from outside interference. Water remained a precious commodity, subject to the whims of nature. 'At Kumzar,' it was said euphemistically, 'the well will dry up at the bark of a dog.'

ON 2 MARCH 1940, an Imperial Airways aircraft, HP42 *Hannibal,* was lost somewhere on the approach to Sharjah on the Trucial Coast. The aircraft, flight CW197, was travelling from Calcutta through Alexandria to London, and made its last radio call to Karachi, expecting to arrive at Sharjah at 1.35 p.m. local time.

The most likely explanation for the loss was multiple engine failure. The *Hannibal,* a four-engined plane, could fly on three engines, but not on two. So, the official report concluded, as one and then two engines failed, the aircraft would have begun to descend, with the last transmission breaking up as the aircraft's radio antenna came into contact with the surface of the sea. Squadron Leader A. J. Young, then serving in the Royal Air Force at Karachi, was in command of the search for the crashed aircraft. Despite a wide search over the Gulf of Oman and himself carrying out a low-flying search over the mountains, no trace of the aircraft was ever found.

Belief in Shihuh ferocity persisted: one RAF officer said that they were like the Ethiopian tribes in taking the testicles of their victims as trophies. The difficult terrain, was also a formidable barrier to a land search being carried out.

It remained a possibility that *Hannibal* had crashed in the mountains, and that its passengers and crews had perished. Since there was little or no communication between the Arabs of the Trucial Coast and the tribe that inhabited the mountainous terrain, it was possible that the aircraft had crashed without a report reaching the outside world.

In 1971, after the ban on foreign visitors was lifted, the virtually unexplored Peninsula attracted the attention of the Royal Geographical Society (RGS), and an expedition of scientists was planned. When news of an expedition came to Squadron Leader Young's notice he wrote to the Secretary of the Society, venturing the possibility that *Hannibal* may have come down in the mountains, its wreckage undetected for the past 30 years:

It is this thought that prompts me to write to you with the suggestion that it might be useful if members of the Society's expedition were to make enquiries among the Shihuh people regarding any aircraft crash in the area, particularly if they see what appears to be parts of an aircraft, e.g. interplane struts, being used in Shihuh villages.[4]

There, it was hoped, the connection ended: no one wanted *Hannibal* as a *leit-motif* for the expedition, nor for the party to suffer the same fate as its poor doomed passengers and crew.

IN THE SUMMER of 1971, Mike found himself at a loose end. He had retired from the Company in July, and there were not many vacancies for 47-year-old exploration geologists at that time.

Mike joined the RGS expedition by default. A member of the original party, one Captain ffrench-Blake, was unable to obtain permission from the Ministry of Defence to join the expedition, so an approach was made to Mike to join as deputy leader. Much as Mike welcomed the opportunity to take part in a field expedition again, there was the difficult matter of finance: his pension from IPC was not sufficient to sustain his family during his absence on a four-month expedition. It was at this point that IPC stepped in and agreed to make up the difference between his pension and his former salary for the duration of the expedition.

Mike's experience of Oman made him the ideal candidate for the role. Indeed, Mike had been a member of an IPC field party which had made a geological reconnaissance of the Ruus al Jibbal in January and February 1952. Mike's presence also added geological weight to the RGS team – but perhaps too much weight. As Team Leader Norman Falcon[5] was quick to point out, the inclusion of an experienced erstwhile employee of the Iraq Petroleum Company might have led some people to believe that this was an oil survey in disguise. Those fears were unfounded, of course, since the expedition's objectives had been set down long before Mike's involvement.

In the light of all that was known (or what little was known) about the Musandam Peninsula, it was hardly surprising that one of the first questions Mike asked on joining the expedition was: 'When are we meeting the Shihuh?'

IT STARTED WELL enough. The Musandam (Northern Oman) Expedition Committee met on 23 August 1971 and confirmed Mike's appointment as deputy leader. It was reported that outward transport arrangements had been finalized with the Ministry of Defence. Personnel and equipment would be flown from RAF Brize Norton to Bahrain, shipped to Dubai and then on to Khasab in the expedition dhows. A list of camp equipment, drawn up by Mike, was approved for shipment. There were two expedition dhows: *Tarak*, a 15-metre *sambaq* hired in Dubai, and the *Nasser*, a 9-metre launch obtained in Sharjah. Two Gemini inflatable dinghies with outboard engines were loaned by the Royal Navy. The expedition would also have the occasional use of a Land Rover hired in Khasab. On account of the difficulty in traversing the terrain, the expedition planned to visit most sites of interest by sea. A submarine survey would be conducted by Hunting Surveys, using a towed 'Sparker'[6] to draw up seismic maps of the drowned valleys.

On 11 October, the RGS issued the following press release:

AN RGS EXPEDITION TO NORTHERN OMAN

The Sultan of Oman has given the Royal Geographical Society permission to send a scientific expedition to the extreme north of Oman. The expedition, which leaves next month for four months in the field, will be working in the Musandam Peninsula, bordering the Strait of Hormuz, and in parts of the mountainous area to the south, the Ruus al Jibbal. Until quite recently this remote region of south-east Arabia has largely been closed to Western travellers. This will be the first scientific expedition to work there.

The expedition will be led by Mr Norman Falcon, FRS. It will consist of three geologists, a geographer, two surveyors, and a zoologist, and has the support of the Royal Society, the British Museum (Natural History) and the Natural Environment Research Council.

The same day, members of the expedition were presented to the Duke of Kent at the Royal Geographical Society: in addition to Norman Falcon and Mike, the party comprised: Lieutenant Hugh May, Royal Navy, hydrographic surveyor; Capt. Phillip Robinson RE, land surveyor;

Dr Paul Cornelius, zoologist from the Natural History Museum; and Dr Claudio Vita-Finzi, geographer at the University College, University of London. The third geologist, Dr Derek South, would join the party later from BP. Following drinks in the Director's office, Professor Dorstal of Berne University gave an illustrated lecture on the Shihuh of Oman.

As planned, Mike and Norman Falcon left for the Persian Gulf on 21 October, flying from RAF Brize Norton to Bahrain. Mike busied himself with last-minute preparations in Bahrain and Dubai, visiting the camp site at Khasab, making arrangements with the expedition's local suppliers, Gray Mackenzie & Co. British Petroleum provided an initial supply of drums of diesel fuel, for subsequent refilling at a depot in the creek at Dubai. Leaving Norman Falcon in Dubai, Mike took a dhow to Manama in Bahrain to pick up the other expedition members, who were flying into Manama on the evening of 7 November 1971.

By the time the flight landed, however, Mike had landed up in hospital.

Earlier that day, taking a short-cut across a patch of waste land in Manama, Mike had fallen down a three-metre hole. His upper front teeth were knocked out. In mild shock, he had managed to clamber out of the hole and take himself off to hospital.

After checking in at the Middle East Hotel, on hearing the news, a member of the expedition immediately went to see Mike, whose face was 'considerably battered'. Despite his injuries, Mike was able to mutter that the expedition dhow *Tarak* had arrived from Dubai and was due to leave for Khasab with a full complement of stores and passengers at 7.30 the following morning.

The following day the pace quickened. The party, alarmed that they would miss their last opportunity of stocking up on essential supplies, jumped into taxis at the break of day, visited Mike in hospital, and got their departure time extended to 9.30 a.m. Then Phillip Robinson dashed off to the Muharraq military base, and persuaded the local NAAFI manager to open up early to enable them to purchase the expedition's alcohol, tobacco and other comfort supplies. Heading for the jetty, he was diverted to the offices of Gray Mackenzie: a *shamal* was blowing and the dhow captain was unwilling to leave. By 11 a.m. the party was back at the hotel and the pace slackened for the rest of the day, allowing a leisurely shopping trip to town. Mike appeared at the hotel in the evening. 'It will be some time before the dentist will be finished with him,' Phillip Robinson noted grimly.

They were told that the dhow was due to go to Dubai, after all, to pick up Norman Falcon and Derek South. The party assembled on the jettyside at 8.30 next morning, and waited for their passports to be returned from Immigration.

And they waited. First, Phillip was summoned to the office. His passport revealed that he was a British subject born in Pakistan, resident in southern Ireland with the passport itself issued in Cyprus. And there was no *entry* stamp on Phillip's passport. Next, Hugh May's passport was found to bear an *exit* pass but not an *entry* pass, and Hugh was duly summoned back from the dhow. Both men were ordered to return to Muharraq to obtain the necessary entry stamps.

Then it began all over again, the explanations – and officials – criss-crossing the dusty floor while electric ceiling fans re-circulated a rising heat. Eventually, after negotiations lasting one-and-a-half hours, the matter was resolved, and the two servicemen were free to rejoin their party.

At midday on 9 November, with all its passengers and crew of seven present and correct, *Tarak* left its moorings. The dhow was relatively new with stout, well-fitted timbers. It had a powerful Perkins diesel engine that was poorly insulated from the hull, with the result that the entire vessel vibrated constantly and the noise of its engine made it difficult to talk.

With a stiff north-west breeze blowing, the dhow rode rough for the hour it took to round Muharraq and then set a south-south-easterly course for Dubai. Party members spread themselves around the poop deck and, without landmarks or charts to guide them, they had to crane their necks to see the compass binnacle. The voyage was an opportunity to break out the cigarettes after the restrictions of Ramadan and generally relax but – for some – the toilet facilities gave the most pleasure. The toilet was an open box nailed on to the stern, utilized by 'squatting with a sea breeze cooling one's genitalia while languidly watching the frothy wake endlessly pursuing the dhow.'[7]

Later in the day, the sinking sun heralded a growing anticipation of the moment when the sailors would break their Ramadan fast. Around the cooking area, a wooden box with earth flooring near the bow, the evening meal was prepared:

> The approach of dusk heralded frenetic activity by the dhow cook-boy. Flame, smoke and jets of steam issued from the Primus stove in the galley box. As the sun sank into a deep horizon of bright scarlet, the whole crew lined the starboard gunwale and, with silent eagerness, keenly watched for the blue flash. At the instant of setting they broke into a happy chatter, broached the case of minerals we had given them and speedily settled around their dish.[8]

The party, having waited in deference to Ramadan, now plunged their hands into a large bowl of fish and rice prepared by the dhow's cook. It was a choppy night due to a stiff following breeze as the dhow shuddered down the Gulf, passing the occasional orange glow of oil-rig flares on its way towards the dawn.

Their destination was Dubai. With adjacent Sharjah, they were arguably the boom towns of the Gulf. Dubai was a bustling port on a long creek packed with bobbing dhows, evidence of a once-lucrative trade in gold and pearls with India and the Far East, now a major centre for trade and commerce for the lower Gulf. Their stay was brief: two nights in the Sheba Hotel with the intervening day spent buying provisions and sorting out the cargo on the dhow. Meanwhile, Norman Falcon and Derek South joined them for the next stage of their journey.

IT TAKES A certain degree of skill to load 44 crates of beer on to a dhow from a quayside in a Muslim country during Ramadan. No doubt *Tarak's* timbers creaked as the cargo was stowed aboard, the crews of several dhows being enlisted to ensure that it was rapidly accomplished. Next day, amid the chatter and clatter and the comings and goings of the busy port, the loading of the equipment, stores and passengers was completed. With a mighty thump, the diesel engine lurched into life. *Tarak* ploughed a steady course through the wakes of the smaller craft that criss-crossed the creek, and headed for open water.

It was a pleasant day with a clear sky and a slight beam sea. 'Mr Falcon regaled us with tales of big-time oil geology,' noted Phillip, referring to Norman's ten years as Chief Geologist for British Petroleum and his extensive pre-Second World War field experience in Iran. *Tarak* pushed on, reverberating and pungent as diesel fumes mixed with the heat of the day. By mid-afternoon they had their first glimpse of the mountains of northern Oman, barren and almost deserted, rising from the sea six kilometres away.

Presently, the slanting rays of the afternoon sun would accentuate the differences between the leader of the expedition and his deputy – it was like comparing a Victorian headmaster with a recuperating pugilist. Norman Falcon, authoritarian and distinguished, a 67-year-old explorer from a bygone age; Mike Morton with a battered face, a gaping hole where his front teeth should have been, and the first stubble of an exploration beard beginning to take root.

At sunset they squatted around another meal of fish and rice, a diverse but harmonious bunch: Claudio Vita-Finzi, a bilingual bespectacled geographer with a lineage of Russian and Italian descent; Derek South, a tall geologist with a beaming smile; Paul Cornelius, a zoologist on his first professional expedition, the youngest member of the party; and Phillip Robinson and Hugh May, two servicemen coming to terms with the unfamiliar ways of a civilian-led expedition. All of them with stories to tell, all with families or sweethearts left behind, all now reliant for news from home on the fickle processes of an uncertain postal system and a crepuscular BBC World Service news.

On the evening of Friday 12 November, less than a week since they had left the cold dark night of an English winter behind, members of the RGS expedition looked on eagerly as the dhow met a cool breeze and carried them around the westerly headland of a broad bay for their first glimpse of the lights of Khasab, dropping anchor at 7.45 p.m.

1   Paul Craesbeeck, *The Commentaries of Ruy Freyre de Andrade*, translated by C. R. Boxer, Routledge, London, 1930, pp. 403–04.
2   Ibid.
3   Indian Office Records, British Consulate, Muscat.
4   Squadron Leader A. J. Young to L. P. Kirwan, letter dated 21 September 1971.
5   Norman Falcon had been Chief Geologist with BP from 1955 to 1965.
6   A 'Sparker' was an acoustic survey performed by towing a device behind a dhow. The device would emit a loud bang below the surface of the water, sending sound waves into the rocks below which were used to build up a picture of the sub surface rock structure.
7   Phillip Robinson, 'Musandam Expedition: A Personal Narrative'.
8   Ibid.
9   Map by Deidre Yuill, reproduced by permission of IPC Media Limited from the *Geographical Magazine*, Volume XLV, November 1972.

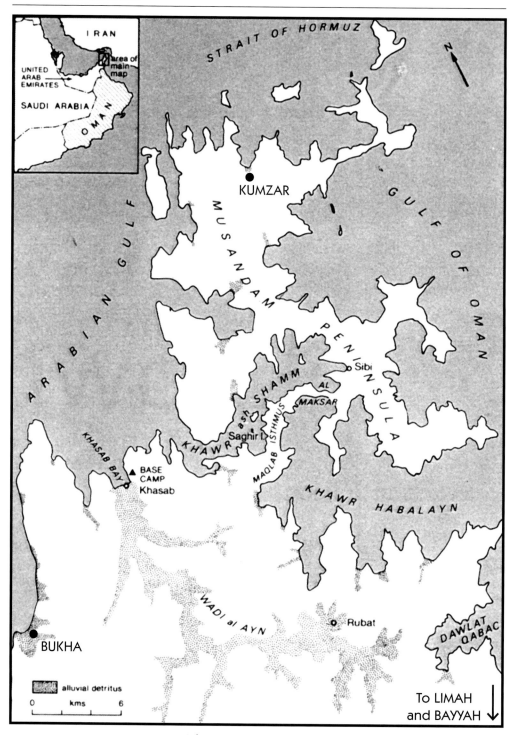

The Musandam Peninsula[9]

Chapter 20: Round the Bend

13 November–18 December 1971

'Laying the cable round the bend of the Gulf gave rise to the expression, since living on Telegraph island must have sent them crazy.'

Omani Travel Guide

Mountains predominated the scene, fringing a wide creek and the Wadi al Ayn, sheering upwards in places to a height of some 1,200 metres, starkly cutting a jagged, rocky line across the sky. On the flat alluvial plain below, the wadi ran seaward through a thick clump of palm groves. Its seasonal creek emerged the other side in a wide meander across sand flats exposed by low tide, as if losing its direction on the way to the sea.

The heat of the morning was settling over Khasab[1] Bay, where the expedition dhows *Tarak* and *Nasser* lay at anchor. Across the estuary stood Khasab village, an unimposing clutter of mud-brick and palm-branch dwellings, and an old Persian fort crumbling like an abandoned sandcastle on the shore. On the nearest side of the bay, just 300 metres below the cliff-top perch, lay a path lined with whitewashed stones leading to the RGS expedition camp in a small re-entrant known as Dib Dibba. They had five two-man tents, a mess marquee, a cook's tent and a cook's shelter. There were two kerosene refrigerators, two gas cookers and numerous tables and chairs. 'The camp itself will be quite comfortable,' wrote Phillip Robinson,[2] who built a path leading to a thunder-box positioned over a hole at a safe distance away from the camp. There was a shallow well near the camp, with saline but potable water about three metres below the surface. Supplies of tinned food came from Dubai, and of fresh food from Khasab.

Now there was movement: a small, inflatable craft – one of the Geminis – was pushing out from the shore, leaving a fishtail pattern in its wake. For half-an-hour at a time the labourers would unload stores on to the boat before carrying them to the camp, their occasional shrieks and hollers ringing out across the water.

Camp life would begin before dawn, with Norman Falcon usually the first to rise. Mike would then supervise the arrangements for breakfast and prepare the expedition for its next outing, staying in camp to negotiate with the local tribesmen and traders, and doing the accounts, joining survey parties only when time permitted.

Paul Cornelius, the zoologist, set about catching specimens of sea life in a manner that initially intrigued and alarmed the Arab workforce. It began with a 75 cm sucker fish caught by the crew of the dhow, who were about to throw it back into the sea until Paul intervened. The next hour or so was spent clattering and splashing about the deck as he tried to inject the unfortunate specimen and place it in a bucket of formalin. On another occasion, the crew of the small dhow was puzzled to know why the fish Paul caught and injected had died. Perhaps the 'fish doctor' had made a mistake?

Phillip Robinson tried another kind of doctoring. He set up an unofficial medical centre, which became hugely popular with the local population. Men suffering with a variety of ailments – heat exhaustion, constipation, verrucae, injuries caused by sea-urchin spines, various cuts and sores – came for treatment. Eye infections, particularly among the children, were frequent. Several camp staff caught dysentery, and at one stage Paul Cornelius had to go to hospital at Ras Al Khaima for treatment of the same.

Then there was 'Khasab fever', an illness of cold sweats, common among the labourers, which laid one low for days at a time. The camp 'doctors' might see its effects and attempt to treat it with palliatives, but it was ever-present, moving from one man to another and back again, making it a regular feature of Phillip Robinson's morning surgeries.

One day, a man came to Phillip with a sore on his lip. Phillip, being suspicious, prodded with questions, finally obtaining an admission from the patient that he had a similar sore on his *minanna zub* (penis). Rather than treatment, a stern warning was administered to the man of the consequences to his wife and future children of the venereal disease if it went untreated – he should go straight away to the proper doctor at Bukha.

Phillip made use of Mike's rudimentary medical knowledge garnered from his experience in the field. Their combined medical expertise was severely tested when it came to the matter of Isia's finger. Isia was a crew member of the small dhow. He came with a bandage that, a few days before, had been applied to his damaged finger by his crew mates, together with a liberal coating of axle grease. When the bandage was soaked and peeled away, the gashed article – swollen, green and smelling – emerged:

> I promptly called Mike over, showed him the finger and told him that Isia would have to go to hospital for probable amputation.

Phillip proceeded to treat the finger pending Isia's admission to hospital. However, four days later, Isia reappeared:

> The bad finger case again – rot now confined to the end, from the last joint onwards. Black in places. Mike and I discuss amputating. Self in favour of morphia and cutting away carefully at joint, Mike in favour of deadening with nupercainal and a quick chop!

In the end, the patient was treated with antibiotics on the basis of 'let's see what happens'. A few weeks later, the finger had healed.

While expedition members set about their surveys, camp life settled into a steady routine. Mike busied himself with acting as front-of-house, meeting the steady stream of visitors, ranging from the Wali, local sheikhs and curious Bedu. The villagers occupied themselves with tending their date plantations, and fishing. As Paul Cornelius noted, all the fishing was inshore, with fish as large as barracuda being caught on hand-hauled lines, sometimes by young lads shorter than the fish they caught.[3] In December large shoals of anchovies were seine-netted in shallow water, dried stinking in the sun and stored for use for fertilizer and animal feed. Crabs were trapped in hand-made wire pots, and seagulls caught in nooses placed on their roosting area.

While those members of the party left in camp got on with their paperwork, the cooks got on with their cooking. Not surprisingly, fish, especially barracuda, was a regular feature of the menu: fish with rice, fish with chips, fish with salad and, as a special treat, marine crayfish. They also had seagull once or twice. As a later arrival, Beatrice de Cardi, noted: 'the excellence of the food was to some extent reflected in the camp cat, which usually sat on the whitewashed stone near the kitchen and grew visibly fatter as the weeks went by.'

There was no shortage of kitchen staff, the party including two Pakistani cooks and a 'coolie' dishwasher. There were four armed watchmen to look after the camp. One labourer, Mohammed, stayed behind on account of a damaged foot, and in time took on the unofficial mantle of camp orderly. Mohammed had two speeds of work: slow and very slow.

Other images of the expedition spring to life: Norman Falcon sitting on a fold-up outside his tent, crouched over a typewriter, trying to type up his reports while the breeze plays havoc with the sheets of paper and carbon; Derek South grinding down rocks to make glass slide samples for microscopic study; Claudio Vita-Finzi on his knees on the foreshore with a cine camera, filming Paul Cornelius supervising a gang of labourers collecting narcotized fish from a tidal pool into white buckets; Paul injecting and preserving the fish; Hugh May dressed in a shirt and tie on his way with the others to meet the Wali of Khasab.

Generally, the members of the expedition were a happy crowd. In the evening, when they would reconvene for pre-prandial drinks and dinner in the mess tent, there was usually a convivial atmosphere as they swapped jokes and stories over the meal and finished the evening by playing liar dice – often uproariously – well into the night.

THE MOUNTAINS WERE a formidable obstacle and the expedition was forced to concentrate on the coastal areas, travelling by dhow. The fjords of Musandam, rocky bays and inlets hemmed in by sheer cliffs, prevented detailed work in the interior. Reconnaissance mapping was carried out from *Tarak* as it chugged slowly along the tortuous coastline and, while Paul Cornelius stayed on board to capture marine life, Hugh May and Phillip Robinson would take the smaller dhow or a Gemini to land for topographical survey work along the shore. But even this was not an easy task, for the rugged coast afforded few accessible landing places.

The Maqlab Isthmus occupied much of their time. Phillip and Hugh set up a survey camp on a shingle beach at Dabshan, on the north-west side of the isthmus, where they spent days at a time completing trig-marks and a beacon, followed by cairns which were then whitewashed.

The principal labourer was Abdur. Lean, tall and cheerful, with a quick mind, he was the hardest worker, a 'frenetic eager beaver'. His strength was his weakness; he was too enthusiastic at times. For example, a simple request to load stores on the dhow resulting in the dhow being so overloaded that it was liable to sink. 'Abdur had quite extravagant ideas on the use of the whitewash,' noted Phillip. 'He managed to cover himself and paint part of my briefcase in the process.'

Next was Abdullah, a good-looking man with a small moustache and a gold-capped smile. Although a good worker who 'humps a good load', when left to his own devices he preferred a comfortable shady corner. He was a persistent sufferer of Khasab fever, once recording a temperature of 40 degrees Centigrade.

Then there was Ahmed. A younger-looking Abdullah in many ways, he was the smallest and the strongest of the three. Yet his strength was relative for, like their counterparts of the interior, all these Arabs were quite puny, unable to lift heavy objects on their own, a feature probably caused by their reliance on a limited diet of mainly fish and rice.

And so, taking to the isthmus with different combinations of labourer – which included one Mohammed when he was fit enough to get out of camp – Phillip carried out his survey, occasionally calling on the services of Mike to help in directing the work. But, although the survey work was at times intense there were some compensations:

> Paddling out of a cove to *Tarak* laid around the point in dead water; a young moon, phosphorescence dripping from the paddles, slight slap of the wavelets, and feeling of timelessness.[4]

SUDDENLY ONE MORNING the thump of a cannon going off on the battlements of the fort reverberated across Khasab Bay, into the re-entrant at Dib Dibba, echoing around the cliffs and into the camp where most of the party were still asleep. It was 7 a.m. Rocked from their slumbers, the party emerged blinking from their tents to discover that this marked the end of fasting and the start of the feast known as Id. There were many celebrating visitors at camp that day. The following day party members went to the fort to pay their respects to the Wali, or Governor, of the province of Khasab, the Sultan's uncle. The euphoria brought on by the end of Ramadan persisted in the village: as the party passed through the main street, they encountered a mob of well-dressed villagers advancing up the street singing and laughing.

On their arrival at the fort they were ushered into an audience room to join a dozen well-armed notables dressed neatly in dazzling white robes, sharp-eyed and bearded, all waiting to meet the Wali, Sayyed Majid bin Taimur. Presently the Wali appeared, a small, bearded man with twinkling eyes. He wore a colourful turban, a white robe, a bandolier and a jewelled *khanjar*. Pleasantries were exchanged, and the party toured a collection of old cannon scattered around the fort. The firing sequence was alarming: the barrels, supported on stones, were loaded and then a guard sprinted out of the fort with a long matchstick, applied it to the touch hole, and then 'ran like hell'!

There were some moments of local diplomacy. On one occasion a local man came to the camp, speaking reasonable English, asking for a crate of beer. This was provided, but a few days later he was back again, making a similar request of Mike. 'When we get more beer from Dubai, we'll gladly send a crate or two down to the fort,' said Mike. The man, clearly agitated, departed.

On 24 November, as the expedition was preparing to leave on a trip around the Peninsula, a Gendarmerie Land Rover came bouncing towards them and jerked to a halt. Out leapt an *askari* with a signal from the Commanding Officer, Major Halstead:

NO MOVEMENT NORTH OF YOUR LOCATION UNTIL FURTHER NOTICE.

There had been an incident at Bayyah, a settlement on the eastern side of the Peninsula. Building contractors had been taking sand and gravel from Shihuh territory without permission or payment. A group of tribesmen had descended from the hills to complain to the Naib Wali who, in his wisdom, did nothing, with the inevitable result that the Shihuh had shot up a contractor's lorry and ambushed a Gendarmerie Land Rover, wounding one man and pinning the remainder down.

The Major had arrived and chased off the dissidents with the aid of a mortar, driving them onto a hill overlooking the town. A parley on the beach was arranged but there was a real danger of escalation:

> The Shihuh respect only those who live in the high mountains, and treat all others with contempt. They are primitive and fiercely proud, and could well band together to clear the Sultan's men out. With the Sultan fighting a considerable war south of Salalah, trouble here would be a considerable embarrassment to him. From our point of view it would severely limit our movement and thus our work.[5]

It was a military situation and, as often happened on the expedition, there was a difference between the civilian and military points of view. Norman Falcon suggested that the Shihuh would never attack the RGS camp because their work was of benefit to them. Besides, they could not have attacked from the land side because of the mountain ranges and the position of Khasab with its small garrison; any attack would have to come round by the sea.

This difference of approach was a constant theme of Phillip Robinson's journal, in which he had earlier recorded:

> The civilian style of working is interesting to note. Whereas a military expedition would start a day with breakfast and a briefing, here we are not told of any firm plan. One either has to pressure with questions or potter along trying to determine and/or influence the direction of events.[6]

Major Halstead arrived the following day to find Phillip Robinson alone, the others having set sail for a survey on the *Tarak* earlier in the day. A thin, wiry man, with an aura of energy, Halstead found the presence of a fellow soldier a pleasant surprise. After a mutual briefing they went their ways amicably, Phillip to return to his survey work and the Major to sort out the Shihuh.

WHEN *TARAK* ARRIVED in the winter of 1971, nothing much had changed in these parts for hundreds of years. Equipped with their axes, or *jerz*, the Shihuh still lived in mountain villages, inhabiting stone huts that had changed little since the Stone Age. It was the *jerz* that indicated their ancient and distinctive origins: a small axe-head on a long, wooden stick. Quite how these people came to make use of a hatchet rather than the traditional Omani weapon, the *khanjar*, was yet another puzzle. Part weapon, part walking stick, the *jerz*, together with a small knife called the *peshak*, were symbols of the Shihuh's distinctive past.

The Shihuh collected water in stone cisterns and guarded them against intruders – yet it was their custom to leave large jars of water by the roadside for passing travellers. If someone came across the jar and drank from it, the jar would be replenished for the next traveller. Mike treated reports of the hostility of the tribe sceptically, especially since, in his experience of Arabia, rumours of hostility rarely pressaged reality.

The Persians had traded with the fishermen of the Musandam Peninsula from earliest times, and their descendants continued to do so through Khasab. In the 1970s motorized dhows would arrive from Iran to trade goats and produce for cigarettes and American goods. More than just passing interest drew foreigners here, and in this a strange paradox arose: the Musandam Peninsula was remote, yet was in a key strategic location, being the gateway for tankers taking crude oil through the Strait of Hormuz to the four corners of the planet.

The incursions of the Persians, Portuguese and British had been mere pinpricks on this impenetrable coast. The British, who had taken the submarine telegraph 'round the bend' of the Persian Gulf to India, found it impossible to live there. The gaunt, empty ruin of the abandoned telegraph repeater station on Saghir Island in the Khwar ash Shamm bore witness to its terrible isolation.

There was a feeling of timelessness about the region. In 1950 a Political Liaison Officer of IPC, Ronald Codrai, arrived at a village on the southern end of the Peninsula to be greeted by a sheikh demanding to know why *he* had shelled his village 'yesterday' – in fact the incident had occurred some 25 years earlier when the British had sent a vessel to 'lob a few admonitory shells' into the village, destroying its fort.[7] It remained to be seen what the Shihuh would make of this curious collection of three geologists, a geographer and a zoologist who dared venture onto their jealously guarded land.

EARLY IN THE evening of 28 November as the camp was settling down, with Claudio and Phillip just starting a game of chess, the sound of gunshots erupted from the direction of Khasab.

'Cut out all lights!' shouted Phillip.

All the symptoms of a major battle were present, with single shots being followed by bursts from a Bren gun; brief silence; then the chatter of an SMG, a crash of rifle fire, a few dull thumps and the clatter of the Bren again. Verey lights rose from the fort, and bullets winged overhead. Echoes sent the sound racing from wall to wall of the Wadi al Ayn to bounce back again, distorting the gunfire and magnifying the impression that a serious battle was in progress.

The two military men, Phillip and Hugh, actually peace-loving surveyors, prowled forward in the shadows, leaving the others standing in a 'nice fat knot' in an open moonlit patch. Unable to see anything Phillip returned for a large whisky, which he sipped while scanning the cliff tops with binoculars. Following his example, Paul also took a hefty swig and Mike held on to the Cointreau. Some of the party started for the *Tarak* to sleep there, surrounded by the sea as the tide came in. Meanwhile two watchmen were sent to Khasab to find out what was going on.

The last few bursts of gunfire had just died away when the watchmen returned to report a false alarm. The shooting was a *feu de joie*, instigated by news that the Wali had consumated his marriage with his latest wife.

The instigator of the gunfire was later identified as the local man who had previously asked for a crate of beer. He returned to the camp the following day and this time asked Norman Falcon for another crate, saying that he wanted it for a sea trip to Dubai. He was given short shrift and retreated, climbing to the cliff top and spending the rest of the day firing shots at the periphery of the camp. 'This might have been showing off to some fisher girls rather than an expression of resentment,' Phillip generously concluded.

Meanwhile in the desolate surroundings of Bayyah to the south, the last moves in the Shihuh drama were being played out. The Beni Hali had failed to turn up for the parley on the beach, preferring instead to step up their fire on the Gendarmerie and the town. They were supported by their womenfolk who formed a rudimentary supply corps, bringing forward rations and water, recovering the wounded and back-loading them.

A brisk action developed. In response to a call from Major Halstead, a company of the Muscat Regiment flew in with a section of 81 millimetre mortars. The soldiers drove the Shihuh from the outskirts of the town, killing two and injuring about ten. With the Minster of the Interior in attendance an ultimatum was delivered to the Shihuh, directing them to send ten men down from the mountains to parley, otherwise the Army would come and get them. And there the matter rested.

WADI AL AYN is the principal wadi of the Peninsula, starting at a rocky hump called the Aqaba and running for 20 kilometres to Khasab on the coast, varying in width between one and two kilometres along most of its length. It carries an alluvial plain which appears to be level along its entirety, although it drops some 150 metres on its journey to the sea. A series of tributaries feeds into the wadi, but for most of the year the higher reaches of the wadi are dry.

The excursion to the wadi began soon after daybreak. The party – Mike, Derek, Claudio, Paul and Phillip – left the camp, skirting the creek and heading for the palm groves of Khasab, carrying the equipment themselves. They had expected a Land Rover to collect them – hired in the village which was cut off by a high tide – but they could see no sign of it when they reached the other side of the creek.

Already the signs were inauspicious. They found the Land Rover by the fort, the vehicle having no brakes and the driver Zaqrab too frightened to drive through the date plantation to meet them. It was one of those Mahra moments: time to rely on native wit and cunning. Mike scribbled out a note for Phillip to take to the driver: 'This man is the most famous driver in England,' it read. Zaqrab, duly impressed, surrendered the steering wheel to Phillip.

It was to be a dubious privilege. He had to drive the car with a mixture of luck and judgement, sometimes controlling the Land Rover's speed through the gears as the vehicle bounced along, its springs broken and its frame breaking up. They travelled – hanging on and tired, limbs bruised – three in the front and two sitting in the open back, with a guard in attendance, standing over the cab with a rifle slung from his shoulder.

You could look up into these barren mountains that rose in stacked precipices up to 1,200 metres thinking they were deserted. But there was evidence of Shihuh dwellings along the way, past and present, small stone-built shelters without wells, many of them deserted. At the head of the wadi they came across a family complex of eight to ten dwellings, a parched cultivation with many trees, the sign of a significant underground supply of water. Two Arabs were working a field with a wooden plough, one pulling it on a rope and the other steering it through an unpromising soil.

And so the scenes of the expedition unfolded: Mike in a straw hat plane-table mapping, Derek in an orange shirt using the rangefinder, both going into ecstasies over a particularly interesting geological formation of grey rocks twisted with red; Paul finding a type of cactus previously unknown in northern Oman; Phillip and Mike ascending the rocky Aqaba and looking down on the Indian Ocean spread out before them on the other side. At the head of the wadi they found evidence of Shihuh graves and a *birkah,* used by the mountain tribes for storing water. They returned to the Land Rover after saying farewell to the village headman and headed back down the wadi in their battered jalopy, somehow stopping to take barometric readings along the way.

Back at camp in the evening they ate beneath the light of a Tilley lamp, their starter a bowl of soup with small beetles swimming about.

THE TIME TO go round the bend had arrived. Next day the scientists, having been given the all-clear, sailed around the northernmost tip of the Peninsula to reach Limah on the eastern coast, the site of Admiral Ruy Freyre's massacre of a Persian garrison. Along the coastline they saw houses built into the rocks, and several huge Manta Rays gliding through the clear sea. Some of the villages, such as Limah and Kumzar, were accessible only from the sea.

Traditionally, relations between the Shihuh and the two smaller tribes of the northern Peninsula were poor. Neither of the latter had reason to be on good terms with their Shihuh neighbours: indeed, the more imaginative tales told to the early travellers about the mountain people may have originated from these disenchanted and destitute people. The Arabic-speaking Dhuhuriyan, the original inhabitants of Musandam, had been displaced by the Shihuh, and by the Persian-speaking Kumzar now living in a small group on the northern coast and earning a living from fishing.

The inhabitants of these coastal villages were generally welcoming, with a history of contact with others through their connection with the sea. The survey party would encourage a good reception with gifts of clothing, tinned food, household utensils and medicines for the local people. On the return trip they set up camp in the bay of Khawr Habalayn, still on the eastern side of the Peninsula.

As part of their investigation into ways of improving the local economy, the party looked at the Maqlab Isthmus, a thin ribbon of land separating the Persian Gulf from the Gulf of Oman. By cutting a canal through the isthmus, shipping would be saved a round trip of 65 kilometres and thus avoid the strong currents of the Strait of Hormuz. It would also open up the possibility of water tankers accessing the remoter parts of the long fjords of the Peninsula. Hugh May placed tide gauges on either side of the isthmus to measure the difference in the tidal ranges and times of the Khawr Habalayn and the Khawr ash Shamm inlets. The varying effect of barometric pressure, currents and wind could result in a significant difference in the tide level between the two sides of the isthmus.

Dawn broke and silhouetted the outline of a single fishing boat being rowed out into the bay. The heat of the day would surely follow, but at this time they felt only a hint of the sun's warmth on their faces, as an early morning haze dimmed the sun. As the expedition dhow sailed along the limestone-piled, twisted coastline, Mike stood at the bow and looked through his binoculars. He could see in the exposed rocks the whole calcareous Mesozoic succession of the Arabian shield.

In the Musandam mountains rocks had been thrust to the west, exposing structures which included the Ghail Formation, massive light-coloured typically dolomitic limestone with calcite veins. In this formation fractures and cavernous weathering had taken place, suggesting the presence of evaporites in the original rock that had now disappeared. The formation stood out from the softer, less extensive Elphinstone Group of rocks and the grey limestones of the Musandam Group that lay in sequence above it.

A hazy dawn over Khawr Habalayn, the local fishermen out in their rowing boats with their lines and nets at the ready, *Tarak* chugging gently along the zig-zag coast, dolphins cruising alongside. It was a primitive scene, the fishermen carrying out their tasks in much the same way as their forefathers had done for hundreds of years.

Mike scanned the mountain ridge and followed it to the water's edge, its sharp, rocky edge dipping suddenly and plunging into the sea. These cliffs had once been valley walls. During the Pleistocene ice ages vast amounts of water were locked up in the polar ice caps, draining the seas and leaving much of the Persian Gulf as dry land. A great river had flowed through the Strait of Hormuz, entering the sea where the Gulf of Oman now lay. These inlets of the Musandam Peninsula had once been valleys, probably inhabited, the sea level then being some 90 metres below its present level.

The sea, when it rose again, rose rapidly in terms of geological time. Approximately 20,000 years ago the ice caps began to melt, releasing water to fill the seas that would invade the valleys of Musandam and the settlements of the people who lived there; the Musandam area was sinking throughout the Pleistocene; the Peninsula is on the sharp end of the Arabian plate as it is pushed northwards and downwards under the Eurasian plate[8]; all this causing the valleys to drown. One of the objectives of the expedition was to investigate these inlets to discover whether archaelogical remains lay buried in the silt.

Another, perhaps far-fetched, notion was that the coast of northern Oman, matching as it did the coastline of the ancient super-continent of Pangaea, had remained unchanged since Palaeozoic times. But this would have been remarkable considering all the tectonic movements that had occurred since the break-up of Pangaea. A more immediate puzzle was how the sequence of rocks found on the Peninsula was linked to other ranges in the region, the Makran range in Persia and the mountains of Pakistan. The sequence seen in Musandam appeared in the Kirthar range north of Karachi; it was an open question whether these represented a continuation of the Omani belt that disappeared beneath the sea bed to re-emerge across the Gulf of Oman in Pakistan.

Later in the day, after the crew of the dhow had been working long and hard without a break, the captain decided to take matters into his own hands and bring their excursion to a premature pause. With great skill, standing in the bows directing the helmsman, he deliberately steered *Tarak* towards the shore so that the dhow grounded on the beach at a slow speed. It was just after high tide, just the right time to ensure that the dhow could not be relaunched before the next high tide, and long enough to afford his men a well-earned rest.

It certainly came as a surprise to Mike when *Tarak* ran aground. Nothing could be taken for granted on this querulous Peninsula, especially the actions of a frustrated captain whose last thought had possibly been the Arabic equivalent of 'blow this for a game of soldiers' before he so deftly grounded the dhow. *Tarak* was duly hauled off the beach several hours later to continue its survey work around the Peninsula, undamaged, but the subject of much mirth.

ONE DAY IN mid-December, Phillip Robinson was on a hilltop surveying with the labourers Abdur and Mohammed when their attention was attracted by shouts from an adjacent hill. They might have feared the worst, but the encounter developed in an unexpected way:

> We were distracted by the shouts of two women, collecting wood, on a ridge about 1000 yards [metres] away. Abdur yodelled back and quite an exchange followed, shouted

through the clear air. The natural amphitheatre formed by the mountains permits these 1000-yard [-metre] conversations.

What the women were not to know was that I had a surveying telescope with 40x magnification! Of course I trained the theodolite on them. A couple of pretty young things. What was amusing was that they were entertaining themselves by making obscene gestures in our direction. One had lifted her skirt suggestively while the other watched and giggled. Abdur too had a look through the telescope and had a terrific laugh. Young Mohammed was too abashed.[9]

It was not entirely clear which tribe these women represented, the Shihuh or their disaffected neighbours, and it was not a situation that required any further scrutiny. But one thing was certain: the time of hostilities appeared to have ended.

1   *Khasab* means 'fertile place'.
2   Phillip Robinson, 'Musandam Expedition: A Personal Narrative'.
3   P. F. S. Cornelius, 'The Musandam Scientific results, Part I: The Biological Aspects', the *Geographical Journal*, Vol. 139, Part 3, October 1973.
4   Phillip Robinson, 'Musandam Expedition Personal Narrative'.
5   Ibid.
6   Ibid.
7   David Holden, *Farewell to Arabia*, p. 187.
8   From Ras Masud, south-west of Khasab, it is possible to see the gradual bending of the strata as they dip to meet the Asian plate. The valleys drowned, and there was no sign of their existence above sea level: Paul Cornelius in a letter to the author, October 2005
9   Philip Robinson, ibid.

Chapter 21: The Lights of Bukha

19 December 1971–4 February 1972

'I see the lights of Bukha but they never seem to get closer.'

Phillip Robinson

In later life, whenever the subject of Musandam cropped up, Mike would be circumspect, preferring to rely on an illustrated article published in the *Geographical Magazine* of December 1972 rather than tell his own story. The article shows him at the helm of a dhow, standing with his back to the camera, looking across the sea towards the imposing mountains of the Musandam Peninsula. Perhaps this is how he wished the expedition to be remembered, as described in the official reports and photographs.

As a result of his work on the expedition, Norman Falcon wrote a number of papers on the Musandam mountains and their relationship with the Makran mountains of Iran, which confirmed his reputation as a leading authority on the geology of the Middle East.[1] In 1973 he was awarded the RGS Founder's Medal 'for contributions to the geographical history of the Persian Gulf region'.

The biological survey studied the phenomena of cliff undercutting by molluscs, and small coral reefs were found in two sites. Important specimens of animals and a few plants were collected, mostly by offshore dredging, hand-hauled and thereby limited in number. The steep drop of the coastline beneath the sea limited operations to a narrow strip of the coastal zone, some 50 to 100 metres wide.

The zoological collections included by far the largest and most species-rich collection of corals made from the Persian Gulf, more than doubling the number of species recorded from the region before. They also included two specimens of lizard, about 20 centimetres long that proved new to science.[2] To his chagrin, Paul Cornelius was instructed by his Natural History Museum managers not to work on the collections he had made, leaving others to reap the benefit. The numerous hydroid specimens of Paul's specialist group, so tediously gathered by shore collections and by the strenuous hand-hauling of dredges off carefully selected headlands and the like, remain unworked to this day.

Owing to the difficulty of the terrain, survey work in the interior was restricted. Expectations of helicopter support from the Omani Gendarmerie were not fully realized, and the southern Peninsula was not penetrated. Surveying the land from the sea, however, was more straightforward and, overall, the expedition's land and hydrographic surveys in the northern Peninsula were successful.

Archaeologist Beatrice de Cardi[3] joined the expedition towards the end of 1971 and carried out a survey along the west coast of the Peninsula. Near Khasab, she found several stone-built tombs of the late third Millennium BC type that were destroyed just a few years later when the town was developed and an airport built. She also came across the remains of a settlement on the island of Umm al Ghanam and, on the nearby shore, evidence of sustained occupation for many hundreds of years, with pottery shards suggesting trading links with Persia. Elsewhere deserted

Shihuh settlements were found, and the remains of Chinese porcelain. But the difficult terrain and uncertain weather conditions prevented a survey of Kumzar and the east coast, much to her disappointment.

Good weather in January aided the 'Sparker' survey, which attempted to define the bedrock topography of the inlets and determine the extent of infill in them. However, steep submarine slopes made this a difficult task, and considerable rock debris in the sediment required more powerful equipment to penetrate it. So another objective of the survey, to confirm exactly what happened to Musandam during the Pleistocene Ice Ages, was not achieved.

The hydrographic survey of the Maqlab Isthmus found that, between the two sides of the isthmus, the sea level could differ by as much as one metre. If, as had been postulated, a canal were built at Al Maksar, its narrowest point, there would be an unacceptable rate of water flow through the isthmus. This led Hugh May to state that, 'if a canal is to be built at all, there must be a lock: a break in the isthmus without a lock would have disastrous effects'.[4] The economic arguments were against it as well: it was estimated that the Army could build a canal in 18 months at a cost of £700,000, and a private contractor at a cost of £2 million. Therefore, it was concluded that the money would be better spent on projects to aid the local population and to date no canal has been built.

Hugh May's work recording a whole fortnight's tidal cycle enabled much better tidal predictions to be made than before for the important marine bottleneck, the Strait of Hormuz, invaluable, for example, for larger tankers leaving the Gulf. His tide-cycle date would have fed into tide tables available during the Iraqi conflict some 20 years later.

Phillip Robinson's astro-sightings, and telemetry and triangulation between the mountains to the south of Musandam and those of southern Persia, closed a key triangulation gap. He made the last link in a chain uniting Europe and Asia Minor with Africa, a goal of surveyors for more than a hundred years previously. The exact distance between London and Cape Town thus became known!

They found no sign of aircraft debris on the Peninsula: no fishermen's tales about a plane coming down in the Strait, no interplane struts holding up the roof of a local dwelling. The mystery of the *Hannibal* lives on.

Apart from a few brief entries in his geological notebook, Mike wrote nothing about the expedition. He did mention 'a few anxious moments', such as the occasion when he paced along the shore with Norman Falcon discussing the problems confronting the expedition, the turn in the weather and the difficult terrain.

There was another story to tell of the Musandam expedition, a personal one that will not be found in the official reports of the Royal Geographical Society. To understand this story, it is necessary to consider the days leading up to Christmas.

IT BEGAN WITH the foxes. The party would occasionally be woken in the early hours by blood-curdling shrieks from the cliffs behind the Dib Dibba camp. The shrieks were identified by Paul Cornelius as coming from sand foxes, looking much like English foxes but with big ears and sand-coloured coats. Then, on the night of 19 December, a gusting wind silenced the foxes, bringing swirls of dust into the camp.

Later they would count their blessings. A fully-fledged *shamal* came in next day, twisting the rain and mixing it with dirt and sand, flattening most of the tents and leaving the camp in a thick, grey sludge, but the equipment was preserved and the most serious loss was a box of Derek South's cigars, trampled in the rush to stop the fridge setting fire to the mess marquee as it collapsed in the wind.

A more severe loss was narrowly averted: the storm almost claimed the *Tarak*. A heavy metal mast had been fitted to the dhow to support a grabbing and dredging boom. It rested precariously on the keel. Sailing back to Khasab Bay from the east coast with Paul Cornelius on board, the dhow met the full force of the storm just before rounding the north of Musandam. Caught abeam, she rolled right over on her scuppers. One of the four inadequate mast-stays slipped its clamp, and the supporting crown slid down the mast, which began pounding the keel like a battering ram. The dour skipper seized the moment, turning sharply to port to find shelter where temporary repairs could be effected. The mast was tied fast, somewhat tenuously, with Paul's dredge-hauling rope. The party paused before venturing forth again. Leaving the shelter, the dhow rolled beam-on in a wave-fetch from India for twenty minutes before finally heading south to Khasab with a safer, following sea. The mast was discarded at the earliest opportunity.

As the storm blew in, with sand hurtling through the camp, Norman Falcon kept trying, knee deep, to sweep his tent clean. And when in the morning he was found on his hands and knees, peering into Mike's tent, he explained that he was trying to work out why Mike had no sand in his tent while there was a pile of it in his own. By now Norman was anxious to call off the whole expedition, announcing that it was 'impossible to work if this sort of thing happens'.

The rigours of the expedition were taking their toll. It had first come to light in the little things: a 'daily parcel of dithers', as one member described it. The expedition's budget was a constant theme: they were overspending and must cut down on the use of gas and kerosene, and then, suddenly, they had sufficient funds to equip the whole camp with further mats, to hire a tent and build another *barasti*. Norman worried that the camp was not a suitable place for a woman, referring to the impending arrival of Miss Beatrice de Cardi when he said 'We must have new tablecloths and floor mats'.

Later, when the *shamal* had subsided, Norman paced up and down the shore, with Mike in attendance talking him through the problems. It was typical of Mike's Yorkshire grit that he wanted to see the expedition through, since he viewed the damage caused by the storms as minimal. But attitudes among the members had changed: from that day on no-one had complete confidence that the expedition would run its full course, and it was later confirmed that the expedition would end a month earlier than planned.

AT THE SURVEY camp on the Sibi Isthmus, it was a different story. At 6 a.m. on the Monday, Hugh May and Phillip Robinson woke to the patter of rain. They sprang into action, gathering all the sensitive equipment under shelter before the downpour hit them like a drum roll. Then they brewed tea and waited, while everyone sat around in a state of collective despondency. With the rain came wind, which threatened to circumscribe their activities for the rest of the day.

Presently, the servicemen left camp and took the Gemini to motor around to a place where they had placed a tidal gauge, known as the north gauge landing. They tried to manoeuvre the small, inflatable boat against wind and waves, but they were suddenly blown on to a sharp rock that gashed the rubber skin of the boat, causing it to deflate. Undeterred, they hauled the Gemini on to the shore and started up the scree on foot to meet up with Derek South, who was waiting on the other side of the ridge where strong squalls were whipping up a choppy sea.

While Paul Cornelius stayed on board *Tarak* to dredge for hydroids before returning to Khasab, the servicemen looked on from the shore. After an hour they concluded that the wind was not going to abate, so they chose to carry out sounding work in the sheltered fjords of the Peninsula. The next three hours were 'pretty wet and even colder'. Although completing four sounding runs across the fjord, it became obvious that the weather was worsening and that their work would have to be curtailed.

The wind strengthened. White horses appeared in the bay as lines of dark water indicated squalls sweeping in across the jagged peaks of the western shore. The small party retreated over the isthmus to devour a tinned Dundee cake, partly to lift their spirits, partly to celebrate the approach of Christmas, and set up a survey camp.

The wind rose all evening. By the time Phillip and Hugh retired to their camp beds in the early hours the more powerful blasts were threatening to rip off the roofs of their shelters, waking them with alarm as they battered the canvas. In the night, the labourers lost their roof, while the other – which had been reinforced before dark – survived.

They emerged at daybreak in various states of disarray, the wind and cold having caused a restless night. Supplies of fresh water were critical, with only two-and-a-half litres per person, and the small dhow likely to be storm bound. They tried to carry on business as usual: a wet and very cold morning, with constant squalls whipping spray across the Gemini as Phillip and Hugh struggled to complete their soundings in the bay, shipping water over the bow as they went.

Then events took a turn for the better. News reached them of the small dhow's arrival off Dib Dibba, bringing supplies of food and fresh water, cigarettes and whisky. The weather began to ameliorate at midday, making the afternoon's soundings easier and allowing them to finish by mid-afternoon and return to their small camp. Although in the evening, as they huddled together over the cooking stove, it was still very cold with the wind persisting, the storm had left a beautiful legacy in its wake:

> A new magic in the mountains in these conditions. The orange grey rocks are now a
> solid grey. Clouds hang over the higher summits and scud by above. The sea is black-
> blue laced with white. Gulls swarm with shrill cries in sheltered corners. These views
> and the moan of wind in rocks brings a strong sensation of home, or Irish mountains
> or – more so – the Western Highlands.[5]

Two nights later, when the wind had diminished, the Peninsula revealed another aspect of its complex nature:

> A cold night again with the odd slight chill gust, but otherwise flat calm. The still warm
> reaches of the bay are more luminescent than I've ever seen them before. Each time a
> fish jumps there is a great blaze of green. Whilst communing on my haunches on the
> tidal foreshore I noticed the shallows sparkling and flashing green, as small insects
> brushed the surface. Very beautiful and very calm.[6]

MIKE LEFT THE camp at Dib Dibba and joined the survey party at Dabshan on 23 December, no doubt relieved to get away from the devastation of the main camp, and happy to act as Phillip Robinson's staff director in his survey of the Maqlab Isthmus. It was an arrangement which suited them both, since Phillip appreciated the help of an Arabic speaker to assist in their dealings with the labourers. Phillip and Mike would make several survey trips together over the next few weeks.

Christmas was rapidly approaching, and soon it was time to suspended work for a few festive activities. At midday on Christmas Eve they left the isthmus and joined *Nasser*, returning to the main camp at Dib Dibba where Phillip, Hugh and Paul could witness the scene of destruction for themselves. Much had changed in their absence. The basic layout of the camp was the same, but the tents had been reinforced and to some degree rearranged. Phillip's own tent and the office tent were in chaos, with jumbles of paper, sand, books, containers and equipment scattered all around.

Nonetheless an attempt had been made to decorate the forlorn camp with fluorescent flags and buoys, red bunting and a line of stockings decking out the mess tent, which was topped by a chimney pot. There were a few pencil and chalk sketches around the tent, one sketch characterizing the members of the expedition: Norman Falcon in his bath with a pile of forty of the loathsome camp *chapattis* beside him, based on his axiom 'Why do you need bread when you can walk to Muscat on forty *chapattis*?'; Mike sitting amidst a pile of beer cans and cases; Paul Cornelius in his sleeping bag; Derek South breaking rocks; Hugh May shipwrecked in a Gemini alongside a broken tide pole; Phillip Robinson with a theodolite standing on a sharp jebel.

The Wali was expected to visit the camp at some point during Christmas Day. When he did not arrive in the early morning, the party set about their own tasks: Norman contemplating a tour of the old fort, Mike enjoying a lie-in, and so on. For Phillip, it was time to stock up for his surgery. But he quickly discovered that Khasab was not the ideal place to find a pharmacy. In the *suq*, certain essential items – bandages, plasters, gauzes, cotton wool – were non-existent. Others – Chinese liniments, French-labelled tubes of penicillin, gripe waters, unlabelled tablets – were so bizarre as to be useless. But he was not entirely disappointed, and he found a few items that could be used in his work, such as Aspirin, Sloane's Liniment, a single packet of cough drops, linctus and Dettol.

As Phillip was leaving Khasab the Wali appeared with his bodyguards, driving a brand new Land Rover, exchanging greetings and offering a lift back to the camp. Phillip accepted, but almost immediately regretted his decision; the Wali was a terrible driver. Showing intense concentration in every line of his chubby face, with his mouth pursed and his brows tightly drawn, he leaned forward with his more-than-ample belly pressed against the steering wheel. He painfully negotiated each corner, scattered people and goats, and narrowly missed several houses, on his less-than-stately progress through the dilapidated streets of the storm-damaged town.

Upon his arrival at the camp, where small eats had been laid out Arab-style on the mess table for the visitors' delectation, the Wali turned to his minions and told them they could drink alcohol if they wished – an offer that they all declined. After exchanging pleasantries the Wali and his retinue departed, leaving the party with the sand, flies and a single, sad acacia tree for company.

They made the most of their situation. Derek presented Mike with a fancy dress outfit – a stocking hat, black eye patch, belt, knife and cardboard cut-out parrot – 'with his battered mouth and stubby beard, he looked every inch a pirate'.[7] Christmas dinner – as near as such – was served in traditional style beneath the tattered canvas of the mess tent:

MENU
Gulf Turtle soup
Roast Duck à la Rahman
Roast Potatoes
Peas à la can opener
Cabbage à la Iran
Apple sauce
Pud à la Christmas
Mince pies à la Khan
Lumpy custard
Fruit

Among the Christmas cards was one from the RGS with a picture of Captain Scott's camp at Cape Evans, 1911, with a message – 'We envy your idyllic site' – and one from Sayyed Majid bin Taimur, the Wali of Khasab.

'It was a good day,' noted Phillip in his journal, as they rounded it off with the Queen's Speech heard on the BBC World Service, just a few drinks and noisy rounds of liar dice.

28 DECEMBER WAS a day that would be 'long pressed' in their memories.

Daybreak saw the whole group leaving Dib Dibba on *Tarak*, taking the labourers with them. One of the labourers, Mohammed, was an uncomplicated man who always tried his best. He was nick-named 'Charlie's Aunt' because of his habit of wearing robes, whatever the circumstances, and arranging his *shemag* in the manner of a ladies' head scarf. Mohammed the camp orderly, whose foot injury had confined him to camp for long periods in the past, was now detailed to join Mike and Phillip on a tachymetric survey of the Maqlab Isthmus:

We all went to the isthmus together with the labourers and Lal Khan. Hugh went to finish the levelling and Norman went to help him; Paul to root for seashore creatures at low tide; Derek to stay and do a detailed geological section; Mike to stay and work with me on tachy and Lal to cook.

Mike and I got into our tachy by 14.00 – I'd had to organise the camp. Norman, Hugh and Paul finished by 14.30 and left on *Tarak* with Abdur and Ahmed.

My tachy station was on a small bluff looking in on all the north east side of the isthmus. From there I shouted to Mike who perched on a rock higher up and directed Abdullah and Mohammed with the staves. Poor Mohammed. A likeable chap hobbling around with his head scarf and dirty green robe – but so slow he drove Mike to distraction.[8]

They worked methodically through the afternoon, Mike directing the labourers as best he could, no doubt growing increasingly annoyed by Mohammed's lack of urgency, and relieved when Phillip called it a day and made to return to the survey camp at Dabshan:

At 16.50 I announced to Mike, who had joined me at the instrument, that I reckoned I'd enough readings and we call it a day. It was cold in the shadows and we'd been going hard. 'Righto,' said Mike, 'I'm for tea,' and stumped off towards the camp calling in Mohammed and Abdullah at the same time.

I continued sketching in, then for no very apparent reason glanced towards Mohammed, only about 40 feet [12 metres] away, at the instant he developed a fit. His arms jerked out in front of him – dropping the staff – his neck twitched visibly, he crumpled at the waist and knees and fell backwards. With a clatter of rocks he tumbled ever faster down the boulder/scree and disappeared over the small shore cliff.

Yelling to Mike – who turned in time to see him drop over the cliff – I ran like a Shihuh goat down the scree reaching Mohammed only 20 to 30 seconds after he had fallen.

He was lying just out of the water on a flat ledge of rock still violently twitching. I immediately restrained his movements, aided by Abdullah who was hot on my trail and, as he subsided, checked the damage.

Briefly, he had sustained a terrible gash across the top of his head, three or so inches [8 cm] long, a half inch [1.3 cm] wide and down to the bone. I later found a hole punched into his head but that was not immediately apparent. No bones broken, a variety of cuts and abrasions, but nothing else.

They were far from civilization, without a radio to summon help, with a darkening sky to the east and a restless sea to the west:

I started staunching the blood, first with my *shemag*, then with my vest. Quickly instructed Mike to take the Gemini, moored almost alongside, and get my haversack pack from the survey camp (patrol pack), then return with *Nasser* and with Derek. Of course first the anchor jammed and then the outboard played up.

In the ten minutes Mike was away, Mohammed came round in glazed fashion. I comforted him, satisfied myself he had no spinal injuries and made him more comfortable. An interminable wait during which the blood flowed steadily through my improvised pads.

Severe shock was setting in and it was clear he would best be moved immediately and treated thereafter, so as soon as *Nasser* appeared we ran her bow against the rocks, laid out the gangplank and assisted by Derek and the crew got Mohammed aboard.

Quick instructions. Get to camp. Blankets, bags (not yet unpacked), camp bed, supplementary medical box, Derek and Abdullah stay, Mike come with me. At the same time, got Mohammed, who was part conscious, to take two sulphatriad. I couldn't get at the wounds – head so matted with blood – so sprayed the whole area with cicatrin [an antibiotic powder] and applied a pressure pad of gauze.

They shouted instructions at the agitated crew, who shoved *Nasser* off the rocks and set the dhow's course through the sheltered Elphinstone Inlet (Khawr Dabshan) for the rough open sea:

As we thumped out of Dabshan in the dusk, Mohammed was grey and complaining of cold and pain. Tarpaulin on bed under him. One, two, three blankets on top. Not enough. Sleeping bag and valise cover. Sips of hot tea. But what about the pain? A dangerous factor in shock. Distalgesic perhaps, but that tranquillizes. Is that a good thing or not? Might slow him up. But pain could be worse. Right, one distalgesic.

Pulse 105 and weak. Blood everywhere. Lord, where is it coming from? Scissors. Cut away hair, but hurts him and so blood-clotted it won't come away. More gauze pads. Keep up pressure. Smile at patient. 'Mike a torch please.' '*Sif, chai min fadlak.*' ['Tea please.'] Still the blood. Search with torch. Cold wind. Sea spray. Boat rising and falling in swell. I find it. The unnoticed hole, welling out thick lumpy gore. Cotton wool. Cicatrin. Plug it – more tea. More smiles. Bandage on pads. Where are we? Turned out of Khawr Shamm. Sky threatening.

'Mike we must go straight to Bukha, the nearest doctor.' Agitated conversation between Mike and crew.

'Sorry Phil, crew do not like the look of the weather. Could get in real trouble off Bukha. Must go to Khasab. Try and get aero-medivac from Gendarmerie.'

Agreed. A bad sea would certainly finish him off.

Ah. Bleeding checked. Swab up the gore all around me. Pulse better. Mohammed sleeping. Less grey. For first time relax a little. Light a shaky cigarette. Find tip blood-stained. Who cares?

'Mike.'

'Yes,' from the darkness.

'You'll find a bottle of whisky in my bag. Time for the doctor to treat himself for shock.'

God it's cold. Whisky, tea, cigarette. Feel better, Khasab coming up. But no Gemini to get ashore.

Lay alongside *Tarak*. 'Where's your dinghy?'

'Fishing off the point.'

It was vital to find the dinghy so that Mike could be put ashore to contact the Gendarmerie to radio for aero-medivac help. Searching around, they found the dinghy and Mike set off. On the shore the lights of a Land Rover switched on indicated that he had made it and was on his way to the Gendarmerie post. Meanwhile, Phillip stayed on board *Nasser* with his patient:

Mohammed sleeping. Pulse 90. Not too weak. No more blood. (Had) told Mike that if no aero-medivac until daylight best not move Mohammed in case of relapse into severe shock. Would treat on boat. But a big swell running. Motion quite violent. Decide better take risk and get him ashore. Can handle him better there.

Tarak dinghy took note to camp. Abdul arrives with Tilley lamp, tea towels, more bandage and gauzes – all emergency stock being finished. Also flask of coffee and biscuits. Send note back with Abdul. 'Severe swell. Decided to transfer to shore. Need Gemini. Should appreciate Mohammed is critical and may die.'

Moon appears from scudding clouds. See a cold oily darkness, rising and falling like a large sinister animal asleep.

'Oh God, he's having another fit.' '*Sif taltal sare.*' ['Come come quickly.'] Battle to hold him down. Try to support head but bandages torn off. Blood again, pulsing everywhere. Suddenly falls quiet. Pulse still there. Last of the gauze. Pad with tea towels. Gemini arrives with Hugh at helm and – God bless – Geoff Harcourt dressed only in his underpants. He'd had to swim the creek.

Geoff says he cannot get an aero-medivac before morning. Says take him to Bukha. I realize that crew won't. However, weather is clearing and Geoff persuades crew. Says he'll signal ahead. Gendarmerie will be waiting.

Hugh takes a look. Turns a bit green.

'You OK then Phillip?'

'Certainly Hugh, I'm all right.'

But I've been tending him three hours now. I'm tired and I'm cold.

The two men returned to Khasab in the Gemini while Phillip, his only option now to head for Bukha, inwardly cursed his predicament and turned back to the task in hand:

Head for the open sea. Bleeding checked. Mohammed woke again. Most worried about a cut on his hand which is hurting a lot, and pain in his kidney. Give him another distalgesic, and apply nupercainal to the cut. He goes to sleep again.

Round Ras Sheikh Masud [the western headland of Khasab Bay]. Some stars but little moon. White caps. Spray. Thud of the bows and thump of the engine. Leave Mohammed briefly to grab some handfuls of fish and rice from crew's meal. Gives me indigestion and pains in the stomach. Coffee and chain-smoke. Take an edge of one of the blankets and sit alongside camp bed under it holding Mohammed's hand. Sing quietly. It seems to please him.

I see the lights of Bukha but they never seem to get closer. About 21.00. Rolling heavily and hold Mohammed's head. He's very quiet but awake again. Give him more coffee.

A certain nightmare quality sets in. Those unattainable lights, the Tilley lamp packed in, battery torch low. Spray kicking back out of the darkness. Shadows of the three crew hunched around the tiller. Find I've been leaning in a pool of blood.

Mohammed suddenly sick. Then another fit. More bleeding. Not a single bandage or gauze left. Press a tea towel hard against the head.

Eyes very glazed. Can't feel pulse any more but can feel breath. Bukha so close now. Pain in my stomach a dull throb. So very, very cold. Take a bit more whisky and coffee. Another cigar. Still no apparent pulse but breathing. Glance into red book to check on how to do cardiac massage. Damn it, why have I no stimulants in all that mass of drugs in my pack? My fault.

We've arrived off Bukha. A few lights. Sea smashing against a low shore cliff. No sign of life. Repeatedly flash SOS. What happened to that signal?

Unbeknown to Phillip, there was life on the shore. But the first sign of it was not quite what Phillip had been expecting:

A couple of Arabs amble on to the rocks. Long exchanges with boat crew. For God's sake – what is anyone doing? Decide to swim for shore if we can find a beach but locals finally amble off saying they'll get a British officer.

'Hello, ahoy!' from the darkness.

Thank God.

'Get around headland to beach there. We are trying to launch a raft for you.'

'OK,' I yell back over the wind, 'as quick as you can please, he's nearly dead.'

Back to Mohammed. Can hardly feel breath. Flash torch in his eyes. He looks back. Is awake and alive. I take a hand. He grasps at mine as if he can draw life from me. Perhaps in a way he can.

The crew steered the *Nasser* round the headland, to reveal frantic activity taking place on the shore:

Opposite the beach. See shadows of a score or more people hauling a heavy object along the sand. A little later it's in the sea and headed for me propelled by four men with sweep oars. A flash of moonlight shows a great big box – the Khasab raft. Not exactly made for heavy swells and injured men.

Couple of Brits jump aboard and two Arab soldiers. Get Mohammed on to stretcher. Now the difficult bit. Boat goes up, box down. Box down, boat up. Lurch apart, crash together. Fast patter of Arabic with an Oxford accent and sudden lift – he's in. I grab bag and follow.

'*Bukha, Saa tossa.*' ['Tomorrow, nine o'clock'] I call to the dhow and with a thump of heavy diesel *Nasser* claws her way off this treacherous lee shore.

No time for talk. I continue to hold Mohammed's hand as we are taken by the surf and borne in. Not quite there. Drawn back in a mass of foam. The Brits leaning heavily on the oars. Another wave. Leap forward. Crash on to the sand. A half-dozen men struggling in the sea to get hold of the raft which had been hastily built by lashing together empty forty-gallon [180 litre] drums and decking with planks. Ropes snake out and another dozen heave from the beach. Foam. Roaring waves. Up, down, crash. Up, down – silence. On the beach.

'Sorry old boy, doctor won't come to beach but I've got a stretcher party here.'

Six Arabs lift stretcher and start off at a jog. I thrust my bag into the hands of a Brit and follow. Another Brit jogs alongside.

Five minutes to the hospital. At least the doctor's waiting. A young doctor, seems at a bit of a loss. Stretcher bearers all stand around and gawp at nearly dead figure on the stretcher. Door swings open. A pretty and smiling Pakistani girl sweeps in. The hospital sister. 'Out, thank you,' she orders the stretcher bearers. Gets doctor in hand. Mohammed quickly lifted on to bed. Obtains quick history. Blood pressure – very low.

'Better come along,' my companion says, 'you need a drink and you can't help here.'

Phillip was led away to a small, sparsely furnished mess to enjoy a drink with a couple of service personnel. At 12.30 a.m., he was called back to the hospital, where Mohammed's situation looked bleak:

Back to hospital. Mohammed now got tubes sticking out of him. 'Sorry,' says the doctor, 'I think he'll die very shortly, but if he does last the night we must fly him to Dubai in the early morning. Has lost a lot of blood and I've almost none here. Also has probably damaged skull. Needs an X-ray.'

With nothing more to do Phillip retired to bed, only to be woken shortly by a hammering on the door:

Doctor appears. He gives a grin. 'Patient has rallied,' he says. 'Should survive until morning.'
'Thanks doc,' I reply. Gone up a bit in my estimation. Needn't have walked over here.
Back to sleep until the duty orderly sweeps in with the dawn dew and a cup of tea.

Phillip flew back to Khasab at 6:30 a.m., while the aero-medivac flew Mohammed to Dubai where he made a complete recovery. Mohammed returned to the Dib Dibba camp on Sunday 9 January looking undimmed and very cheerful, his wounds having healed up well. Mike agreed to keep him on the expedition payroll for the time being, a gesture that greatly pleased the other men.

Mohammed was back in the fold.

As the sun was going down, the calm of a gentle evening in Khasab Bay was broken by a flashing light signalling the return of *Tarak* from a survey to the north. In the camp Phillip waited for Norman, Derek and Hugh to arrive from the dhow, his quiet idyll about to end.

Stepping ashore were Barry and Clive, the 'Sparker' men. Over drinks they were introduced to the other members of the party, looking much like fish out of water. Barry was a regular guy who knew his job well, young with frizzy hair and beard. When on board *Tarak*, Barry would strip to his waist and, wearing jeans and boots, lie on a camp bed on the deck of the dhow. Clive was quietly spoken with a London accent, a graduate from Leeds University.

Days later, when Phillip was working on the Isthmus again, he encountered the Sparker survey in Khawr ash Shamm. Norman was disappointed as he read the print-outs which showed that the Sparker was only penetrating about 90 metres into the sediment without finding the main rock bed. It was no surprise when it was announced that the Sparker crew would be leaving a week earlier than planned.

While Mike and Derek concentrated on measuring sections along Wadi al Ayn, Beatrice frantically collected pottery, Paul wandered about shooting lizards and Phillip caught up on his paperwork.

Sometimes camp life could be a depressing business. Once, awoken by rumbles of an approaching storm, the party gathered in the mess tent as the thunder came over and the rain lashed in. 'It's a fine soft morning,' declared Phillip. Outside, the sight of the watchman's wife plodding over from Khasab with his breakfast might have raised a smile. But Norman, standing in the doorway watching the rain, remained utterly and heavily despondent, good cheer and banter only serving to increase his gloom.

It was time to call it a day. There was no sadness among the party: the survey had run its course, and although Phillip was still making plans to return for a survey of the southern part of the Peninsula, they were all relieved to be heading back to civilization. On 30 January 1972 they packed up the tents and cleared the site, presenting the Gendarmerie with a fridge and the Wali with some chairs, and then ceremoniously burnt the thunder-box. The next morning, when the site was finally cleared, the only sign of their occupation was a few scuff marks in the sand and a pile of whitewashed stones neatly stacked to one side.

They boarded *Tarak* bound for Dubai. As they sailed out of Khasab Bay, a squall blew up. After sailing a short distance south-westwards along the coastline, they saw a water spout, a smudge on the horizon, a thin column of water twisting upwards in a crooked line to meet the threatening clouds that were massing over their heads.

Against this backdrop of an angry sky, the members of the expedition sailed towards the calmer waters of the Persian Gulf, the water spout gesturing a dark farewell from one of the remoter parts of the Earth that had retained most of its secrets for another day.

The RGS party, winter 1971 – 72: colour section p. xiii
A drowned valley of Musandam: colour section p. xiv
Paul Cornelius carrying out 'field' work in Musandam: colour section p. xv
Tachyometry on the Maqlab Isthmus with Mike Morton and labourer, December 1971:
colour section p. xv
A view of the Musandam Peninsula, Khasab from the north: colour section p. xvi

1   N. L. Falcon, 'From Musandam to the Iranian Makran', *Geographical Journal*, London, Vol. 141, Part I, p. 165.
      N. L. Falcon, 'The Musandam Expedition 1971–72. Scientific results, Part I, II. Vertical and horizontal earth movements', *Geographical Journal*, 1973, Vol. 139, Part 3, p. 404.
      N. L. Falcon, 'The Musandam, Northern Oman, Expedition 1971–72', *Geographical Journal*, 1973, Vol. 139, Part I, p. 24.
2   Later named *Lacerta coerulea Arnold* on account of the blue underbelly of the male.
3   Then Secretary of the Council for British Archaeology.
4   Lieutenant May's report is included in 'The Musandam Expedition Scientific Results, Part II', *Royal Geographical Journal*, Vol. 140, Part I, p. 103.
5   Phillip Robinson, 'Musandam Expedition: A Personal Narrative'.
6   Ibid.
7   Ibid.
8   This and the following quotations in this chapter are from Phillip Robinson, 'Musandam Expedition: A Personal Narrative'.

Epilogue

What makes the desert beautiful is that somewhere it hides a well.[1]

Mike always spoke highly of the Bedu, and it was with these nomads of the desert that he felt a strong affinity. Fluent in Arabic, well respected by the tribes, *Shaib al-Ahmar* would roam the interior with a confident air. Yet, much as Thesiger predicted, it appears that the roaming Arab has declined with the advent of modern life.

Indeed, much of the Middle East as Mike knew it has changed. It is a far more dangerous place. Palestine has become subsumed in violent conflict, with declaration of the state of Israel; and two major wars in 1948 and 1967 have redrawn the boundaries of a troubled region. The state of Jordan still exists albeit surrounded by conflict. The modern history of Iraq is of course well known and with it the ongoing fate of Kurdistan. Only the Trucial States avoided bloody conflict in their transition to the United Arab Emirates.

In the Hadhramaut, 'Ingrams' Peace' did not hold. Following a guerrilla war the British retreated from Aden in 1967 and civil war ensued, with the Protectorates coming together and eventually being swallowed up by the Republic of Yemen.

Some things didn't change: in 1982 when Mike and Dr Gerhard Martin returned to Yemen working for the Hunt Oil Company, they were met in the traditional way with a modern twist:

> On a visit to a reported surface exposure of salt at Safir dome, the geologists were fired upon by riflemen at the dome as they drove towards the feature. They stopped immediately and took cover, and they were soon approached and informed that, although they were welcome, their vehicle was not, since it 'might contaminate the salt'. The mine, located along a one-time principal caravan route, had been in operation for centuries, and those in charge, although in a rather remote corner of the world, were intensely aware of the necessity of at least attempting to maintain immaculate environmental conditions.[2]

Ultimately the search for oil in the Yemen bore fruit: the Hunt Oil Company made the first commercial discovery at Arif in July 1984, followed by eleven fields in the next eight years.

Sometimes the question is asked: 'How much oil did Mike find?'

Mike would have been the first to acknowledge that oil exploration is a team effort and that correctly ruling out the presence of oil can be as vital as finding it. Aspects of his work contributed towards the discovery of oil: helping to open up and map territories such as the Aden Protectorates and Oman for oil exploration; taking part in the stratigraphic research programme which led to further oil discoveries in Iraq – Mike and René unravelled the geology of many parts of nothern Iraq and their field work in the 1940s and 1950s has never been repeated and is still the foundation of our knowledge of Mesozoic outcrops today; overseeing geological operations in Abu Dhabi at a time when the massive Bu Hasa field was discovered. He would not be drawn on the subject but mischievously perhaps he would sometimes say: 'I know where the world's largest oilfield lies and it still hasn't been found.'

Mike in Kurdistan, c.1950
© Iraq Petroleum Company

THERE WAS ONE loose end in Mike's story. The man known as El Khalidi intrigued me: who was this mysterious figure who emerged from the gloom, told incredible stories and then disappeared into the desert again? In November 2003, when the tales of El Khalidi must have been a distant memory for Mike, an article appeared in *The Independent* newspaper:

THE TRUTH SEEKER – VETERANS RECALL THE PALESTINE REGIMENT[3]

Hazim Khalidi in 1973

The article told the story of Hazim Khalidi, an Arab who fought alongside Jews in the Palestine Regiment for the British during World War II and then against the Jews in the First Arab War of 1948. This Khalidi bore remarkable similarities to the El Khalidi described in Mike's journal. But there was no evidence to prove that Hazim Khalidi had ever visited the Hadhramaut or the fort at Bir Asakir, so I couldn't be sure that they were one and the same. I set out to find Sa'ad Khalidi, referred to in the article as Hazim Khalidi's son, to check what I suspected: that my father had met his father in the Western Hadhramaut all those years ago.

Early in 2004, I attempted to contact Robert Fisk, the author of the article, at first without success. Then, out of the blue, an answer came. I arrived home one evening to find a message on my answerphone: it was Robert Fisk from Baghdad, with Sa'ad's address and telephone number. 'Greetings from Baghdad,' Robert ended his call, 'if it is possible to send greetings from such a place.'

I contacted Sa'ad, and he confirmed that his father had indeed been in the Hadhramaut in November 1949, having been parachuted in with a bandolier of gold and a belt of ammunition on behalf of the United Nations. El Khalidi had come home to roost.

On an overcast day in October 2004 my wife and I met Sa'ad Khalidi outside the imposing gates of the Saudi Arabian Embassy, W1. We had arranged to visit an exhibition of Arabian travellers and, as we toured the exhibits, the poignancy of the moment was apparent. There we were, the sons of Mike and Hazim, surrounded by photographs of famous explorers – Thomas, Philby and Thesiger – exchanging stories, much in the same way that our fathers had almost fifty-five years before, in the whitewashed fort at Bir Asakir.[4]

THE HISTORY OF oil production is littered with abandoned derricks, the skeletal remains of unsuccessful attempts to find oil in the ground; but drilling remains the only sure-fire way of finding oil. Today, computer-aided technology allows exploration companies to build models of the Earth's subsurface. New surveys are compared with old to monitor and predict how fluids in an oil or gas reservoir are migrating. And yet, for all this technology, there is truth in the saying 'oil is only found with the drill bit'.

Nothing is ever certain in the oil game. Dire predictions are made about the world's petroleum reserves running dry. Nonetheless, as consumption increases, new oil deposits are being discovered and opened up. New methods of extraction are being developed. Territories once thought to be marginal can be transformed into profitable ones by a rise in the price of crude oil on the world markets. Politics and war also have a part to play in the never-ending search for new oil reserves. No place illustrates these themes better than Oman.

In the mid-sixties, the Americans withdrew from the Dhofar oil concession. Civil war broke out in the province in 1965, presenting new problems for oil exploration. When Shell arrived on the scene and began to reappraise the concession, times had changed dramatically since Mike and René had travelled in the company of the paramount sheikhs, and feasted with them under a desert moon. Guerrilla activity now made it highly dangerous to travel through the interior of Dhofar, as a Shell employee reported in his field notebook:

> It seems that the whole area from Jebel Qara to Jebel Samhan and the sea are extremely unsafe except the coastal plain around Salalah. To escort us properly would require about sixty soldiers.[5]

Oil prospectors in Dhofar proved remarkably determined in the face of disappointment. It is a tribute to the Sultan Said bin Taimur, his son Qaboos and the companies involved, that they persisted in their efforts. In 1974 the Omani Government took a 60% shareholding in PD(O) Ltd, with a foreign interest comprising Shell, Total and Partex. By 1977, a long-term agreement was reached which provided for the development of the oil fields of Dhofar, continued investment by the private shareholders (Shell, Total and Partex), and an active level of exploration.

Several factors assisted in this process: successes in finding oil in north and central Oman; uncertainties over the boundary between Dhofar and Oman being resolved; a sharp rise in world oil prices in 1973 making heavy-oil fields such as Marmul a viable economic option; the end of the civil war in 1975; and improvements in seismic techniques.

Oman prospers on its oil revenues. Today, the province once known as Dhofar contributes about one-fifth of Oman's oil production, a fulfillment of H. H. Said bin Taimur's dream. Tourists visit Muscat and Salalah in increasing numbers, and expats from Oman and the United Arab Emirates visit the Duqm coast in air-conditioned Four-Wheel Drives at Ras Duqm to enjoy its beaches, birdlife, and relative solitude. Metalled roads make it possible to drive all the way from Dhofar to Muscat and beyond. Musandam, too, has shed its mystery and welcomes tourists to its rocky coast.

JEBEL FAHUD ON a windswept day. We are standing on a ridge overlooking the oil field as Egyptian vultures wheel above us in a cloudless sky.

The days of discovering giant oil fields are nearly over. Emerging industrial nations such as India and China are making growing demands on precious oil resources. Production is likely to peak in the next few decades. Countries are stepping up their gas consumption but gas is not going to meet the world's energy needs for long. Ahead lies the Holy Grail, the move from carbon-based fuels to new energy sources, such as hydrogen fuel.

In many ways Fahud symbolizes the past, present and future of world oil production. There has been much talk about the failure to Fahud No. 1 to strike oil, of the decision not to extend the seismic survey line north of the well site and to abandon drilling in 1957 after only one attempt. Why? Did 'bean counting' accountants in IPC headquarters call it a day? Did the absence of the Jurassic Arab Zone – a formation of rocks in which oil had been discovered elsewhere in the Middle East – deceive senior Company geologists into thinking that there was no oil to be found at Fahud? Or was there simply a loss of faith? As Dr Alan Heward of Petroleum Development Oman put it: 'Once confidence is lost in a project, it is very difficult to get it back.'

Natih opened the door to Fahud in 1963 when the newly-constituted PDO returned there: the discovery of oil at Natih strongly suggested the presence of oil at neighbouring Fahud. Today, as if to mock the work of the early explorers, Fahud well no. 153 stands a few hundred metres away from the site of the first doomed well, discreetly feeding oil into a network of flow lines that eventually leads to the sea. Four hundred and ten wells have been drilled so far, leaving one side of the once-barren jebel dotted with well heads. The marks of a recent seismic survey remain, with stripes drawn across the Leopard's flanks. The easy oil has been recovered but nearly four times as much still remains in the ground.

Geologist Dr Volker Vahrenkamp is now explaining what the next fifty years might have in store for the Fahud oil field. One hundred geologists, engineers and researchers in PDO, Shell and many universities around the world are investigating its future development. Visions of unconventional methods of extraction are conjured up. Steam-assisted gas-oil drainage, where vast quantities of clean water are pumped from desalination plants on the coast, boiled in a power plant near the field and then injected into the ground. Or open-cast mining, creating a huge hole in the ground and digging out the oil. Volker concludes: 'Who knows, maybe in 100 years there will be a huge inland lake with beaches and resorts in Fahud. Ready to buy some property?'

So much lies in the future but finally we must consider the past.

IN 1955, MIKE was driving through the desert in the Wadi Amairi when he came upon a tribesman squatting beneath a *samr* tree.[6] They struck up a conversation in Arabic. The man asked for a job and Mike engaged him as a rod man. Although Aziz was more accustomed to riding a camel, bringing charcoal up from the south to trade in the Trucial States and digging salt from the salt domes, he proved a willing and dependable worker and taught himself to drive. Mike and Aziz became good friends.

The field party was returning from the desert to the oil camp one day when they came upon a poster advertising Watneys brown ale pasted to an outside wall of the bar known as The Swinging Tit. This should not have been a great surprise to the geologists because the General Manager was a keen proponent of the brand but the sight of it amused them nonetheless. They took turns in having their photographs taken in front of it; and someone took a photograph of Mike and his driver Aziz facing each other, mimicking the characters portrayed on the poster.[7]

After Mike's stint in Oman ended in 1957, there was no contact between the two. Aziz got on with his life, using the money he had earned from his driving job to buy camels and cultivate palm trees in the village of Adam. He became relatively prosperous and had three wives and ten children, five boys and five girls. He died in 1981.

Fast-forward to 20 January 2006. Don Sheridan and I had been invited to Oman by the Geological Society of Oman to take part in the 50th Anniversary of the spudding-in of Fahud No.1. On Don's behalf, an Omani geologist Raid Jamali raised the possibility of tracing the sons of Aziz. The oil company found five brothers and to help confirm that they were the sons of the correct Aziz, the eldest son Hamoud brought a photograph of their father with a 'well-dressed Englishman' into the PDO office at Fahud.

It was arranged that we should meet at the Golden Tulip Hotel in Nizwa on our return from the Fahud oil field. As I walked into the lobby, a French geologist said to me excitedly, 'Aziz's sons are here and they've brought a photograph of *your* father!'

And there it was, emerging from the mists of time, the photograph of Mike and Aziz taken outside The Swinging Tit. It was the only photograph the brothers had of their father. I had not seen this photograph before and – more than fifty years on – it felt as though my father had just walked into the room.

The brothers were not finished yet. Hamoud approached and presented me with a red box which was opened to reveal a *khanjar*. 'We are giving you this *khanjar* because your father gave our father a job when times were hard,' he said.

I remembered what my father had told me about the Bedu being a proud and noble people. Here, in the lobby of a modern hotel, the heart of the desert had opened to me at last and I knew that my journey was at an end.

MIKE, AFTER A decade of consultancy work for various companies, retired from the oil business in 1984. The Iraq Petroleum Company became a shadow of its former self, a small company without subsidiaries administering the Company pension fund (which in due course was contracted out).

Mike took an active interest in the Middle East until he passed away on 22 November 2003. Some might say that he found it difficult to break away from the past. It is true that he always liked to reminisce about his desert life, telling stories which we took with a pinch of salt, little realizing that they were entirely true. Perhaps, if he were alive today, we might have listened a little more closely to the stories he told, but now that he is gone, a little part of each story has been lost for ever.

There are still vast tracts of land untouched by human beings. Satellite photographs show wide expanses of the Earth unscathed by progress - no houses, no roads, no tracks, no cars, no planes, no airstrips, and no oilmen to disturb the virgin soil. It was the very isolation of the desert that captured Mike:

... the challenge of a new country, another people and the excitement of arriving in a stretch of desert and have the *feeling* that you are discovering it for the very first time.

All these things drew a young man from a bleak northern town into the heart of the desert. As I looked around at the last remaining evidence of Mike's time in the Middle East – the ragged books of scribbled notes piled on the desk, the books, maps and geological reports strewn across the table – I realized that he had left something more precious behind.

The heart of the desert beats on.

Mike and Aziz outside 'The Swinging Tit', 1955

The author with the sons of Aziz, January 2006: colour section p. xvi

1   Excerpt from *The Little Prince* by Antoine de Saint-Exupéry, copyright 1943 by Harcourt Inc. and renewed 1971 by Consuelo de Saint-Exupéry, English translation copyright © 2000 by Richard Howard, reprinted by permission of Harcourt Inc.

2   *The Oil Finders: A Collection of Stories About Exploration* edited by Allen G. Hatley, Jr., originally published by the American Association of Petroleum Geologists.

3   Robert Fisk, *The Independent*, 11 November, 2003.

4   El Khalidi's tales live on. See Appendix 5, 'The Truth about El Khalidi'.

5   J. J. K. Poll's field notebook in PDO papers, relating to C. H. Mercanton and J. K. Poll's 'Geological Study of Dhofar'. with kind permission of PD(O) Ltd.

6   See page 182.

7   See the photograph above.

Appendices

Appendix 1

Geological Time

EON	ERA	PERIOD		EPOCH	DATES in millions of years before present	AGE of	
Phanerozoic	Caenozoic	Quaternary		Holocene	0-2	Mammals	Humans
				Pleistocene			
		Tertiary	Neogene	Plerocene	2-5		
				Miocene	5-24		
			Palaeogene	Oligocene	24-37		
				Eocene	37-58		
				Palaeocene	58-66		Extinction of dinosaurs
	Mesozoic	Cretaceous			66-144	Reptiles	Flowering Plants
		Jurassic			144-208		First birds / mammals
		Triassic			208-245		First dinosaurs
	Palaeozoic	Permian			245-286	Amphibians	End of trilobites
		Carboniferous	Pennsylvanian		286-320		First reptiles
			Mississippian		320-360		Large primitive trees
		Devonian			360-408	Fishes	First amphibians
		Silurian			408-438		First land plant fossils
		Ordovician			428-505	Invertebrates	First fish
		Cambrian			505-570		1st shells, trilobites dominant
Proterozoic	Also known as Precambrian				570-2,500		1st multi-celled organisms
Archean					2,500-3,800		1st one-celled organisms
Hadean					3,800-4,600		Approx age of oldest rocks 3,800

Appendix 2

Middle East Oil Concessions, 1948

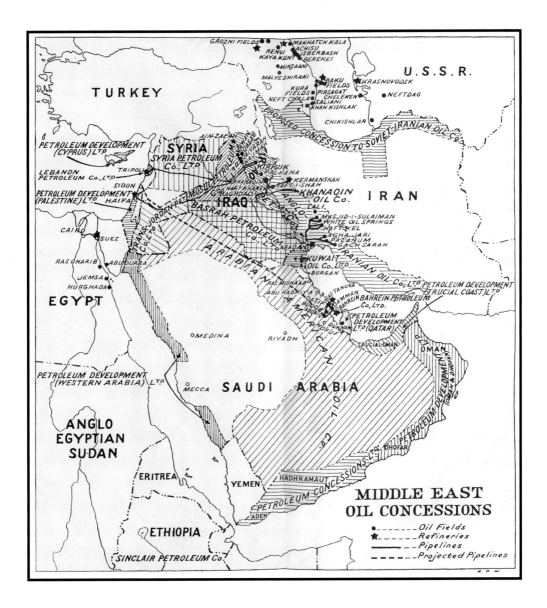

Appendix 3

The Trek to Buraimi

IF YOU'VE HEARD OF THE COAST CALLED
BATTINAH AND P.D. (OMAN & DHOFAR),
YOU SHOULD KNOW OF THE TREK TO BIREIMI,
THAT STARTED ONE DAY IN SONAR

THE VULTURES WERE EVER SO FRIENDLY.

THE PEOPLE DON'T
OFTEN GET VISITS

THOUGH THEY'VE
MADE A FIVE
HUNDRED FOOT
DROP.

EXPLORERS BEFORE WERE ON CAMELS.

PAST THE WATERSHED
WE WENT ON SHELL

WE'D HEARD OF A PASS UP THE JIZZI,
THOUGH THEY SAID IT MIGHT BE A BIT STEEP,
YOU MAY THINK THAT'S EXAGGERATING,
BUT FORD DOESN'T MAKE MOUTAIN SHEEP,

AND THE SCENERY COMPELLED US TO STOP,

BUT UPWARDS AND ON WENT THE CONVOY,
AND THE TRANSPORT STOOD IT QUITE WELL

AND SO TO THE PEACE OF BIREIMI,
WHERE ABOVE THE SOFT SAND PALM TREES LOOM,
AS A HEALTH RESORT BASIS,
I COULD STICK THE OASIS,
AND THE JIZZI AS WELL- IF THERE'S ROOM!

DRAWN: MIKE MORTON
BIREIMI 1949
TRACED: I. KENAN
TRIPOLI 28.3.49

Appendix 4

① It was not long ago, in the wastes of Iraq
That they said "Let's drill by that bush."
And so this skilled judgement (some may call it luck)
Caused the great Kirkuk Oilfield to gush.

② Now we've come a long way from those bad old days,
And our methods are highly refined.
If we view our past record of locating oil,
Our future is clearly defined.

④ Take Basrah f'rinstance, that wide barren plain,
Which RAYCO & SEISMIC pushed hard.
Was it due to the dials on all those machines,
Or their shares in the Scherezade?

⑦ Terbol deep test, or otherwise known,
As profound penetration sub-strata.
A structure no doubt, but what carried the vote,
Was the sea-bathing clause in the charter.

⑧ Geophysicists swear by the far Trucial Coast.
" Drill now, or forever be cursed"
The Company alerted, got on with the job
And located Ras Sadr as first.

③ A mariner's message from Qatar's domain,
Brought the Company rushing to toil.
He said "There's nowt 'ere, but earth, sea, and sky,
And it's 'ot, so there ought to be oil."

⑤ Ain Zalah, where drilling is all hit or miss,
Geological prospect of course;
Or was it the fact that in Northern Iraq,
It's the best place for riding a horse?

⑥ Gaza we know was the genius' touch,
Science told us to drill through that sand,
But recommendations were bound to be right,
With oranges so close at hand.

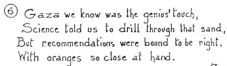

Mike Morton
Qatar 1949
I. Kerray Traced
Tripoli 28.6.49

⑨ To all in Alep, & the man in Amman,
If it's oil that you want with a rush,
Just bury those slide-rules, and burn all your maps,
Get out there, and drill by that bush.

247

Appendix 5

The Truth About El Khalidi

Sa'ad El Khalidi writes:

My father was in the Hadhramaut in 1949 at the behest of the United Nations. I was born in 1949 and so was only a 'babe in arms' at the time in Damascus. I understand that he was parachuted in, armed, given supplies with the drop and a bandolier containing gold sovereigns. Gold and ammunition was an important form of barter to the Bedouin. His brief was to find out more about the Bedouin tribes and advise the UN about short- and long-term famine relief. In the six-month period he was there he covered almost 3,000 miles [5000 kilometres] travelling and living with the Bedouin.

There may have been other motives in sending him there – certainly oil prospecting had created a need to 'understand' the Bedouin of Arabia, equally locust swarms were known to breed in that part of Arabia and then catch winds that would allow them to fly hundreds of miles and drop on to the coast of East Africa and devastate the farms of Kenya and Rhodesia.

My father was educated at Schmidt's (the Kaiser's foundation school) in Jerusalem in the 1930s under the Palestine Mandate, so when matriculation was introduced he was able to progress to the LSE with a scholarship. He spoke good English and also German. In 1954/5 my father was invited to join Shell and help them with Gulf operations. By 1965 he was made Shell's Deputy International Director of Supply and Trading – an amazing position for an Arab to achieve. However, he found his way blocked from further promotion – and left for Beirut (which he found too corrupt for his tastes) and finally Jerusalem – having made his peace with King Hussein. He then took up the post of Director of Tourism for Jordan which he held until the 6-day war in 1967, when he was also mayor-elect of Jerusalem.

My parents sadly separated and divorced when I was 4-5 years. Although I knew my father, this came about more through visits and correspondence as I grew older, we only became really close after the 6-day war.

For the sake of historical accuracy – although your father's notes are excellent – please note the following. My mother attended Owen's College (Manchester University) and obtained two BA degrees, one in French and one in Spanish. My father may have thought it to be a Cambridge college.

Equally, I think my father was decorated twice in WW2 – it may have been DSO and MC. He lost his medals along with all his household possessions when the Haganah[1] captured the suburb of Katamon, Jerusalem, where he had a home with my mother. His darker complexion comes from his mother's Moorish descent – my grandmother Munira (Abdel-Kadr) had the rank of Princess and was the great granddaughter of the Emir of Algiers. The French captured Algiers in 1830 when the Emir was only 18 and after several years he was captured and taken to France. He was kept prisoner in the chateaux of Pau and Amboise before being released in the 1870s as an old man and allowed to settle in Damascus. Amboise has two portraits of the Emir and the resemblance is clear. His father was killed in the Jerusalem earthquake of 1927.

Finally, he may have been 'economical with the truth' about my maternal grandmother who was Jewish (not Basque). She was born a Levison from a French/Belgian Jewish banking family – they had important links with the Middle East. Joseph Levison was the honorary American consul in the 1850s in Ghent, Belgium, and a very wealthy man. They helped to finance the building of the Suez Canal and had diplomatic links with Morocco (Sultan Mullay). Ironically my grandmother's few relatives were lost in the Holocaust – a point not lost on my father – but she was never a Zionist and felt it [Zionism] was wrong. Her family were followers of Rabbi Moses Mendelsohn's teachings. My father spoke a reasonable Hebrew – something that the Israeli leadership didn't realize when he conducted the first Arab-Israeli peace talks in Jerusalem – he could listen to all their asides!

---

1   The Zionist Underground Army.

Appendix 6

A Chronology of Mike Morton

1924	9th July: born at Huddersfield, England.
1945	Graduates from Leeds University with a B.Sc. in geology. Appointed field geologist to the Iraq Petroleum Company. 9th November: leaves Liverpool on a troopship bound for Haifa, Palestine.
1945 – 47	Stratigraphy and structure field work in Palestine and Trans-Jordan. July 1946: the bombing of the King David Hotel, Jerusalem.
1947 – 48	With René Wetzel, takes part in geological explorations of the Hadhramaut, Mahra and Dhofar. IPC exploration headquarters is moved from Haifa to Tripoli, Lebanon. May 1948: British Mandate in Palestine ends.
1948	Appointed leader of a geological party, North West Syria (stratigraphy field work).
1948	Appointed leader of a geological survey of Qatar (structure mapping).
1949	February: the shoot-up at the Wadi Jizzi. August: Marries Heather Howells. November: with René Wetzel, takes part in a geological exploration of the Western Aden Protectorate: Shabwa, Leyadim and Beihan.
1950	Undertakes a survey of water resources for the Government of Trans-Jordan.
1950 – 53	Takes part in stratigraphic studies in Iraqi Kurdistan with some work in Palmyra, and adjacent areas of Iraq. Also (1952) surveying in the North Oman mountains (Ruus al Jibbal).
1953	Appointed Area Geologist, Aden Protectorate, in charge of a field party based at Thamud. December: hands over the field party to Ziad Beydoun.
1954	Appointed Area Geologist in charge of field operations in Oman. February: takes part in the Duqm landings. October: the field party reaches Jebel Fahud.

1956	18th January: 'spudding-in' of Fahud No.1.
1957	April: appointed Head of Department with responsibility for surface/ subsurface operations in Qatar, Trucial States, Oman and Aden Protectorates. Continues to visit exploration crews in the field. May: drilling at Fahud No.1 is abandoned. IPC eventually withdraws from Oman.
1959	Delivers 'The Geology of Oman' to the 5th World Petroleum Congress at New York.
1962	Petroleum Development (Oman) Ltd strikes oil at Fahud No. 2.
1962 – 67	Head of the Geological Department for the Qatar and Abu Dhabi Petroleum Companies.
1967 – 71	Appointed Review Geologist, Persian Gulf. This includes field work in eastern Abu Dhabi (Oman mountain front).
1971	July: retires from the Iraq Petroleum Company. August: appointed deputy leader of the Royal Geographical Society. Expedition to the Musandam Peninsula, Oman. November to February 1972: takes part in the RGS Musandam expedition.
1972 – 73	Leads a team of Mobil geologists to Oman and United Arab Emirates.
1973 – 78	Engaged in varied consulting advice.
1980	Employed by Marathon Oil in geological exploration in Syria.
1980 – 81	Advises the World Bank on oil prospects in Turkey.
1981	Engaged by Hunt Oil International in geological exploration in North Yemen.
1982 – 84	Engaged in varied consulting advice.
1984	Retires from the oil business.
2003	22nd November: dies at Shrewsbury at the age of 79.

Bibliography

Allfree, P. S., *Warlords of Oman*, London, 1967

Asher, Michael, *The Last of the Bedu: In Search of the Myth*, London, 1996

Belgrave, Sir Charles, *The Pirate Coast*, London, 1966

Beydoun, Z. R., *The Stratigraphy and Structure of the Eastern Aden Protectorate*, London, 1964

Bibby, Geoffrey, *Looking for Dilmun*, New York, 1969

Boustead, Colonel Sir Hugh, *The Wind of the Morning*, London, 1971

Brent, Peter, *Far Arabia: Explorers of the Myth*, London, 1977

Centre National de la Recherche Scientifique, *Lexique Stratigraphique International*, various volumes relating to the Middle East

Codrai, Ronald, *The Seven Sheikhdoms: Life in the Trucial States before the Federation of the United Arab Emirates*, London, 1990

Codrai, Ronald, *Abu Dhabi: An Arabian Album*, Dubai, 1992

Coriat, Percy, *Soldier in Oman*, 1960

Craesbeeck, Paul, *Commentaries of Ruy Freyre de Andrade*, translated by C.R. Boxer, London, 1930

Fiennes, Ranulph, *Atlantis of the Sands: The Search for the Lost City of Ubar*, London, 1992

Hamilton, A. P, the Master of Belhaven, *Kingdom of Melchior: Adventure in South West Arabia*, London, 1949

Hamilton, A. P. Lord Belhaven, *The Uneven Road*, London, 1955

Hatley, Allen G., *The Oil Finders: A Collection of Stories About Exploration*, Utopia, Texas, 1995

Henderson, E., *This Strange Eventful History*, London, 1988

Henderson, E., *Arabian Destiny – The Complete Autobiography*, Dubai, 1999

Holden, David, *Farewell to Arabia*, London, 1966

Ingrams, Harold, *Arabia and the Isles*, London, 1942

Innes, Hammond, *The Doomed Oasis*, New York, 1960

Innes, Neil M., *Minister in Oman*, Cambridge, 1987

IPC Society, the, Newsletters, 1975 – 2005

Iraq Petroleum Company Handbook, London, 1948

Iraq Petroleum Company, Various Reports, 1945 – 1971, BP Archive, Warwick University

Iraq Petroleum Company, I.P.C. magazine, 1955 – 1957

Lawrence, T. E., *Seven Pillars of Wisdom*, London, 1935

Longrigg, Stephen H., *Oil in the Middle East: Its Discovery and Development*, Oxford, 1961

Morris, James (now Jan), *Sultan in Oman*, London, 1957

O'Connor, Richard, *The Oil Barons: Men of Greed and Grandeur*, London, 1972

Morton, D. M., *The Geology of Oman*, Proc. 5th World Petroleum Congress, 1959

Osborne, Christine, *The Gulf States and Oman*, London, 1977

Owen, Edgar W., *Trek of the Oil Finders: A History of Exploration for Petroleum*, Tulsa, Oklahoma, 1975

Pethick, Derek, *Vancouver: The Pioneer Years 1774 - 1886*, Vancouver, 1984

Petroleum Development (Oman) Ltd, Field Reports, 1954 – 1958

Reeves, E. A., *Hints to Travellers, Volume One: Survey and Field Astronomy*, London, 1935

Royal Central Asian Society, the, Royal Central Asian Journal, various articles relating to the Middle East

Royal Geographical Society, *Hints to Travellers, Volume One: Survey and Field Astronomy*, London, 1935

Royal Geographical Society, The Geographical Journal, various articles relating to the Middle East

Schiff, Stacey, *Saint Exupéry: A Biography*, London 1994

Searle Pauline, *Dawn Over Oman*, London, 1979

Sheridan, Don, *Fahud – The Leopard Mountain*, Dublin, 2000

St. Exupéry, Antoine de, *Wind Sand and Stars*, London 1939

St. Exupéry, Antoine de, *The Little Prince*, New York, 1971

Stark, Freya, *The Southern Gates of Arabia*, London, 1935

Stevens, E. S., *By Tigris and Euphrates*, London, 1923

Stock, Pastor John, *History of the Salendine Nook Chapel*, Huddersfield, 1874

Stock, Percy, *Foundations*, Halifax, 1933

Thesiger, Wilfred, *Arabian Sands*, London, 1959

Thesiger, Wilfred, *Desert, Marsh and Mountain*, London 1979

Thomas, Bertram, *Arabia Felix: Across the Empty Quarter*, London, 1938

Townsend, John, *Oman: the Making of a Modern State*, London, 1977

Van Der Meulen, D., *Aden to the Hadhramaut*, London, 1947

Wellsted, J.R., *Travels in Arabia*, London, 1838

Wendell Phillips, *Oman: A History*, London, 1967

Wendell Phillips, *Unknown Oman*, London, 1966

Wilkinson, John, *The Imamate Tradition of Oman*, Cambridge, 1987

Wetzel, R. and Morton, D. M., *Contribution à la Geologie de la Trans-Jordanie: Notes et Memoirs sur le moyen-orient; Contributions à la Geologie de la Peninsule Arabique; Mus Nat. and Hist. Natu.*, Paris, 1959

Yergin, Daniel, *The Prize: The Epic Quest for Oil, Money and Power*, New York, 1991

Glossary

Aba = robe

Ain = spring

Anticline = convex fold in rock strata, typically in the form of an arch, with the oldest rocks at the core, and beds dipping away on either side

Aqaba = pass

Askari = native soldier

Bait = tribe

Beni = the sons of

Barasti = Bedouin dwelling constructed from palm branches and goat skins

Bin = son of

Bir = well

Birka = stone cistern built by the Shihuh tribe to retain water in the moutains of Musandam

Cambrian = geological period 505 - 570 million years ago

Cretaceous = geological period 66 - 144 million years ago

Dhow = Arab sailing vessel

Falaj = water channel

Feu de joie = rifle shots fired in the air, in celebration or welcome

Futah = loin cloth

Geosyncline = a continent-size downwarp, or trough, in the earth's crust into which rock sediments have accumulated over many millions of years

Ghazzu = tribal raid

Harmel = a leafy, light green shrub growing in clumps

Himyars = pre-Islamic race

Imam = religious leader

Imamate = area ruled by Imam

Jebel = mountain or hilly land

Jidda = plain

Jiddat al Harasis = plain of the Harasis tribe

Jol = plateau

Jurassic = geological period 144 - 208 million years ago

Kohl = powder used to darken the skin around the eyes

Khanjar = highly decorated dagger, symbol of manhood

Kifi = a thorny bush with violet small flowers

Majlis = meeting room

Miocene = geological epoch 5 - 24 million years ago

Mudhahs = freed slaves

Muezzin = holy man who calls the faithful to prayer

Muqaddam/Mugaddem = tribal leader, chieftain

Nasrani = Christian

Nejd = the great desert of central Arabia

Oligocene = geological epoch 24 - 37 million years ago

Palaeontology = the study of fossils

Pleistocene = geological epoch up to 2 million years old

Pliocene = geological epoch 2 – 5 million years ago

Pre-Cambrian = geological era 570 – 4,600 million years ago (oldest rocks approx. 3,800 million years old)

Rafiq = guide

Ramadan = a fast lasting a month, during which time Muslims are forbidden to eat in the day. The fast is broken by a festival called 'Id'.

Ras = headland

Rub al Khali = the great sand desert of southern Arabia, the 'Empty Quarter'

Sabkha = salt flat, evaporation pan

Saif en Nebi = 'Prophet's Sword', a rainbow

Saiyid = Holy Man

Sambaq = type of Arab sailing vessel

Samr = tree of southern Arabia

Shaib al-Ahmar = literally 'Old Red Man', Mike's Bedouin nickname which he interpreted as 'Angry Red Man'

Shamal = wind from the north

Sharwish = sergeant

Shemaq = lead wrap

Siyarra = Bedouin passport

Spudded in = term used to describe the start of drilling of an oil well

Strata = layers of rock

Stratigraphy = the study of rock strata, especially the age, distribution, deposition and age of sedimentary rocks

Suhaili = wind from the south

Suq = market

Syncline = a concave fold of rock, with the youngest rocks at its centre

Thawb = long shirt or robe

Triall = a green plant with a small, daisy-like yellow flower

Triassic = geological period 208 – 245 million years ago

Trucial Coast or Trucial States = the seven sheikhdoms of the lower Persian Gulf region: Abu Dhabi, Dubai, Ras al Kharma, Sharjah, Fujaira, Ajman and Umm al Quurain. In the nineteenth century their rulers had entered into a truce with the British Government to end piracy. In 1971 they became the United Arab Emirates.

Ubar = the reputed site of the 'Atlantis of the Sands'

Wadi = dried up river bed or valley

Wasia = geological term referring to a certain stratum of rock

Abbreviations

ARAMCO = Arabian American Oil Company
EAP = Eastern Aden Protectorate
HBL = Hadhramaut Bedouin Legion
MOFF = Muscat and Oman Field Force
PDO = Petroleum Development (Oman) Limited
RCS = Royal Corps of Signals
RGS = Royal Geographical Society
WAP = Western Aden Protectorate

Acknowledgements

In the Heart of the Desert has been more than 50 years in the writing. When Mike returned from the expedition to south-western Arabia in the spring of 1948, he talked about writing a book of his travels. Eventually, René and Mike published an account in the Iraq Petroleum magazine in the autumn issues of 1955. Mike himself kept journals of his travels, and Heather kept many of his letters describing life in the Middle East. I was surprised at how much material Mike had gathered together and equally surprised at how much material I went on to collect.

When I came to set these reminiscences down in the form of a book, I was immensely grateful for the help I received from Mike's friends and colleagues: Clari Wells for his memories of Huddersfield; Ron Miller for sharing with me his extensive knowledge of IPC, its subsidiary companies, and of Mike's career, for proof-reading the manuscript and making many helpful suggestions; Adrian Humphreys for his invaluable account of the Thamud and DEF expeditions; Peter Walmsley for his recollections and superlative film of the Fahud days; Tom Jameson for his account of life in the camp in the Wadi Semail as he and Mike waited to gain access to the Birket Gorge; Rodney Collomb for reading the Omani chapters and making suggestions; Tom Harris for his comments and helpful advice on the early and later years of Mike's career with IPC, for correcting my clumsy attempts at describing the essentials of geology and for redrawing geological diagrams; David Heard and Tony Smith for their advice on Chapter 18; John Scott for his advice on Mike's career in Iraq; and many others who have assisted and encouraged me.

I received much help from Dr Alan Heward of Petroleum Development (Oman) Ltd. in accessing records and photographs from the early days of exploration in Oman, and for his advice on the geological issues, particularly in relation to Fahud Nos. 1 & 2 and the Wadi Mu'aydin, proof-reading the Dhofar and Oman chapters, rewriting the passage about the Tethys ocean and commenting on my geology and the script generally. His wife Felicity gave advice on Oman which helped to make our trip so memorable. Petroleum Development (Oman) Ltd. assisted my research by giving permission to use company records and photographs. The Geological Society of Oman kindly published my first attempt at telling Mike's story and its members generously shared their knowledge with me on the Fahud field trip.

My thanks to Dr Paul Cornelius for proof-reading, editing and making numerous suggestions which vastly improved the manuscript; to Hugh May, Derek South, Claudio Vita-Finzi and Beatrice de Cardi for their material and comments; and to Phillip Robinson for allowing me to use his 200-page journal which breathed new life into the Musandam episodes.

I am grateful to Don Sheridan who received my enquiries over many months and answered each one; for his invaluable contribution to the chapters on Oman and for his comments on the photographs I sent him; for reading and commenting on a draft of the Oman and the Aden chapters; and for generally sharing his extensive knowledge and experience with me.

My research led me to unexpected quarters: thanks to Robert Fisk of *The Independent* for putting me in touch with Sa'ad Khalidi, and thanks to Sa'ad himself for providing me with the information that enabled me to round off the story of El Khalidi and for the photograph of his father. My thanks to Peter Housego of the British Petroleum Archive for assisting me with the IPC archive and, together with Andrew Whitehead of IPC, for giving me permission to use extracts and photographs from it; and to George McGeechie for sending me material from the IPC magazine and for publishing the story of the crashed Dove.

I am indebted to Gill Williams and Catherine Williams of Able Publishing for their advice, hard work and patience, and to Penny Green for her meticulous proof-reading and comments.

Ethiopian Airlines kindly provided me with details of the aircraft they were flying into Aden in 1947; Ian Buttershaw commented on Mike's photographs depicting soldiers from the Muscat and Oman Field Force; and the Natural History Museum in Paris provided me with a copy of *Contribution à la Géologie de la Trans-Jordanie*. As a result of my research, Mike has entered 'immortality' on the Internet (although I am not sure that this would have greatly pleased him!), with details of his travels being provided on two websites – one on Nabataean Railways (www.nabataea.net/workinglocos.html) and the other on the crash of the Hannibal (www.rrhobby.ca/flight_cw197.htm).

Ian Fairservice, Managing Partner of Motivate Publishing, kindly gave permission for my use of extracts from Edward Henderson's book *This Strange Eventful History*, which was expanded and republished in 1999 as *Arabian Destiny - The Complete Autobiography* and is now available at Motivate Publishing, P O Box 2331, Dubai, United Arab Emirates, and also through www.booksarabia.com.

My thanks to all those who have given me permission to use excerpts and photographs. Every effort has been made to trace copyright holders and I apologise in advance for any unintentional omission. I would be pleased to insert the appropriate acknowledgement in any subsequent edition.

I am especially grateful to Heather for all her assistance and encouragement, her comments on the manuscript and for her contribution in describing life in Tripoli, Kirkuk, Greenaway Gardens and the Persian Gulf; to my brother Peter for fielding questions on aircraft and geology, reading the manuscript and providing useful advice; to Ann and Gareth for their helpful comments and for supporting me in this project.

My love and sincere gratitude to my wife Gill, who has cheerfully listened to stories of the desert, learned the finer points of camel-riding, eaten sweetmeats – the list is endless. Without her help and encouragement, none of what has been written would have been possible, and 'Mike's story' would never have been told.

And finally to Buster and Jasper, my apologies for all the walks in the summer sunshine they have forfeited.

Index

R

S

Y

Z

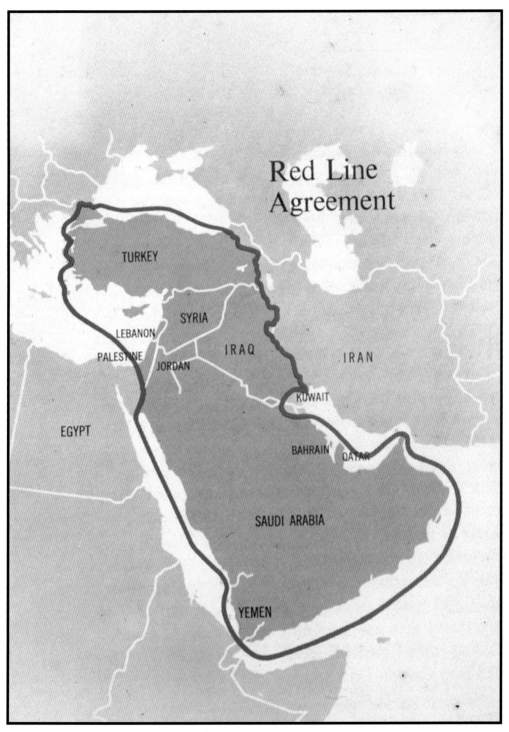

Red Line Agreement, 1928

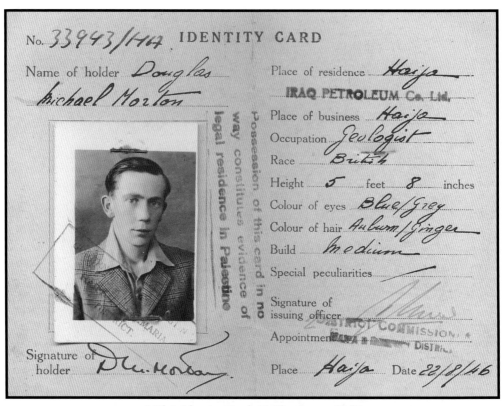

Mike's Identity Card, Haifa, August 1946

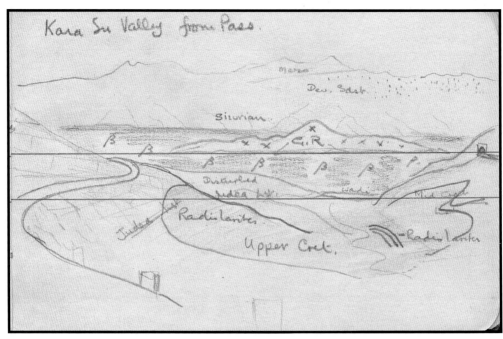

Mike's sketch of the Kara Su Valley from Pass, 1948

A street scene in Mukalla, 1953

The Wadi Hadhramaut, Eastern Aden Protectorate (EAP)

Bedouins taking water from the well at El Kareef, EAP

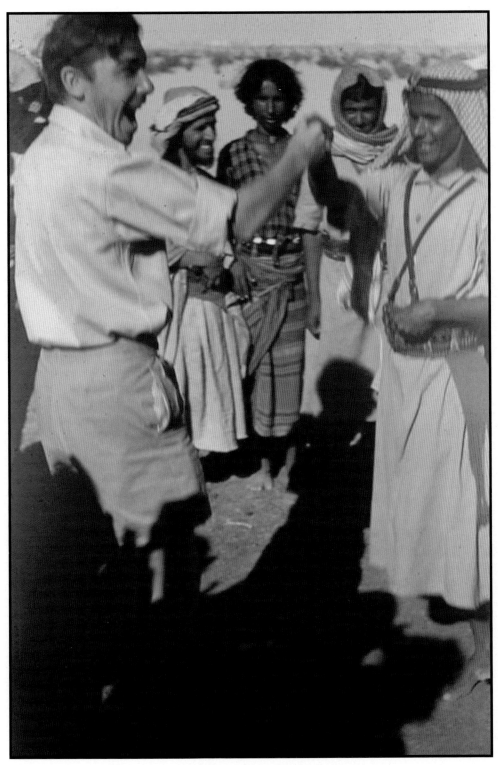

Peewee joining the dance

The Bedouin well at Thamud, December 1953

'Jesoura' offloading on Duqm beach, February 1954

Mike at Duqm camp, February 1954

18th March 1954, tribesmen line up to greet the Sultan at Duqm

The Sultan arriving on the Duqm shore

The Sultan strides along the shore with various advisers in tow

The tribesmen celebrate his arrival with dancing

1955: Camp scene with Rodney Collomb and Tom Jameson in the foreground, and with Don Sheridan approaching from the right.

F. E. Wellings at the Fahud 'spudding in' – January 1956

The approach to Nizwa, 1956

The fort at Nizwa

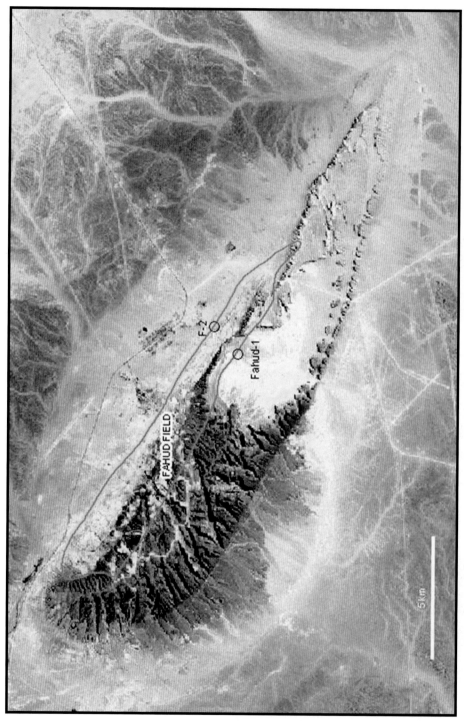

Satellite image of Fahud showing the presently defined field and the location of wells 1 and 2
(Reproduced with permission from the PDO Archive)

Jebel Akhdar, the Green Mountain

The RGS Party, Winter 1971 – 72 (photograph by courtesy of Phillip Robinson – inset)
From L-R: Camp Guard, Mike Morton, Abul Rahman, Lal Khan,
Wadi of Khasab, Norman Falcon, Derek South, Hugh May and Paul Cornelius

A drowned valley of Musandam

Paul Cornelius carrying out 'field' work in Musandam

Tachyometry on the Maqlab Isthmus: Mike Morton and labourer, December 1971
(photograph by courtesy of Phillip Robinson)

A view of the Musandam Peninsula, Khasab from the north

The author with the sons of Aziz, January 2006
(photograph by courtesy of Xiomara Marquez)